A PROGRAMMED COURSE IN
basic electricity

OTHER BOOKS PREPARED BY THE STAFF OF
NEW YORK INSTITUTE OF TECHNOLOGY

A PROGRAMMED COURSE IN
basic electronics

A PROGRAMMED COURSE IN
basic transistors

A PROGRAMMED COURSE IN

basic electricity

SECOND EDITION

THE STAFF OF ELECTRICAL TECHNOLOGY DEPARTMENT
NEW YORK INSTITUTE OF TECHNOLOGY
ALEXANDER SCHURE, PROJECT DIRECTOR

McGRAW-HILL BOOK COMPANY

NEW YORK   ST. LOUIS   SAN FRANCISCO   DÜSSELDORF
LONDON   MEXICO   PANAMA   SYDNEY   TORONTO

A PROGRAMMED COURSE IN BASIC ELECTRICITY

07-046390-5

10 11 12 13 14 15 16 17 18 19 20 BABA 8 7 6 5 4 3 2 1 0

This book was set in Times Roman by Graphic Services, Inc., and
printed on permanent paper and bound by George Banta Company, Inc.
The cover was designed by Marsha Cohen.
The editors were Alan W. Lowe and Albert Shapiro.
Peter D. Guilmette supervised production.

preface

The programmed course in basic electricity contained in this book offers a tested procedure for taking the first step toward electronics specialization. Starting with the assumption that the student has only a meager background in electricity, this course develops the basic electrical concepts essential to later studies in electronics. The carefully organized logical sequence of interrelated steps permits the student to proceed at a pace best suited to his abilities and needs. He is constantly aware of his progress by means of immediate feedback as well as many checks and repetitions. He is his own tutor and his own examiner. Visual instruction is aided by clear, uncomplicated diagrams. Mathematics has been kept at a minimum, especially in the earlier sections of the work, to enable the nonmathematically minded reader to achieve a firm grasp of the necessary concepts.

There is one major prerequisite for the successful completion of this course: *interest*. An inner drive to learn is often a more important ingredient than a high IQ. Armed with determination and perseverance, the man with a strong desire to learn simply cannot fail.

The text is designed for an introductory two-semester course; it is followed by two additional texts, also in linear programmed form: *A Programmed Course in Basic Electronics* and *A Programmed Course in Basic Transistors*. Each may be used independently, or the three may be studied in sequence.

The intervening years between the publication of the first edition of *Basic Electricity* and the present have seen an increasing number of greatly refined studies concerned with the improvement of programmed educational strategies. The gradually emerging pattern has lost much of its complexity; it has by now assumed sufficient clarity of structure to permit its incorporation into the format and content revisions of the second edition.

Deletions: Validation studies have indicated that the Completion Summaries which concluded each chapter of the first edition did not contribute significantly enough to student performance to warrant the time required for student handling. These have been replaced by organized measurable behavioral objective listings to be described later. The Self Tests and Answers have been altered in form and location to improve their validity and usefulness to the student.

Additions: Each chapter ends with a list of Measurable Behavioral Objectives (MBO's) that are keyed to the frame or frames that relate to each objective. Each MBO is considered a terminal objective for a specific, limited phase of the work and is correlated with a group of enabling objectives which present the proper sequence for achievement. At the conclusion of a chapter, the student is expected to review the MBO's carefully, determine for himself whether or not he has met the requirement of the objective, and then proceed to remedial work, if necessary, or to the Criterion Check Test for that chapter.

The Criterion Check Tests for student use are bound into the text. These tests have a one-to-one relationship with the MBO's for the chapter. If the student has conscientiously performed the remedial study indicated by his first review of the MBO's, his score on the Criterion Check Test will be high. These tests are to be self-graded; the answers to the questions are also included in the text. Since all the test questions are of the four-distractor multiple-choice type, the likelihood of misinterpretation is minimal.

A second set of Criterion Check Tests, one for each chapter, is available to the instructor in the Instructor's Manual for this text. Every effort has been made to preserve parallelism of difficulty in the second set of tests so that these may be used either for grading purposes or for second-stage self-checking of learning achievement. The answers for the second set of tests are included in the Instructor's Manual.

Text modifications: Careful editing has removed most or all of the mechanical errors that may have been present in the first edition. A number of the frames have been rephrased, emphasis has been altered, and clarifications have been introduced to improve the content material and sequencing.

The instructor is urged to review carefully the Preface to the Instructor's Manual.

History and development of material: The three books had their beginnings in 1958. At that time, faculty members of the electrical technology department of New York Institute of Technology undertook the development of an integrated series of programmed learning materials relating to electronics. In conferences held with training directors and curriculum specialists, an agreement was reached on the topics comprising those segments of electronic training considered essential in the majority of industrial and formal educational programs. The conferees further agreed that variations in background would require structuring the programs on several levels, with one major program being fundamental in aproach. The overall project was termed the PRINCE project (*P*rogrammed *R*einforced *I*nstruction *N*ecessary to *C*ontinuing *E*ducation). This volume is part of the series dealing with the *basics* of electricity, electronics, semiconductors, transistors, and pulse circuits.

By early 1961, preliminary versions of the programs had been prepared and tested by the programming teams. The next step required extensive field testing under various instructional conditions. In May of 1961, the Institute requested the assistance of the Educational Coordinating Committee of the Electronic Industries Association, offering the developed programs to industry on a cooperative data-exchange basis. Participating companies were asked to make their test data available for use in refining, revising, and developing a validated teaching instrument. Through the efforts of the committee, and through the interest of other industrial groups, a number of companies became aware of the project and agreed to aid in the validation. Among these companies were:

Aerovox Corporation, *New Bedford, Massachusetts*
The Boeing Company, *Renton, Washington*
Corning Glass Works, *Corning, New York*
E. I. du Pont Nemours & Company, *Wilmington, Delaware*
Eastman Kodak Company, *Rochester, New York*
General Dynamics/Pomona, *Pomona, California*
General Electric Company, *Philadelphia, Pennsylvania*
Hycon Manufacturing Company, *Monrovia, California*
International Telephone and Telegraph, *Belleville, New Jersey*
Lockheed Aircraft Corporation, Missiles and Space Division, *Sunnyvale, California*
McDonnell Aircraft Corporation, *St. Louis, Missouri*

Concurrent with the industrial validation, a validation program in a number of technical institutes and community colleges was undertaken with the cooperation of McGraw-Hill Book Company. Thus, all material was thoroughly tested for the first edition of *Basic Electricity*.

Grateful acknowledgment is hereby extended to Benjamin Edelman of Western Electric, Chairman of the Educational Coordinating Committee of the Electronic Industries Association; George Maedel of RCA, Chairman of the Curriculum Development Task Force of EIA during the major portion of this study; the training directors of the participating companies; the programming teams and faculty of New York Institute of Technology; and the many others who through their efforts brought the first edition to fruition.

ALEXANDER SCHURE

contents

to the user

Programmed instruction

No matter how deeply you probe the nature of electronics, you will always be dealing with certain basic principles. The understanding necessary to become an electronics technician comes from a grasp of the fundamental concepts of electricity.

As your skill in electronics grows, you will realize how important these basic ideas are. To understand the complex, you should know about the simple. Much of this basic information is in the program which follows.

The information in this course is organized in a relatively new manner. As you work with the materials in the lessons that follow, you will find that the information you are asked to learn has been arranged to provide for your participation in the instruction. This method of teaching is called *programmed learning.*

In presenting the information, the subject matter is divided into small units called frames. Most of the time, each frame requires that the statement in the frame be completed. With a little thought you should be able to provide the correct answer, or response. The correct answer is enclosed in parentheses and appears at the beginning of the frame which follows. You should look at the correct answer only after you have written what you feel to be the proper one.

In order to introduce you to this method, the following section is programmed. Cover the answers with a cardboard or paper sheet. Lower the sheet only *after* you have written your answer. Use reasonable judgment to decide whether your response is the same as the printed answer. Now try the sample frames which follow.

---

1. Self-instructional materials will be given to you in the same form as the frames which follow. Your first feelings may be that you are taking a test. You are not! Understand this clearly— programmed learning is a teaching method and is much more than just a t_____ . (Complete the statement.)

---

2. (test) The purpose of this book is *to teach you* in just the same way as if you were receiving individual instruction. So, your self-instructional text, called a program, acts as your private teacher. We can now say: A self-instructional book is called a p_____ .

---

3. (program) A program presents the information to be learned in small bits, a few sentences at a time. You will either complete a statement, find information on a diagram, or make a choice. For example, you might be asked to complete this statement:

What you learn from each frame of this program will not be graded because the program is a (test, teaching device).

---

4. (teaching device) Let's move on now. We've said the program presents information in small amounts at a time. These small segments are called frames. Each numbered statement in the program is a frame.

This is the fourth _____ in this series.

---

5. (frame) Thus, we see each frame leads us further into the subject by giving a little additional information or by searching for information learned in that frame or a previous one. After receiving this information, you check the next frame to determine, immediately, if you are _____ .

---

5. (correct)

Information Panel

Some frames or chapter introductions give you information and do not ask you to make a response. Information and summaries given in this way are important. Read them carefully. Then, just go on to the next frame. Do so now.

6. Let's summarize: Programmed learning involves breaking up the subject matter into small units, called _____ .

---

7. (frames) Each frame will require a(n) _____ from you.

---

8. (response or answer) In the frame below, you will find the correct _____ .

---

9. (response or answer) From time to time you will be given supplementary material in the form of problems and exercises. You will be required to do these _____ and _____ .

---

10. (problems, exercises) Proceed at the rate best suited to you. One of the great advantages of programmed material is that each student can proceed at his own _____ .

11. (rate or pace) Because you are working at your own rate, there will be no _____ limit for your completion of "daily lessons."

12. (time) Remember the difference between the words teach and learn. The program will teach, but only you, the _____ , can learn.

13. (student) You must, therefore, make the effort to _____ from the program.

14. (learn) No matter how a course is taught, the responsibility for learning is with you, the _____ .

15. (student) The program is a teaching device and not a _____ . Since this is so, there is no reason to look ahead for an answer. If you do so, you will merely be cheating yourself of the opportunity of le__ing.

16. (test, learning) Extra *learning* steps are built into the program. Measurable behavioral objectives and criterion check tests will help you _____ .

17. (learn) You are to complete each of these criterion check tests. Be sure to answer every question. You may then check your answer with the _____ answer.

18. (correct) The measurable behavioral objectives provide a comprehensive outline of what you should achieve in each

_____ .

18. (chapter)

You are now ready to proceed with the program.

A PROGRAMMED COURSE IN
basic electricity

part one

direct current

static electricity

States of matter

Any fundamental study of the universe in which we live must begin with an understanding of the *states of matter*. The familiar states of matter are solid, liquid, and gas, although other states representing transitions between the fundamental ones are also possible. Matter may also exist in subdivided forms that are of interest to the nuclear physicist but which are not of great interest to us at this point. We shall begin by characterizing the state in which a given substance appears by means of three criteria:

1. If the substance has a given shape and volume regardless of the container in which it is placed, we shall call it a "solid" (e.g., ice).

2. If the substance changes its shape to fit the vessel in which it is placed, we shall call it a "liquid."

3. If the substance changes its shape to fit the container and also changes its volume to match that of the vessel, then it is called a "gas" (e.g., water vapor).

1·1 The universe is composed of matter. Rock is matter in the solid form. An ocean is matter in the liquid form. The atmosphere is a gaseous form of ＿＿＿＿＿＿ .

1·2 (matter) Solids are characterized by the fact that they retain their own shape and volume wherever placed. A sphere of iron with a volume of 1 cu ft made in Cincinnati would be a sphere of iron with a volume of 1 cu ft in New York as well. Hence, iron is normally a ＿＿＿＿＿＿ .

1·3 (solid) When the sphere of iron is melted in a cylindrical vat, it retains its own volume (1 cu ft) but flows freely and assumes the shape of the vat. Thus, a liquid is a state of matter which retains its volume but can easily change its ＿＿＿＿＿＿ .

1·4 (shape) If the iron is heated still more, it can change into a vapor or gas. If the vaporizing chamber is 10 cu ft in volume, the original cubic foot of iron will expand to fill every crevice of the chamber. Thus, a gas assumes both the shape and _____ of the container.

1·5 (volume) When a substance changes state from solid to liquid to gas, or vice versa, its mass and weight remain the same. Hence, when 10 lb of ice changes to liquid water, the weight of the water formed is ___ _____ .

1·6 (10 lb) The same mass of water, when vaporized to steam, has a weight of ___ _____ .

1·7 (10 lb) Iodine crystals change directly from the solid to the vapor state when heated. Ten grams of iodine crystals when vaporized have a weight of ___ _____ in the gaseous state.

1·8 (10 grams) Joss is a mineral. A cube of joss measuring 1 in. on each side retains its shape and volume when placed in a large can; the cube has a fixed mass no matter where it is placed. The cube is, therefore, the form of matter known as _____ .

1·9 (solid) Ethanol is a kind of alcohol. A 2-oz medicine bottle full of ethanol when poured into a large can flattens out on the bottom but retains its volume of 2 oz and its original mass. Ethanol is, therefore, the form of matter known as _____ .

1·10 (liquid) Glycerin assumes the same shape as its container but does *not* change its volume and mass. Glycerin is a _____ .

1·10 (liquid)

Elements, compounds, and mixtures

An *element* cannot be broken down into simpler substances which will retain the original characteristics. For example, hydrogen and oxygen are elements; they cannot be reduced into anything simpler without destroying their properties. When elements are chemically combined so that they cannot be separated from each other by simple physical means, such as by dissolving one out and leaving the others behind or by filtering or by distillation, they form *compounds*. Elements may be recovered from compounds only by chemical reactions. It is possible, however, to mix elements in such a way as to permit separation by simple physical means. These "temporary" combinations of elements are termed *mixtures*.

1·11 A substance that cannot be broken down into simpler substances is called an element. No matter what we do to a sample of iron, it still remains iron, hence iron is an element. No known chemical or physical process can break mercury down into simpler substances, hence mercury is an _____.

1·12 (element) Bromine is normally a liquid. When cooled sufficiently, bromine solidifies and when heated enough, it vaporizes. In these various states, and under any other kind of physical or chemical stress, bromine remains bromine. Hence, bromine is a(n) _____.

1·13 (element) When two or more elements combine to form a new substance, the new substance is called a compound if its components can be restored by chemical means but not by physical means. Iron rust is a compound because it is a chemical combination of iron and oxygen. Lime is a chemical combination of calcium and oxygen, hence lime is a _____.

1·14 (compound) Limestone is a combination of calcium, carbon, and oxygen. The original elements can be restored only by chemical action, hence limestone is a _____.

1·15 (compound) A combination of elements that can be separated by physical means is known as a mixture. Dry table salt combined with limestone flour can be separated by dissolving out the salt. The process of dissolving one substance out is a physical, not a chemical process; thus, this combination of salt and limestone is a _____ rather than a compound.

1·16 (mixture) A combination of sulfur and iron filings stirred together in a bowl can be separated by pulling out the filings with a magnet. This combination of elements is, therefore, a _____.

1·17 (mixture) Table salt, a very familiar combination of elements, contains sodium and chlorine bound to each other in such a way that chemical reaction is necessary to separate them from each other. Limestone contains the elements calcium and carbon and oxygen tied together in much the same way. Ordinary sugar consists of carbon, hydrogen, and oxygen—all elements—united to each other chemically. All these substances are, therefore, _____.

1·18 (compounds) Gunpowder contains the elements sulfur and carbon, in addition to potassium nitrate. When water is allowed to filter through gunpowder, the nitrate is dissolved out leaving the sulfur and carbon behind. Gunpowder is, therefore, a ———————— .

1·19 (mixture) Carbon dioxide can be broken down into carbon and oxygen only by chemical action. Carbon dioxide must, therefore, be a ———————— .

1·20 (compound) Tantalum cannot be reduced to any simpler form by any chemical method. Tantalum is, therefore, a(n) ———————— .

1·21 (element) Air is a ———————— of elements, since it can be separated by physical means.

1·21 (mixture)

Atoms and molecules

There are at least 30 different kinds of fundamental particles which go into the structure of *atoms.* We shall confine our attention to only three of them: *electrons, protons,* and *neutrons.* In Frames 1·22 to 1·37, we use a mechanical model of the atom in which the protons and neutrons are imagined to be located in the *nucleus,* while the electrons are visualized as being in planet-like orbits around the nucleus. Remember, electrons do not actually exist like this inside the atom; we are just picturing them this way for simplicity.

1·22 Elements contain identical units which are called atoms. Normal iron contains atoms bound together in the solid state; mercury contains atoms bound together to form a liquid; oxygen contains atoms bound together to form a ————— .

1·23 (gas) Nitrogen is an element in gaseous form. A vessel filled with nitrogen contains billions of nitrogen ———————— .

1·24 (atoms) The building blocks of an element such as chlorine are the ———————— of which it is composed.

1·25 (atoms) If a compound is reduced to smaller and smaller sizes, the smallest particle that will retain the properties of the original compound is called a molecule. When table salt is reduced to the smallest particle size, we finally obtain a molecule consisting of 1 atom of sodium and 1 atom of chlorine. When water is broken down to smaller sizes of particles, we end up with a _____ containing 2 atoms of hydrogen and 1 of oxygen.

1·26 (molecule) Hydrochloric acid is a compound of hydrogen and chlorine. The smallest particle size that is still hydrochloric acid is a _____ containing 1 atom of hydrogen and 1 of chlorine.

---

* A nucleus is ordinarily about 1/10,000 the size of the atom. This imaginary picture is for purposes of explanation.

1·27 (molecule) An atom can be broken down into three basic particles: electrons, protons, and neutrons. The simplest atom of all is hydrogen, containing 1 proton at the center and 1 electron revolving around it. The next simplest is helium, with 2 protons and 2 neutrons in the nucleus and _____ electrons revolving around it (Fig. 1·27).

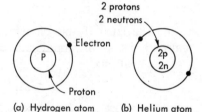

(a) Hydrogen atom   (b) Helium atom

Fig. 1·27

1·28 (2) An atom of lithium contains 3 protons and 4 neutrons in its central mass around which 3 electrons revolve like planets. This central mass is called the _____ (Fig. 1·28).

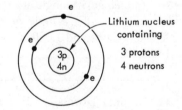

Fig. 1·28

1·29 (nucleus) As substance X is acted upon chemically and physically, it is found that it can be broken down into a "package" containing 1 atom of sodium, 1 atom of nitrogen, and 3 atoms of oxygen. This package behaves in every way like the original mass of substance X. Hence, the package is a(n) _____ of substance X (Fig. 1·29).

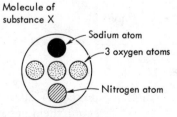

Fig. 1·29

1·30 (molecule) An atom of a certain substance is acted upon by a special machine. The machine causes the atom to disintegrate. The particles that appear as a result of this disintegration are neutrons, protons, and _____.

1·31 (electrons) A gas contains atoms in which no neutrons can be found. These atoms still contain _____ and

_____ .

1·32 (electrons, protons) All the protons and neutrons of an atom are contained in the *nucleus* of the atom, while the electrons are in orbits. If the planetary electrons are all removed, the part of the atom that still remains is its central

_____ .

1·33 (nucleus) All the protons and neutrons in complex atoms are located in the _____ of the atoms.

1·34 (nucleus) If the planetary electrons of helium were removed, its atom would still contain _____ protons and _____ neutrons.

1·35 (2, 2) Two atoms of hydrogen and one atom of oxygen can be combined to form one _____ of water.

1·36 (molecule) A single atom of hydrogen contains 1 proton and 1 electron. If a sample of hydrogen is found to contain 1,000,000 protons and 1,000,000 electrons, there must therefore be 1,000,000 _____ of hydrogen in the sample.

1·37 (atoms) Normally, 2 atoms of hydrogen will tend to cling together to form a larger, stable particle. Such a particle could only be called a(n) _____ of hydrogen.

1·37   (molecule)

Electrostatic forces

Forces of attraction and repulsion can be set up between bodies by treating them in certain ways. The act of stroking or rubbing a body with fur or cloth charges the stroked substance so that it can exert a force on another treated body. These forces are electrical in origin. In these frames, we wish to establish the following facts: **1,** two bodies treated in exactly the same manner repel each other; and **2,** it is possible to get two bodies to attract each other by treating them in different ways, these treatments being quite specific in nature.

1·38 Under certain conditions, two identical substances treated in like manner repel each other. For instance, a glass rod rubbed with silk repels a second glass rod that has been rubbed with silk. Similarly, a rubber rod rubbed with fur will _____ a second rubber rod rubbed with fur.

1·39 (repel) A sulfur roll rubbed with flannel will _____ a second sulfur roll rubbed with flannel.

1·40 (repel) A force of attraction is often found between different substances treated in different ways. For example, a rubber rod stroked with fur attracts a glass rod rubbed with silk. There is a similar force of _____ between two different plastics stroked with different materials.

1·41 (attraction) Sulfur rubbed with flannel behaves exactly the same as rubber stroked with fur. Since rubber stroked with fur attracts a glass rod stroked with silk, we would expect the sulfur treated with flannel to _____ the glass rod rubbed with silk.

1·42 (attract) Polystyrene stroked with nylon behaves exactly like glass stroked with silk. Since two treated glass rods repel each other, we would expect a treated polystyrene rod to _____ a treated glass rod.

1·43 (repel) We compare all substances that show attraction and repulsion to fur-treated rubber and silk-treated glass. Fur-treated rubber repels fur-treated rubber, and silk-treated glass _____ silk-treated glass.

1·44 (repels) On the other hand, fur-treated rubber _____ silk-treated glass.

1·45 (attracts) Thus, any substance that repels fur-treated rubber is said to behave just like fur-treated rubber. Also, any substance that attracts fur-treated rubber is said to behave like _____-treated glass.

1·46   (silk)   A rod of substance X is seen to repel fur-treated rubber. It is, therefore, behaving exactly like fur-treated rubber. Thus, if substance X is brought near silk-treated glass, there will be a(n) _____ force between them.

1·47   (attracting)   A rod of substance Y is seen to attract fur-treated rubber. It is, therefore, behaving exactly like silk-treated glass. Thus, if substance Y is brought near a rod of silk-treated _____, the force between them will be one of repulsion.

1·48   (glass)   If rod X is now near rod Y, the force between them will be one of _____ .

1·49   (attraction)   Rod A repels a fur-treated rubber rod. It will, therefore, _____ a silk-treated glass rod.

1·50   (attract)   Rod B attracts a fur-treated rubber rod. It will, therefore, _____ a silk-treated glass rod.

1·50   (repel)

Law of electric charges

>   There are two kinds of electric charges: *positive* and *negative*, symbolized respectively as "$+$" and "$-$." When a pair of bodies carry the same charge, that is, both "$+$" or both "$-$," they are said to have *like* charges; when a pair of bodies carry different charges, that is, one "$+$" and the other "$-$," they are said to have *unlike* or opposite charges. The original naming of the charges was entirely arbitrary, since it makes no difference whether you call a certain charge positive or negative just as long as you are consistent from that time onward. Thus, all bodies that behave like a rubber rod stroked with fur are now called negative bodies, while all bodies that behave like a glass rod stroked with silk are called positive bodies.

1·51   A rubber rod rubbed with fur is said to be charged negatively, while the fur itself is said to be charged positively. These are called opposite charges. After charging, the fur attracts the rubber, hence opposite or unlike charges _____ each other.

1·52   (attract)   It is found that glass rubbed with silk attracts rubber rubbed with fur. If the rubber rod is negative, this means that the glass rod must be _____ .

1•53 (positive) A glass rod repels a second glass rod. Since both rods are positively charged, we can say that like charges _____ each other.

1•54 (repel) A rubber rod repels a second rubber rod. Since both rods are negatively charged, this verifies the conclusion that _____ charges repel each other.

1•55 (like) The law of electric charges may thus be stated: _____ charges repel each other while _____ charges attract each other.

1•56 [like, unlike (must be in that order)] A positively charged object is hung halfway between another positive object and a negative object of the same size. The suspended positive object will swing toward the _____ object.

1•57 (negative) When a light ball of bamboo pith is touched to a charged glass rod that has been stroked with silk, the pith ball immediately springs away. This shows that there is a force of repulsion in action. Since the glass was positively charged and the pith ball was repelled, we may conclude that the ball received a _____ charge from the rod.

1•58 (positive) An inflated rubber balloon is charged by rubbing on a rough cloth. It is then found to be repelled by a rubber rod stroked with fur. Since the rubber rod was negative in charge, and since it *repelled* the charged balloon, the balloon must have had a _____ charge.

1•58 (negative)

The constitution of charges

The fundamental "−" charge is thought to be produced by a single electron, while the fundamental "+" charge is that of a single proton. A body is *net* negative if it carries more electrons than protons; it is *net* positive if it carries fewer electrons than protons. The numerical value of the net charge is found by subtracting the number of one type of charge from the number of the other type. Whether the net charge is "+" or "−" is determined by inspecting the problem to see whether there are more electrons or protons present.

1•59 The electron is the unit of negative charge. A single electron is said to have 1 unit of negative charge; 2 electrons have 2 units of negative charge; thus, 8 electrons have _____ units of _____ charge.

1•60 (8, negative) If a body carries an excess of 4 electrons, it has a net negative charge of 4 units. Hence, a body that has an excess of 12 electrons carries _____ units of _____ charge.

1•61 (12, negative) A body is given an excess of 150 electrons. This body has a net _____ charge of _____ units.

1•62 (negative, 150) The proton is the unit of positive charge. A single proton has 1 unit of positive charge; 2 protons have 2 units of positive charge; thus, 9 protons have _____ units of positive charge.

1•63 (9) A body that contains an excess of 3 protons has a net _____ charge of 3 units. Thus, a body that has an excess of 14 protons carries a net positive charge of _____ units.

1•64 (positive, 14) An insulating rod has an excess of 325 protons on its surface. Thus, this rod is carrying a _____ charge of 325 units.

1•65 (positive) The charge on an electron is the same magnitude as the charge on a proton, only opposite in sign. One electron added to one proton causes a cancellation of charge, and the body is said to be neutral electrically. If a body contains 3 excess electrons, it can be neutralized by adding 3 protons. Thus, a body with 10 excess electrons can be neutralized by adding _____ protons.

1•66 (10) A rubber rod contains 10,000 excess electrons and carries a net negative charge. This charge can be completely neutralized by adding 10,000 _____ .

1•67 (protons) A polystyrene rod contains 25 electrons and 20 protons, hence its net charge is 5 units negative. Similarly, a body with 120 electrons and 150 protons has a net charge of 30 units _____ .

1·68 (positive) If 10 electrons are added to 8 protons, the net charge is −2. If 10 protons are added to 8 electrons, the net charge is +2. If 6 electrons are added to 3 protons, the net charge is _____.

1·69 (−3) If 12 electrons are added to 11 protons, the net charge is −1. If 12 protons are added to 10 electrons, the net charge is _____.

1·70 (+2) If 15 electrons are added to 10 protons, the net charge is _____.

1·71 (−5) A rod of X rubbed with the proper material loses 3 electrons per atom so that its net atomic charge is +3. Substance Y, similarly stroked, loses 2 electrons per atom and takes on a net atomic charge of +2. Substance Z loses 4 electrons per atom. Its net atomic charge is _____.

1·72 (+4) A rod of material A gains 4 electrons per atom to attain a net atomic charge of −4. Substance B gains 1 electron per atom and, therefore, attains a net atomic charge of _____.

1·73 (−1) Substance C, which loses 6 electrons per atom when stroked, takes on a net atomic charge of _____.

1·74 (+6) An atom of helium contains 2 neutrons and 2 protons in its nucleus; 2 planetary electrons circle the nucleus. The net atomic charge of this atom is zero. An atom of lithium contains 4 neutrons, 3 protons, and 3 electrons. Its net charge is zero. An atom of oxygen contains 8 protons, 8 neutrons, and 8 electrons. Its net charge is _____.

1·75 (zero) An atom of sodium contains 11 protons, 12 neutrons, and 11 electrons. Its net charge is _____.

1·76 (zero) An abnormal atom of a given substance contains 18 protons and 17 electrons. Its net charge is _____.

1·76 (+1)

A <u>normal atom</u> has exactly <u>the same number of protons in its nucleus as it has electrons in orbit.</u> Since the charge on an electron is equal in magnitude but opposite in sign to that of a proton, 1 electron can electrically neutralize 1 proton. Since normal atoms contain equal numbers of these opposite particles, normal atoms are neutral or uncharged. <u>In certain situations, electrons may be forced out of atoms by external influences.</u> When this occurs, the atom has one or more excess "+" charges that are no longer neutralized because it has <u>more protons than electrons.</u> Such atoms are called "<u>positive ions.</u>" It may also happen that an atom gains <u>one or more electrons;</u> since this type of charged atom is predominantly negative, it is a "<u>negative ion.</u>"

1•77   Normal atoms are electrically neutral. A normal hydrogen atom contains 1 electron and 1 proton for a net charge of zero. A normal helium atom contains 2 electrons and 2 protons for a net charge of zero. A normal sodium atom contains 11 electrons and _____ protons for a net charge of zero.

1•78   (11) A neutral oxygen atom contains 8 electrons and 8 protons. Thus, a neutral carbon atom contains 6 protons and _____ electrons.

1•79   (6) A neutral lithium atom has 3 protons in its nucleus, hence there must be _____ planetary electrons.

1•80   (3) A neutral hydrogen atom has 1 planetary electron but becomes a positive ion when it loses this electron. A neutral carbon atom has 6 electrons but becomes a positive ion when the count goes down to 5. Neutral lithium has 3 electrons per atom; hence a positive lithium ion forms when the count goes down to _____ electrons per atom.

1•81   (2) Neutral oxygen has 8 electrons per atom, but ionized oxygen may contain 7 electrons per atom. Similarly, neutral boron contains 5 electrons per atom, so that its positive ion might contain _____ electrons per atom.

1•82   (4) A neutral atom of silicon contains 14 electrons. Thus, a silicon ion with a positive charge might contain _____ electrons.

1•83 (13) When a hydrogen atom gains an electron, its electron count rises to 2 and it becomes a negative ion. A normal oxygen atom has 8 electrons; if it gains one more, its electron count goes up to 9 and it becomes a negative ion. A lithium atom has an electron count of 3, but when this count rises to 4 it becomes a negative _____ .

1•84 (ion) Normal neon contains 10 electrons per atom and forms negative ions when its atomic electron content becomes 11. Similarly, a normal argon atom contains 18 electrons, so that a negative argon ion may contain _____ electrons.

1•85 (19) Normal krypton atoms contain 36 electrons. A krypton atom with 37 electrons must be a _____ ion.

1•86 (negative) If a neutral atom gains or loses 2 or more electrons, it is said to be doubly ionized. If the gain or loss is 1 electron, it is singly ionized. If normal helium (2 electrons) loses 2 electrons, it becomes a doubly ionized positive ion. Thus, normal neon (10 electrons) becomes a doubly _____ positive ion when its electron content goes to 8 electrons per atom.

1•87 (ionized) Krypton forms doubly ionized positive ions when its normal electron count goes from 36 to _____ .

1•88 (34) A certain atom is acted upon by a strong electric force and emerges from the action with 18 nuclear protons and 17 planetary electrons. It is then called a singly charged positive ion. A second atom contains 12 protons and 10 electrons. This is a doubly charged positive ion. If an atom has 23 protons and 21 electrons, it is a _____ charged positive ion.

1•89 (doubly) An atom that has 42 protons and 43 electrons is a singly charged negative ion. If this atom gains 1 additional electron for a total of 44, it would then be a _____ charged _____ ion.

1•90 (doubly, negative) A singly charged positive ion that takes on one additional electron becomes a neutral atom. A doubly charged positive ion becomes a neutral atom when it takes on ___ _____ .

1·91 (2 electrons) An ion that has a net negative charge of 3 must lose 3 _____ to become a neutral atom.

1·92 (electrons) A neutral sodium atom contains 11 protons in its nucleus. When such an atom becomes a positive ion, it will contain _____ electrons in orbits around the nucleus.

1·92 (10)

Coulomb's law of electric charges

Coulomb's law expresses the relationship between *four* quantities: **1,** the amount or magnitude of the charge on body 1; **2,** the magnitude of the charge on body 2; **3,** the distance between the two bodies; and **4,** the resulting force of attraction or repulsion between the two bodies. In mathematical shorthand it may be written

$$F = \frac{q_1 \times q_2}{d^2}$$

where q_1 is the charge on body 1, q_2 is the charge on body 2, d^2 is the *square* of the distance separating the two bodies, and F is the force of attraction or repulsion between them.

It is very helpful to view such a relationship as a *proportion*. To see what this means, let us first assume that q_2 and d are held constant; of course, this signifies that the magnitude of the charge of body 2 and the distance between the two bodies are not going to change in any way. If this is so, it is easy to see that F is now proportional to q_1. If q_1 is doubled, then F will double; if q_1 is tripled, then F will triple; and so forth. This is what a proportionality means. Whatever multiplier or divisor you use on one side will also have to be put in on the other side of the equals sign.

Exactly the same effect is obtained if we assume that q_1 and d are held constant. In this case, F is proportional to q_2. Any arithmetical activity performed on one side will be followed by the same activity on the other.

Finally, if both q_1 and q_2 are held constant, we say that F is *inversely* proportional to the square of d. Looking at the equation above, imagine that $q_1 \times q_2$ is held fixed. For this condition, F will have some value that depends inversely on the square of d. Now imagine that we double the distance d. This doubling process is done *before* we square the term. Thus, if we double d, then d^2 will be four times larger than before; if we triple d, then d^2 will be nine times larger than before; if we quadruple d, then d^2 will be sixteen times larger. Since d^2 is a *divisor* on the right side, in order to keep the validity of the equals sign, we will have to divide the force F by the same quantity. Thus, if d is doubled, the force will be one-fourth as great as previously; if d is quadrupled, the force will be one-sixteenth as great as it was originally, and so on.

You will practice these manipulations in Frames 1·93 to 1·114.

1·93 This equation is a statement of Coulomb's law:

$$\text{Force between charged particles} = \frac{\text{charge No. 1} \times \text{charge No. 2}}{(\text{separation distance})^2}$$

If each charge is 1 unit of strength and the distance between charges is 1 unit of distance, then the force $= 1 \times 1/1^2 =$

$\frac{1 \times 1}{1^2} = \frac{1}{1} = 1$

_____ .

1·94 (1) If two charged bodies have charges of 10 and 20 units, respectively, and a separation of 2 units, then the force is 10×20 over $2^2 = 200/4 =$ _____ units of force.

1·95 (50) If the charges are 3 and 12 units and the separation is 3 units, the force is 4 units. Thus, if the charges are 4 and 25 units and the separation is 2 units, the force is _____ .

1·96 (25) Two unlike charges of 8 units each are separated by 4 units of distance. The force of attraction between them is 8×8 divided by $16 = 64/16 = 4$ units. Similarly, if two unlike charges of 20 units each are separated by 10 units of distance, the force of attraction between them is _____ units.

1·97 (4) Two like charges of 25 and 10 units, respectively, are separated by 5 units of distance. The force of repulsion between them would be _____ units.

1·98 (10) If we double the size of charge No. 1, the coulomb force doubles; if we triple the size of charge No. 1, the coulomb force triples; if charge No. 1 is made five times as large as it was previously with no other changes, the coulomb force will become _____ times as great.

1·99 (5) If charge No. 2 is cut in half, everything else remaining the same, the coulomb force will also be cut in half since we are dividing both sides of the equation by 2. If charge No. 2 is divided by 4, then the force will be one-fourth of its original value because we must divide both sides by _____ .

1·100 (4) If both charge No. 1 and charge No. 2 are doubled, the coulomb force increases by a factor of 4; if they are both tripled, the coulomb force goes up by a factor of 9; if they are both quadrupled, the coulomb force increases by a factor of _____ .

1•101 (16) If charge No. 1 is doubled and charge No. 2 is tripled, the coulomb force goes up by a factor of 6. If charge No. 1 is tripled and charge No. 2 is quadrupled, the coulomb force increases by a factor of _____ .

1•102 (12) If charge No. 1 is quadrupled and the coulomb force (distance unchanged) goes up by a factor of 20, then the value of charge No. 2 must have been multiplied by _____ .

1•103 (5) If charge No. 1 is tripled and charge No. 2 is changed so that the coulomb force remains *unchanged* (distance constant), then charge No. 2 must have been reduced enough to neutralize the increase of charge No. 1. Thus, for the case of a tripled charge No. 1, charge No. 2 must be reduced to one-_____ of its former value to keep the force unchanged.

1•104 (third) If the size of each charge is increased by a factor of 10, the coulomb force must rise by a factor of _____ .

1•105 (100) When any number is divided by the square of another number, the original number is reduced by a factor equal to the square of the divisor. For example, 144 divided by 2^2 means that 144 is reduced by a factor of 4, or 36. If 100 is divided by 2^2, it is reduced by a factor of 4, or down to 25. If 1,200 is divided by 10^2, it is reduced by a factor of 100, or down to _____ .

1•106 (12) The number 18 divided by the square of 3 is thus reduced to 2. The number 25 divided by the square of 5 is reduced to _____ .

1•107 (1) In Coulomb's law, it must be remembered that the product of the charges is divided by the square of the distance between them. Thus, if each charge has a value of 10 units, and if the charges are separated by 2 units, the total force is 10×10 divided by $2^2 = 25$. If each charge has a value of 12 units and the separation is 4 units, then the force is _____ units.

1•108 (9) If the distance between charges is doubled (with no change of charge), the force is reduced to one-fourth its initial value because it goes down by the square of 2. If the distance is tripled, the force is reduced to one-ninth. If the distance is quadrupled, the force is reduced to _____ .

1·109 (¹⁄₁₆) If the distance between charges is increased by a factor of five, the force is reduced by 25. If the distance is increased by a factor of seven, the force is reduced by a factor of _____.

1·110 (49) If the distance between charges is increased tenfold, the force between charges is reduced to _____ of its initial value.

1·111 (¹⁄₁₀₀) We can calculate the combined action of changes in both charge strength and distance as follows. Suppose charge No. 1 is doubled and charge No. 2 is made eight times as great as it was; suppose that the distance is simultaneously increased to two times its former figure. The force then changes by a factor of

$$\frac{2 \times 8}{2^2} = \underline{\hspace{2cm}}$$

1·112 (4) Now try this: Charge No. 1 is increased by 5, charge No. 2 is decreased by a factor of 5, and the distance is reduced to one-half its former value. The charge change is

$$\frac{5 \times \frac{1}{5}}{(\frac{1}{2})^2} = \underline{\hspace{3cm}} \text{ times its former value}$$

1·113 (four) If charge No. 1 were increased by 5, charge No. 2 decreased by a factor of 10, and the distance reduced to one-half of its former value, the force would be changed by a factor of _____ .

1·114 (2) Charge No. 1 is quadrupled, charge No. 2 is divided by 2, and the distance is doubled. This gives

$$\frac{4 \times \frac{1}{2}}{2^2}$$

Thus, for this case the force is changed by a factor of _____ .

1·114 (½)

Introduction to the electric field

The ability of charged bodies to exert forces on one another over a distance, with no contact between them, is attributed to the existence of *electric fields* brought into being by the presence of the charges. The actual nature of an electric field cannot be visualized; that is, there is no purely mechanical or objective model which permits us to picture such a phenomenon. Nevertheless, we attempt to describe the field in terms of its behavior and effect upon material objects. This description is made possible by imagining (and this is pure imagination!) the field to be made up of *lines of force* whose characteristics we define in terms of the forces we suppose them to exert.

Lines of force are arbitrarily assigned a direction. That is, they are described by straight lines with arrowheads, always pointing in the direction in which an isolated *positive* charge would move as a result of the force exerted on it by the field. The choice of a positive, rather than a negative, charge is purely conventional. It is important to remember that the lines of force that surround a stationary charge do *not* in themselves move; the assigned direction merely provides information relative to the motion that another charge would follow if it were free to do so.

1•115 All charged bodies are surrounded by an electric field consisting of lines of force. A line of force has a direction indicated by an arrow. Thus, in Fig. 1•115, the line above the "+" charge is shown going upward. Similarly, the line below the "+" charge is shown going _____ .

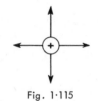

Fig. 1•115

1•116 (downward) The direction of a line of force is taken as the direction in which an isolated positive charge would move if placed on that line. In Fig. 1•116 an isolated "+" charge placed to the right of the positive body would move to the right. Thus, the arrowhead on this line points toward the

_____ .

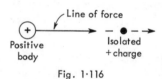

Fig. 1•116

1•117 (right) In Fig. 1•117, the line of force to the left of the central "+" body shows by its arrowhead that the direction of this line of force is to the left. Hence, an isolated "+" charge placed on this line would move toward the _____ .

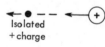

Fig. 1•117

1•118 (left) In Fig. 1•118a, charged body *A* exhibits a line of force directed toward point *B* since this is the direction in which the isolated "+" charge would move in this region. Thus, in Fig. 1•118b, the isolated positive charge would indicate a line of force directed toward point _____ .

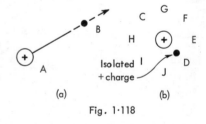

Fig. 1•118

1•119 (*D*) In Fig. 1•119, the unit positive charges show that the lines of force from the central positive body are all directed _____ the central body. (away from/toward)

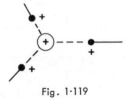

Fig. 1•119

1·120 (away from) In Fig. 1·120a, the "+" charge would move downward toward the negative body since opposites attract. Similarly, in Fig. 1·120b, the unit "+" charge would move from D toward C, hence the line of force has this direction. Thus, in Fig. 1·120c, the line of force has a direction from _____ to _____.

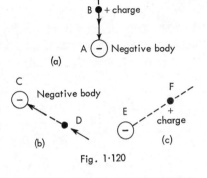

Fig. 1·120

1·121 (F, E) Figure 1·121 shows the lines of force around a *negative* body. Arrowheads could be placed on either the ends labeled A or the ends labeled B. Since this is a negative body, an isolated positive charge would move toward it, hence the arrowheads should be placed on the ends labeled _____.

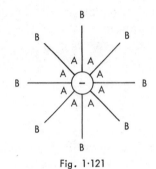

Fig. 1·121

1·122 (A) The strength of a charged body is shown by the number or density of its lines of force. For example, in Fig. 1·122a, a weak positive charge is shown because there are few lines of force. In Fig. 1·122b, a somewhat greater charge is indicated by the greater line density. In Fig. 1·122c, the field strength or charge magnitude is considerably _____ than in either of the other two.

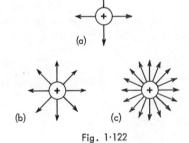

Fig. 1·122

1·123 (greater) Refer to Fig. 1·123. Although the kind of charge is not indicated in this drawing, the charged body at the center must have a _____ charge since the arrows point away from it, showing that this would be the direction of motion of a nearby unit positive charge.

Fig. 1·123

1·124 (positive) Refer to Fig. 1·124. Here again, the kind of charge is not indicated, but we can tell from the arrow directions that it must be a _____ charged body.

Fig. 1·124

1·125 (negatively) Refer to Fig. 1·125. The charged body shown in this figure must be _____ charged and must have relatively _____ strength.

Fig. 1·125

1·126 (negatively, great) When two similar charges are placed near each other, the interaction of their lines seems to be that of repulsion; if the charges are opposite, their lines of force appear to attract each other. The two charges shown in Fig. 1·126 must be _____ charges.

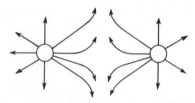

Fig. 1·126

1·127 (similar or like) Refer to Fig. 1·127. These two charges must be _____ in sign.

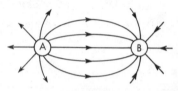

Fig. 1·127

1·128 (opposite or unlike) Judging from the arrow directions, charge *A* in Fig. 1·127 must be a _____ charge.

1·129 (positive) Charge *B* must be a _____ charge (Fig. 1·127).

1·129 (negative)

The electroscope

An electroscope is an instrument used to detect the presence of electric charges. Some electroscopes are also useful for determining the magnitude of a charge. The "leaf" form of electroscope shown in Fig. 1·130 consists of a conducting stem topped by a knob, or disc, and terminated at the bottom by a very thin, lightweight pair of metallic leaves. The lower assembly is enclosed within a protective case. As we will see, an electroscope is often employed to determine the *polarity* (plus or minus) of a charge on a body.

1·130 Figure 1·130 illustrates an instrument called an electroscope. Its knob, stem, and leaves are all initially electrically neutral, since they contain equal numbers of electrons and protons. When a negative body is brought near the knob, some outer planetary electrons of the metal atoms in the knob are torn loose and are driven down to the leaves, giving them an excess of electrons. The leaves will then spread apart because they are both _____ charged.

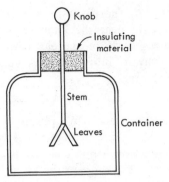

Fig. 1·130

1·131 (negatively) If a positively charged body is brought near the knob of a neutral electroscope, the leaves spread apart because the positive body will attract some of the electrons in the atoms of the metal leaves up to the knob, leaving both leaves _____ charged.

1·132 (positively) If a negative body is touched to the knob, some of its extra electrons will transfer to the knob and run down into the leaves, causing them to spread by imparting a _____ _____ to each.

1·133 (negative charge) A positive body is brought *near* an electroscope that is already negatively charged from previous contact with a treated rubber rod. Since opposites attract, some of the _____ charges already in the leaves will be pulled up into the knob.

1·134 (negative or electron) Owing to the original charge on the leaves, they were <u>diverged.</u> Now, when some of this original charge is withdrawn from the leaves, the amount of divergence will be _____ than it was previously.

1·135 (less or smaller) When a divergence decreases, we speak of this as a condition of "collapsing leaves." Thus, when a positive body is brought near the knob of a negatively charged electroscope, it causes the leaves to _____ .

1·136 (collapse) Note that electrons do not leap across the gap between the positive rod and the knob, since air does not freely carry electric charges. The electrons pulled up into the knob by the presence of the _____ body near the knob simply gather there in more concentrated array.

1·137 (positive) In a similar manner, a negative body brought near the knob of a positively charged electroscope forces some of the electrons initially in the knob to move downward into the leaves, since like charges _____ each other.

1·138 (repel) In a positively charged electroscope, however, the leaves are diverged because of the *deficiency* of electrons there. Now, if more electrons are forced into the leaves by the negative body near the knob, they will help to neutralize the existing positive charge, thereby causing the charge on the leaves to become _____ than it was before.

1·139 (smaller, less, weaker, etc.) When the charge on the leaves becomes smaller, the force of repulsion between them also becomes _____ .

1·140 (smaller) Hence, the leaves would tend to collapse. Thus, when a _____ body is brought near a positive electroscope, the leaves of the electroscope tend to collapse.

1·140 (negative)

Distribution of electric charges

The amount of curvature on the surface of a conductor governs the density of the charges on this surface. To make the language clear, let us first define what we mean by curvature and how this is related to the *radius* of the curve.

A plane surface is flat. Such a surface has no curvature whatever; its curvature is *zero*. A plane may be thought of as a small section of a *sphere of infinite radius*. Such a sphere would be so large that a tiny section of it would appear quite flat. Thus, a surface with zero curvature, such as a plane, has an *infinite* radius. This is, of course, a limiting condition; we are more concerned with intermediate surfaces.

For example, a very large balloon used for stratospheric exploration has a very large radius of curvature but is nearly flat on the surface, hence, has a very small curvature. As we shrink the balloon, its radius becomes smaller and its curvature greater. A very small sphere has a sharp or large curvature. As a limiting condition in this direction, we may consider a *point*, such as the point on the end of a sharpened pencil. The surface of the point has an extremely *small radius* and therefore an extremely *large curvature*.

It is easily demonstrated that when a conductor is charged, the charges are always found in largest concentrations (highest densities) on surfaces of greatest curvature or smallest radius. Since a sphere has uniform curvature (the same all over), the charge density is found to be uniform over the surface. But, on an egg-shaped conductor, the density is highest at the pointed end and least over the straight portions, while the rounded end has a density somewhere between the two extremes.

1·141 When a conducting body is electrically charged, the individual charges distribute themselves on the body according to the curvature at various points. If the curvature is everywhere uniform, the charge distribution is uniform. A sphere has uniform curvature, hence the charge distribution on the surface of a sphere is _____ .

1·142 (uniform) The major surface of a perfect cylinder has uniform curvature, hence the charge distribution on the major surface of a charged cylinder is _____ .

1·143 (uniform) The major surface of a perfect plane has uniform zero curvature throughout. A charged metallic plane would exhibit a _____ charge distribution on its major face.

1·144 (uniform) A metallic egg (Fig. 1·144) displays the largest curvature at the "sharper" end (end *B* in Fig. 1·144). Electric charges tend to concentrate in greater density in areas of greater curvature, hence a greater charge density would appear at end _____ of the egg after charging.

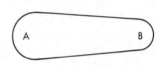

Fig. 1·144

1·145 (*B*) Figure 1·145 illustrates an ellipsoid of metal. When charged, this body would display the largest density at points *A* and _____ .

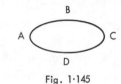

Fig. 1·145

1·146 (*C*) Figure 1·146 illustrates a rounded, three-dimensional cone of metal having a uniformly curved left end (*ABC*) and a pointed right end (*D*). The charge distribution on surface *ABC* is _____ .

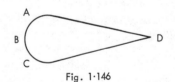

Fig. 1·146

1·147 (uniform) The largest charge density appears at the location labeled _____ (Fig. 1·146).

1·148 (*D*) If a charged body is hollow, all the charges are found on the outside surface and none of the charges on the inside surface. Figure 1·148 shows a thick-walled metallic sphere that is hollow. When this body is charged, the entire charge will appear on surface _____ .

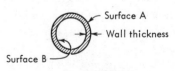

Surface A
Wall thickness
Surface B
Fig. 1·148

1·149 (*A*) Figure 1·149 illustrates the cross section of a thick-walled hollow metal pipe extending along a straight line in and out of the page. The inside surface will be found to have zero charge, while the outside surface will be found to be carrying the entire charge. Therefore, the charge density on the surface *GHI* is _____.

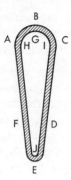

Fig. 1·149

1·150 (zero) In Fig. 1·149 the largest concentration of charges appears in the area labeled _____.

1·151 (*E*) In Fig. 1·149, although the curvature at point *J* is very great, the charge density is zero because point *J* is on an _____ surface.

1·152 (inside) The surfaces *F* and *D* in Fig. 1·149 are perfect planes. That is, they are quite flat and have zero curvature. Thus, there are no points of different curvature on them. Hence, when this body is electrified, the _____ distribution on these surfaces must be uniform.

1·153 (charge) Four perfect charged spheres are shown in Fig. 1·153. Only one of these (*A*, *B*, *C*, or *D*) is correctly drawn with respect to charge distribution. The correct drawing is that of sphere _____.

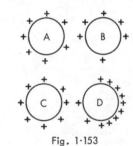

Fig. 1·153

1·154 (*C*) Two charged bodies of nonspherical shape are shown in Fig. 1·154 (*E* and *F*). The one that is correctly drawn with respect to charge distribution is _____.

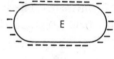

Fig. 1·154

1·155 (*F*) A positive charge is transferred to the egg-shaped metallic body of Fig. 1·155. The greatest concentration of charge would be found at or around point _____ .

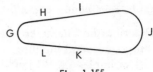

Fig. 1·155

1·156 (*G*) High-voltage discharge can occur across air gaps when enough electrical pressure is applied between two electrodes. The larger the charge concentration at the ends of the electrodes, the larger the gap can be for a given pressure. Three gaps made of differently shaped electrodes are shown in Fig. 1·156. The one that will spark most easily at minimum voltage is that of _____ .

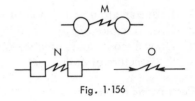

Fig. 1·156

1·157 (*O*) A lightning rod is used to discharge the charge that accumulates on a house during an electric storm. Such a discharge occurs most easily when the house charge can be made to concentrate in one vicinity. Thus, the end of a lightning rod should be as _____ as possible.

1·158 (pointed) Assume that the two hollow brass spheres in Fig. 1·158 have been charged. Each sphere has an *inside* and *outside* surface. Bearing in mind that charges reside on outside surfaces of conductors, which diagram shows the correct behavior of the leaves of the electroscopes? _____ .

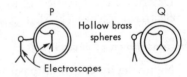

Hollow brass spheres

Electroscopes

Fig. 1·158

1·159 (*P*) Tests with an electroscope show that no charge at all exists on the _____ surface of a hollow charged body.

1·159   (inner)

MEASURABLE BEHAVIORAL OBJECTIVES

Upon completion of a section, you should be able to achieve the objectives listed for it. The frame or frames that cover the related subject matter are indicated immediately following each objective.

States of matter

1   List the three states of matter.   (1·1)
2   Describe the characteristics of each state.   (1·2 to 1·5)
3   Give examples of matter in each of the states.   (1·6, 1·8, 1·9)

Elements, compounds, and mixtures

1 Describe the characteristics of, and differentiate between, elements, compounds, and mixtures. $(1 \cdot 11, 1 \cdot 13, 1 \cdot 15)$
2 List examples of elements, compounds, and mixtures. $(1 \cdot 12, 1 \cdot 14, 1 \cdot 16)$

Atoms and molecules

1 Define an atom and a molecule. $(1 \cdot 24, 1 \cdot 25)$
2 Give examples of atoms and molecules. $(1 \cdot 23, 1 \cdot 26)$
3 Draw a model and name the three fundamental particles which go into the structure of atoms. $(1 \cdot 27, 1 \cdot 30)$

Electrostatic forces

1 Determine when two bodies will repel each other due to electrostatic force. $(1 \cdot 38, 1 \cdot 39)$
2 Describe how one can demonstrate that two bodies can attract each other due to electrostatic force. $(1 \cdot 40)$

Law of electric charges

1 Describe how one can attain a positively or negatively charged body. $(1 \cdot 51)$
2 Determine the direction of force between two charged bodies (law of electric charges). $(1 \cdot 51, 1 \cdot 53)$

The constitution of charges

1 Name the fundamental positive and negative charges. $(1 \cdot 59, 1 \cdot 62)$
2 Determine the net charges on a body if the number of fundamental charges is given. $(1 \cdot 63, 1 \cdot 74)$

Atoms and ions

1 Define what a neutral atom is in terms of its electrically charged particles. $(1 \cdot 77)$
2 Describe the formation of positive and negative ions. $(1 \cdot 80, 1 \cdot 83, 1 \cdot 89)$

Coulomb's law of electric charges

State Coulomb's law in mathematical or verbal form. $(1 \cdot 93)$
a Name the quantities that are proportional and the quantity that is inversely proportional to force between charged bodies. $(1 \cdot 98, 1 \cdot 99, 1 \cdot 107)$
b Solve problems with three of the four quantities given or using proportionalities of Coulomb's law. $(1 \cdot 94, 1 \cdot 98, 1 \cdot 108)$

Introduction to the electric field

1 Discuss the existence of an electric field and its relation to the lines of force. $(1 \cdot 115, 1 \cdot 120)$
2 State the convention for assigning direction to the lines of force originating from positive or negative charges. $(1 \cdot 115, 1 \cdot 120)$
3 Determine the interaction of lines of forces. $(1 \cdot 126, 1 \cdot 127)$

The electroscope

1 State the three principal functions of an electroscope.   (1·131 to 1·134)
2 Describe the operation of a leaf electroscope.   (1·130)

Distribution of electric charges

Determine the distribution of charges: (Introduction)
 a On the surface of a conductor of uniform curvature.   (1·141)
 b On the surface of a conductor of changing curvature.   (1·146, 1·147)
 c On the inside surface of a hollow conductor.   (1·148)

chapter 2
charges in motion

The meaning of electric current

We define an electric current, in a preliminary fashion, as a flow of electrons through a conductor. Static electricity is concerned with electricity at rest; current electricity deals with electric charges in motion. At this point, we will recognize that an electric current will flow when a conductor joins two points, one of which is more negative than the other. As we have seen, electrons must move from more negative regions to less negative (or more positive) regions as long as there is a conductor to carry them.

2·1 An electric current consists of a flow of electrons from a negatively charged body through a conductor to a positively charged body. In Fig. 2·1b, the arrow should be pointing to the _____ to indicate the direction of the current.

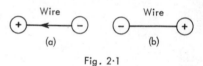

Fig. 2·1

2·2 (right) In the alternating short- and long-line symbol of a battery (Fig. 2·2a), the short line represents a point of negative charge and the long line, a point of positive charge. Thus, the arrowheads show the current in the wire flowing from A toward B or from negative to positive. In Fig. 2·2b, arrowheads should be drawn on the wire CD going from _____ to _____ .

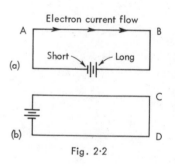

Fig. 2·2

2·3 (D, C) In Fig. 2·3, arrowheads should be drawn to indicate the current flowing into the lamp filament from the _____ side to the _____ side.

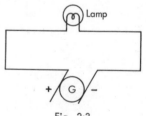

Fig. 2·3

2·4 (right, left) The magnitude of a charge is measured in terms of the number of excess unit charges that are present. The fundamental practical charge quantity is the coulomb. One coulomb contains 6.3×10^{18} electrons. Hence, 3 coulombs contain _____ electrons.

2·5 (18.9×10^{18}) Five coulombs contain 31.5×10^{18} electrons. Ten coulombs contain _____ electrons.

2·6 (63×10^{18} or 6.3×10^{19}) One-half a coulomb could be written as _____ electrons.

2·7 (3.15×10^{18}) The magnitude of an electric current is measured in amperes. A wire carries a current of 1 amp if 1 coulomb flows through it each second. Thus, the current in a wire is 3 amp if 3 coulombs flow through it in 1 sec. Also, the current is 10 amp if _____ coulombs flow through it in 1 sec.

2·8 (10) A wire that carries 4.6 coulombs/sec is carrying a current of ___ _____ .

2·9 (4.6 amp) Three coulombs flowing through a wire in one second constitutes three amperes. Four coulombs flowing through the wire in two seconds constitutes two amperes. Eight coulombs every two seconds would constitute _____ amperes.

2·10 (four) Ten coulombs per second is a current of ten amperes. Ten coulombs in five seconds is a current of _____ amperes.

2·11 (two) Twelve coulombs that require twelve seconds to flow through a wire constitutes a current of _____ ampere(s).

2·12 (one) A current of 30 amp is the same as _____ coulombs/sec.

2·13 (30) To find the current in amperes in any circuit, divide the number of coulombs flowing in this circuit by the _____ required for this number of coulombs to move through any part of the circuit.

2·14 (time) Letting Q stand for coulombs, t for seconds, and I for amperes, the correct equation for finding current is _____ .

$I = \dfrac{Q}{t}$

2·14 $(I = Q/t)$

Conductivity and resistance

At ordinary temperatures, perfect conductors do not exist. All substances, including copper and other metals, offer a definite amount of *resistance* to the flow of current. The actual resistance offered depends upon four distinct factors: **1,** the nature of the material used as the conductor; **2,** the temperature; **3,** the length of the conductor; and **4,** the cross-sectional area of the conductor. For our purposes, it is sufficient to know that the resistance of a metallic conductor will rise if its temperature is raised, its length is increased, its thickness is decreased, and vice versa.

Materials differ widely in resistance. The best conductor known is silver; compared with silver, metals like iron have considerably greater resistance. Some substances such as germanium, silicon, and others offer much greater resistance to current than do normal metals like copper and aluminum; hence, these special materials are called "*semiconductors.*" These are the materials used in the manufacture of crystal rectifiers and transistors. Finally, we have the family known as *insulators* (rubber, bakelite, wood, etc.). Such substances have extremely high resistance per unit length. Just as there are no perfect conductors, there are no perfect insulators. All insulators allow a small amount of current to flow when conditions are set up correctly, but this amount of current is insignificant (usually) when compared with the current that would flow under the same conditions if the insulator were replaced by a semiconductor or a normal metal.

2·15 Every substance offers some opposition to the flow of electricity. This opposition, called resistance and symbolized by R, is measured in ohms (Ω). If lamp A has a resistance of 10 ohms and lamp B a resistance of 20 ohms, then lamp B offers twice the opposition of lamp A to the electric current. If lamp C has a resistance twice that of lamp B, then lamp C offers _____ _____ the opposition of lamp A.

2·16 (four times) The resistance of a toaster is 150 ohms. The resistance of a certain lamp is 75 ohms; thus the opposition offered by the lamp to the flow of electricity is _____ as great as that of the toaster.

2·17 (one-half) The resistance of a certain electric toaster is about 25 ohms. A 200-watt incandescent lamp has about twice this resistance, or 50 ohms. A 100-watt lamp has a resistance of about four times the toaster, hence its R is ____ _____ .

2·18 (100 ohms) The resistance of a 50-watt lamp is about 200 ohms. The resistance of a 25-watt lamp is about 400 ohms. If a 12½-watt lamp were manufactured, its resistance would be about ____ _____ .

2·19 (800 ohms) If the R of a given wire is 0.1 ohm and its resistance is doubled, the new R would be ____ _____ .

2·20 (0.2 ohm) The best electrical conductor is pure silver; the next best is copper, followed in line by aluminum, tungsten, and zinc. This means that iron must have a higher _____ than aluminum.

2·21 (resistance) Tungsten must have a _____ resistance than porcelain, a ceramic material.

2·22 (lower) The resistance of a given piece of wire is 0.04 ohm. The resistance of another piece of wire identical to the first in all respects, except material, is 0.06 ohm. If the first piece is copper, the second might be _____ .

2·23 (aluminum or tungsten or zinc) Materials that have very high resistance are classed as nonconductors or insulators. A short piece of iron has a resistance of 0.01 ohm. The same length of another material has a resistance of 10 million ohms. The second material could be classified as a(n) _____ .

2·24 (insulator or nonconductor) The ability of a substance to conduct electricity is related to the ease with which electrons from the outer orbits of its atoms can be stripped "free" of the nucleus. Under the pressure exerted by electric forces, these electrons can then act as current "carriers." Very good conductors have many free electrons, hence a substance like copper must have _____ _____ _____ .

2·25 (many free electrons) Poorer conductors such as iron and certain alloys like Nichrome and german silver must have _____ free electrons than silver or copper.

2·26 (fewer or less) Nonconductors or insulators like wood and glass, therefore, have extremely _____ free electrons.

2·26 (few)

Factors that control resistance of conductors

We have already mentioned the fact that the resistance of a given conductor depends upon its material, temperature, length, and cross-sectional area. Now let us look at a simple algebraic equation which combines these factors in a single expression:

$$R = \rho \frac{L}{A}$$

where R = resistance, ohms

ρ = specific resistivity of the material at the temperature being worked with (ρ is the Greek character rho, pronounced "row")

L = length, ft

A = cross-sectional area, sq in.

Specific resistivities of materials are given in terms of ohm-feet and may be found in appropriate tables in many books. They are usually given for a conductor temperature of zero degrees centigrade; then by means of another quantity called the temperature coefficient of resistivity, one can determine the specific resistivity at the particular temperature being worked. This gives the factor rho for the given material and temperature. In the equation above, ρ may be considered a constant under a fixed set of conditions.

Thus, the equation states that the resistance of a conductor is directly proportional to its length and inversely proportional to its cross-sectional area. For a given material at a given temperature, if we double its length, we double its resistance; but if we double its area, we *halve* its resistance. This is the meaning of proportions as discussed in the introduction to the previous section.

2·27   The resistance of a conductor is directly proportional to its length. A wire that is 2 ft long has twice the resistance of a 1-ft length of similar wire. A 3-ft length has three times the resistance of a 1-ft length. Thus, a 10-ft length of similar wire has _____ times the resistance of the 1-ft length.

2·28   (ten)   One thousand feet of No. 10 copper wire at 0°C has a resistance of very close to 1 ohm; thus 500 ft of the same wire at the same temperature has a resistance of 0.5 ohm. Also, 2,000 ft of the same wire at the same temperature has a resistance of ____ _____ .

2·29   (2 ohms)   The resistance of 10 ft of very thin Nichrome wire is about 40 ohms. One hundred feet of the same wire at the same temperature would be ____ _____ .

2·30 (400 ohms) If the length of a piece of wire having a resistance of 5,000 ohms is reduced to one-fifth of its initial value, the resistance of the new length must be ___ _____ .

2·31 (1,000 ohms) The resistance of a wire varies inversely as the cross-sectional area of the wire. R is the dependent variable, and A is the independent variable. When two variables are inversely proportional, multiplication of the independent variable by any factor must result in division of the dependent variable by the same factor, and vice versa. For example, if the area of a wire's cross section is doubled, its resistance goes down to one-half of what it was before; if the area is tripled, the resistance becomes one-third. If the area is quadrupled, the resistance goes down to _____ of its initial value.

2·32 (one-fourth) A certain wire with an area of 0.1 sq in. has a resistance of 24 ohms; the same material with an area of 0.2 sq in. has a resistance of 12 ohms. Similarly, when the area is increased to 0.4 sq in., the resistance is 6 ohms; finally, when the area is increased to 0.8 sq in., the resistance is _____ ohms.

2·33 (3) A given wire of fixed length and temperature is replaced by another wire of the same material, length, and temperature, except that its cross-sectional area is twelve times larger than the first. The resistance of the new wire is_____ that of the old one.

2·34 (one-twelfth) Combining the two proportions, we can say that resistance is directly proportional to length and inversely proportional to cross-sectional area. If both length and area are doubled, this means that the resistance is first doubled, then halved. Thus, the resistance must remain the_____ .

2·35 (same) If the length of a wire is doubled and its area is reduced to one-half, we have: doubling length causes resistance to double; halving area also causes resistance to double. Hence, in this case the resistance must become_____ times as great as it was initially.

2·36 (four) If the length of a wire is tripled, its resistance tends to triple; if, at the same time, its area is cut in half, its resistance would tend to double owing to this alone. Thus one action causes the resistance to triple and the other causes it to double; the whole effect is, therefore, the *product* of the two actions. Thus, in this case, the resistance would be _____ times as great as before the two changes were made.

2·37 (six) If the length of a wire is doubled and its area is doubled, its resistance is the same as before, since $2/2 = 1$. Or if the length is tripled and the area is tripled, the resistance again does not change, since $3/3 = 1$. If the length is tripled and the area increased by a factor of 6, the new resistance is _____ as great.

2·38 (one-half) When the length of a wire is doubled, its resistance tends to become *two times* as great; if its area is simultaneously quadrupled, its resistance tends to become *one-fourth* as great. Taken together, the two effects are $2 \times \frac{1}{4}$. Thus, doubling the length and quadrupling the area would cause the resistance to change by a factor of _____.

2·39 (½) As the temperature of a metallic conductor rises, its resistance increases. For example, a given copper wire has a resistance of 100 ohms at 0°C, a resistance of 100.85 ohms at 2°C, and a resistance of 101.7 ohms at 4°C. Thus, if the resistance of a metallic sample is 83.4 ohms at one temperature and 83.04 ohms at the second temperature, we may be sure that the temperature of the wire must have gone

_____ .

2·40 (down) In order to cause the resistance of a given metallic sample to change from 0.001 to 0.0001 ohm, it would be necessary to _____ its temperature.

2·41 (lower or decrease) As the temperature of certain non-metallic conductors such as carbon rises, their resistance decreases. At lower temperatures, the resistance of a given sample of carbon is greater. Thus, to change the resistance of a carbon sample from 1.2 to 1.5 ohms, its temperature would have to be reduced. Similarly, to change the resistance of a block of carbon from 1.8 to 1.1 ohms, the temperature would have to be _____ .

2·42 (increased) Substances whose resistance *rises* with *rising* temperature are said to have *positive* temperature coefficients. Thus, copper has a positive coefficient. Substances whose resistance *falls* with *rising* temperature have *negative* coefficients. Thus, carbon has a _____ temperature coefficient.

2·43 (negative) The resistance of a given conductor is 725.8 ohms at 10°C and 725.9 ohms at 10.3°C. This substance has a _____ temperature coefficient.

2·43 (positive)

As we have previously pointed out, an electric current will flow through a conductor joining two charged bodies if there is a difference in the amount of charge on each body. We have spoken of "positive" and "negative" bodies as though they were unique. Actually, a current will flow from a negative body having a charge strength of, say, 1,000 units to *another negative* body having a charge strength of 500 units, because, as the numbers show, the first body is *more negative* than the other. It would be perfectly all right to state that the second body is *positive with respect* to the first, even though the second body is negative as tested by an electroscope. In other words, positiveness and negativeness are relative terms. If a current flows from *A* to *B*, then *A* is negative with respect to *B*, or *B* is positive with respect to *A*, regardless of their actual polarities as measured by instrument.

When a current flows from one body to another through a conductor, we say that there must have been a *difference of potential* between them. Difference of potential, which is measured in *volts* and is therefore called "voltage," is due to the fact that the bodies have different charge strengths. Potential difference may be produced electrostatically by stroked rods, by means of a dry cell or other chemical battery, and by various means still to be discussed. For the moment, although we confess that we are not being very exact, we shall also call potential difference by other names: electromotive force (abbrev. emf) and voltage.

A volt may be defined as that difference of potential which, when applied across one ohm of resistance, will produce a current of one ampere.

2•44 When a negative body is connected to a positive body, electrons flow until both have the *same excess or deficiency* of electrons. If the negative body has 1 excess electron and the positive body is deficient by 1 electron, this electron will move from negative to positive, making both bodies electrically

_____ .

2•45 (neutral or equal) If a body with 1,000 excess electrons is connected to a body with a deficiency of 1,000 electrons, then 1,000 electrons will move from the "−" to the "+." At the end of the process, neither body will have an excess or a _____ of electrons, making the potential difference between them zero.

2•46 (deficiency) If a body with 1,000 excess electrons is connected to a body with 500 excess electrons, then _____ will flow from the more negative to the less negative body until they both have an excess of 750 electrons.

2•47 (250) When a body with 20 excess electrons is connected to a body with 10 excess electrons, 5 electrons shift over so that both bodies finish with_____ excess electrons.

2·48　(15) If a body with 30 excess electrons is connected to a body with zero excess or deficiency, 15 electrons will shift over so that the net charge on both bodies is now 15. If a net negative body of 250 electrons is connected to a net zero body, there will be a shift of _____ electrons.

2·49　(125) If a net negative body of 120 electrons is connected to a net negative body of 80 electrons, there will be a shift of _____ electrons.

2·50　(20) If a net negative body of 100 electrons is connected to a net positive body of 50 (deficiency of 50 electrons), 75 electrons will shift over so that both bodies finish with a net charge of −25. If a negative body of 500 electrons is connected to a net positive body of 100 (deficiency of 100 electrons), there will be a shift of 300 electrons so that both bodies finish with a net negative charge of −200. Thus, when a body of −80 is connected to a body of +20, there will be a shift of _____ electrons so that both bodies finish with −30.

2·51　(50) When a −150 body is connected to a +100 body, a shift of 125 electrons will cause both bodies to finish with a net charge of _____ .

2·52　(−25) A −2,000 body is connected to a +500 body by a copper wire. A total of 1,250 electrons will then move from one to the other. At the end of this process, the first body will have a net charge of 2,000 − 1,250 = 750 electrons and the second body will have a net charge of 1,250 − 500 = _____ electrons, making the potential difference zero.

2·53　(750) A volt is that difference in potential that will drive 1 amp through 1 ohm of resistance. (Potential difference is often called emf or voltage.) Two volts will drive 2 amp through 1 ohm of resistance. Also, 10 volts will drive 10 amp through 1 ohm of resistance. Thus, 20 volts will drive _____ amp through 1 ohm of resistance.

2·54　(20) If a voltage of 1 volt exists between two bodies and they are connected by a wire of 1 ohm, the current then flowing is 1 amp; if the voltage is raised to 2 volts, using the same wire, the current will be 2 amp; if the voltage is raised to 10 volts, the current will be _____ amp.

2·55 (10) If a potential difference of 0.1 volt exists between two charged bodies connected by 1 ohm of resistance, a current of 0.1 amp will flow; if the potential difference is now raised to 0.5 volt, the current will become _____ amp.

2·56 (0.5) A current of _____ will flow between body A and body B if the emf is 20 volts and the resistance between them is 1 ohm.

2·57 (20 amp) If the resistance is constant, doubling the emf causes the current to double; similarly, trebling the emf causes the current to triple. When two quantities are related in this manner, they are said to be directly proportional to each other. Thus, current must be directly _____ to the emf.

2·58 (proportional) The voltage in a given circuit is 88 volts. For the conditions present in this circuit, the current happens to be 16 amp. The voltage is now reduced to 22 volts. The new current will be ___ _____ .

2·58 (4 amp)

The electric circuit

In Frames 2·59 to 2·66, we define complete and incomplete circuits in electricity. It is important to note that a circuit is complete if the electrons from the source of emf can flow completely around the circuit back to the "+" end of the source.

2·59 A circuit is called complete if electrons can flow from the negative end of a source of emf, through a resistance, and back to the positive end of the source. The circuit in Fig. 2·59 is an example of a _____ circuit.

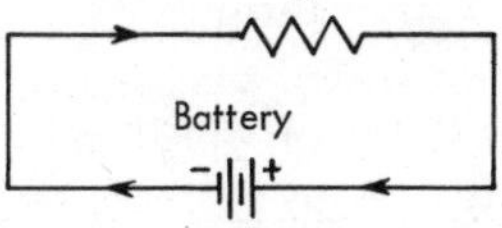

Fig. 2·59

2·60 (complete) A circuit is called incomplete or open if a break in the circuit prevents the flow described in Frame 2·59. The circuit in Fig. 2·59 is not open because electrons can flow from the negative end of the source, through R, and back to the _____ end of the source without interruption.

2·61 (positive) In Fig. 2·61 a switch has been added and the polarity of the battery reversed. This is still a _____ circuit, but the current flows in a counterclockwise direction in this circuit because a polarity reversal means interchanging the _____ and _____ ends of the battery.

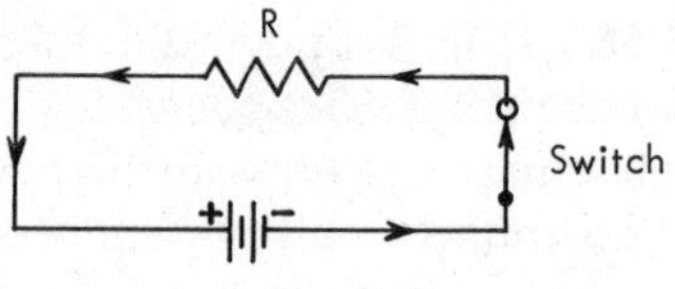

Fig. 2·61

2·62 (complete, negative, positive) The circuit of Fig. 2·62 is a(n) _____ circuit because the switch is shown moved to such a position as to prevent electrons from returning to the _____ of emf.

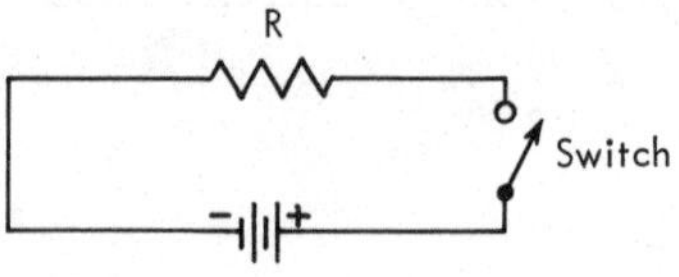

Fig. 2·62

2·63 (open or incomplete, source or positive end) The circuit of Fig. 2·63 is a(n) _____ circuit because the switch is shown moved to such a position as to prevent electrons from flowing through the _____ .

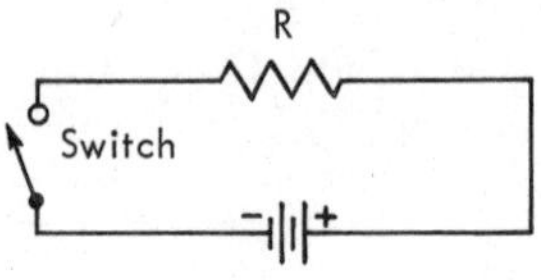

Fig. 2·63

2·64 (open, resistance) In Fig. 2·64, the circuit must be considered to be a(n) _____ circuit if both switches are in the open position, as shown.

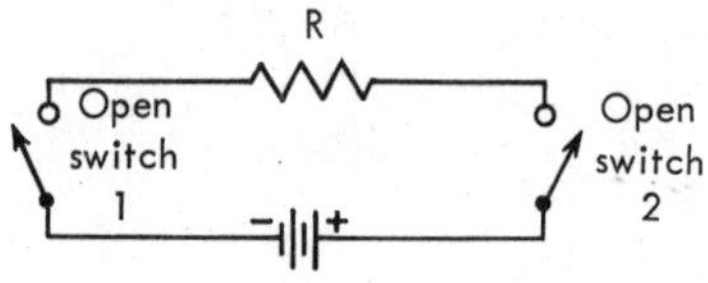

Fig. 2·64

2·65 (open) In Fig. 2·65, the circuit must be considered to be a(n) _____ circuit if switch 1 is closed but switch 2 is left open, as shown.

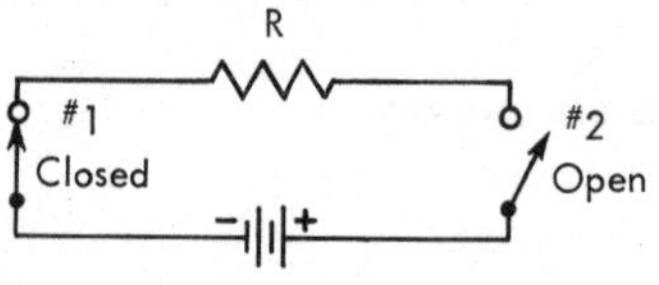

Fig. 2·65

2·66 (open) The circuit of Fig. 2·65 can be considered complete only if _____ _____ are closed.

2·66   (both switches)

Some sources of emf

The most widely used sources of emf are batteries and rotary generators. Beside these, you will find certain applications that employ photoelectric cells, thermocouples, solar cells, and various other devices to develop an emf for specific purposes. In Frames 2·67 to 2·71, we mention only the chemical source (battery) and rotary generator as introductory material.

2·67   Electric batteries are chemical sources of emf. They produce a direct current (abbrev. d-c) when applied to a complete circuit. A dry cell produces d-c in a complete circuit; an Edison storage cell produces d-c in a complete circuit; similarly a lead-acid storage battery produces _____ in a complete circuit.

2·68   (d-c) If a copper penny and a silver dime are embedded in a fresh lemon, an elementary chemical source of emf is formed. The current obtainable from such a source is of the _____ variety.

2·69   (d-c) Many mechanical generators of electricity produce a current that rises to a maximum and falls to zero periodically. This is called pulsating direct current. The reason this is still d-c is because the _____ of electron flow does not reverse; it merely grows and shrinks.

2·70   (direction) Some mechanical generators produce an emf which reverses its polarity periodically, causing the current to flow first one way and then the other in a complete circuit. This kind of current is alternating current (abbrev. a-c). Alternating current differs from either pure or pulsating d-c in that it reverses its _____ of flow periodically.

2·71   (direction) Regardless of whether the output is direct, pulsating direct, or alternating current, the electron flow always occurs from the _____ pole of the source, through the resistance, back to the _____ pole of the source.

2·71   (negative, positive)

Electrical symbols

Frames 2·72 to 2·83 will enable you to become familiar with some of the more common symbols used in the drawing of schematic diagrams of electric circuits. An effort should be made to commit these to memory because they will be frequently encountered in the work that follows.

2·72   Figure 2·72 shows three resistors, one without a tap, or internal connection; one with a fixed tap; and the third with a variable, or movable, tap. The untapped resistor is shown in b, the fixed-tap resistor in a, and the resistor with the _____ tap in c.

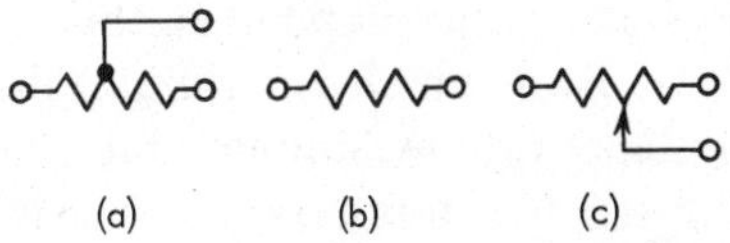

(a)   (b)   (c)

Fig. 2·72

2·73 (variable) In the resistor drawings, a variable tap is normally indicated by placing an _____ on the wire lead that goes to the tap position.

2·74 (arrow) In Fig. 2·74, any meter is indicated by a circle with the appropriate letter inside. For example, the circle containing A represents an ammeter. What kind of meter is most likely indicated by a V inside the circle? _____

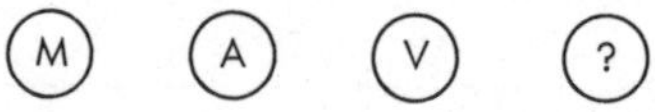

Fig. 2·74

2·75 (voltmeter) In certain experimental work, an electrical meter called a "galvanometer" is often used. What would you put inside the fourth circle (Fig. 2·74) to indicate this instrument? _____

2·76 (G) In Fig. 2·76a, a single chemical cell is shown as one long and one short vertical line, the short line being labeled "$-$" and the long line "$+$." b shows the same cell reversed laterally. Diagram c shows _____ or more cells connected together to form a battery.

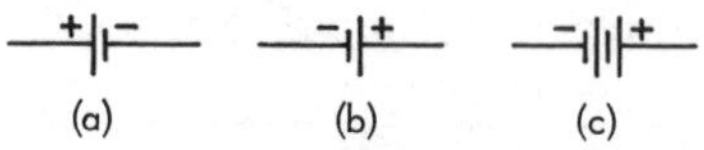

(a)   (b)   (c)
Fig. 2·76

2·77 (two) Merely from the appearance of the drawings in Fig. 2·77, you should be able to select the symbol that stands for a switch, a lamp, and a fuse. The switch is drawing _____.

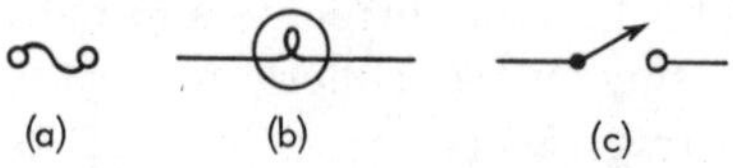

(a)   (b)   (c)
Fig. 2·77

2·78 (c) The fuse is drawing _____.

2·79 (a) The lamp is drawing _____.

2·80 (b) When wires are shown crossing each other in a schematic diagram, we must be careful to distinguish between a crossover where there is no connection between wires and a crossover where a connection does exist. In Fig. 2·80, both crossovers are shown. Which one is the no-connection type? _____

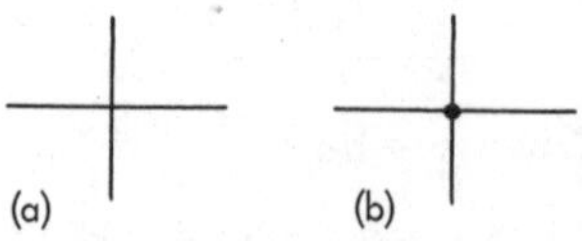

(a)   (b)
Fig. 2·80

2·81 (a) In Fig. 2·81, drawing a shows a ground. This may mean an actual connection to the earth or merely a connection to some common point in the circuit—such as a chassis or bus bar—from which all circuit voltages are measured. Of the remaining two, the one that represents an antenna is _____ and the one that represents a chassis connection (not connected to earth) is _____.

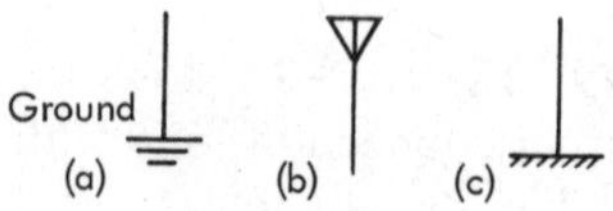

Ground
(a)   (b)   (c)
Fig. 2·81

2·82 (*b, c*) A capacitor is a device consisting of two or more metal plates separated from each other by air or some other insulator. An inductor is a device made up of turns of wire to form a coil. In Fig. 2·82, which group represents the inductors? _____

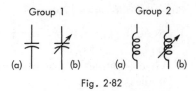

Fig. 2·82

2·83 (2) In both groups—capacitors and inductors—a fixed unit is shown next to a variable unit. In both groups, the variable unit is shown in diagram _____ .

2·83 (*b*)

MEASURABLE BEHAVIORAL OBJECTIVES

Upon completion of a section, you should be able to achieve the objectives listed for it. The frame or frames that cover the related subject matter are indicated immediately following each objective.

The meaning of electric current

1 Define electric current. (2·1)
   a Discuss the flow of electrons through a conductor. (2·2)
   b Determine the direction of electron flow. (2·3)
2 Calculate the amount of current in a conductor from the rate of charge flow. (2·7)
   a Define a coulomb (in terms of electrons). (2·4)
   b Define current (in terms of the coulomb). (2·7)

Conductivity and resistance

1 State the four factors determining the resistance of a substance. (Introduction)
2 Differentiate between conductors, semiconductors, and insulators. (Introduction)
3 Relate conductivity to the number of free electrons. (2·24)
4 Give examples of conductors and insulators. (2·24 to 2·26)

Factors that control resistance of conductors

Express in a simple algebraic equation the relation between resistance, specific resistivity, length, and cross-sectional area of a substance. (Introduction)
   a State the units of each factor in the above equation. (Introduction)
   b Discuss the temperature dependence of the above equation. (2·39, 2·40)
   c Describe the existing proportionalities in the above equation. (2·27, 2·31)
   d Formulate numerical examples of the above equation. (2·28)

Potential difference (voltage)

1 State the criteria for determining the potential difference between two bodies. (2·54)
2 Give examples of potential difference between two negatively charged bodies. (2·49)
3 Define a volt. (2·53)
4 Relate electromotive force, voltage, and potential difference. (2·53)

The electric circuit

1 Define a complete electric circuit. (2·59)
2 Discuss the direction of current flow in a complete circuit. (2·61)
3 Define an incomplete circuit. (2·62)

Some sources of emf

1 Give four examples of sources of emf. (2·67 to 2·70)
2 Discuss direct current sources. (2·67, 2·68)
3 Discuss alternating current sources. (2·70)

Electrical symbols

Recognize the symbols used in the drawing of schematic diagrams of electric circuits. (2·76, 2·77, 2·80 to 2·82)

chapter 3
circuit fundamentals

Introduction to simple schematic diagrams

The symbols studied in Frames 2·72 to 2·83 will be inserted into simple schematic diagrams to help you become familiar with the accepted drawing methods now in use.

3·1 A ground symbol (see Fig. 2·81) is often used to replace a wire that is common to many points of a circuit. For example, in Fig. 3·1a, a return wire from the bottom of R connects the resistor to the battery, while in Fig. 3·1b, the same circuit is shown with two ground symbols. In Fig. 3·1d, the return wire for all the resistors shown in Fig. 3·1c is replaced by the

_____ _____ .

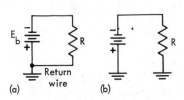
(a) Return wire (b)

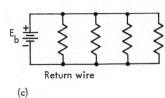
Return wire
(c)

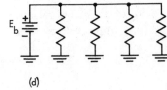
(d)

Fig. 3·1

3·2 (ground symbol) In Fig. 3·2a, three parts are shown connected to a battery. In Fig. 3·2b, the same three parts are shown in the same circuit, except that the ground symbols replace connection H to G to F to E. In Fig. 3·2c, the same circuit is shown with ground symbols replacing connections _____ to _____ to _____ to _____ .

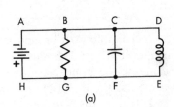
(a)

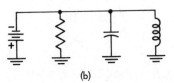
(b)

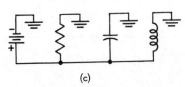
(c)

Fig. 3·2

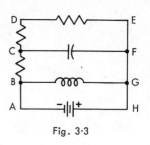

Fig. 3·3

3·3 (A, B, C, D) In Fig. 3·3, ground symbols could be used to replace the common wire that joins points _____ .

3·4 (E, F, G, H) The ground point is often the zero reference level from which all circuit voltages are measured. In Fig. 3·4a, a 12-volt battery is shown connected to two resistors so that the ground point A is zero volts (or reference level), point B is −6 volts, and point C is −12 volts since it returns to the negative end of the battery. In Fig. 3·4b, the same battery is reversed so that point A is 0 volts, B is +6 volts, and C is +12 volts. Using the same reasoning, the voltage in Fig. 3·4c must be _____ volts.

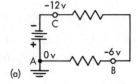

(a)

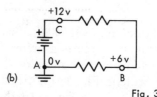

(b)

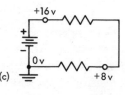

(c)

Fig. 3·4

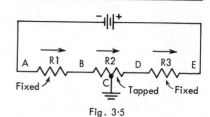

Fig. 3·5

3·5 (16) Resistors R1 and R3 in Fig. 3·5 are ordinary fixed resistors, while resistor R2 is a _____ resistor.

3·6 (tapped) The arrows in Fig. 3·5 indicate the direction of the _____ .

3·7 (current flow) If ground is to be considered the zero reference level in Fig. 3·5, then all voltages in the circuit will be measured to this point. Since the "−" terminal of the battery is connected to point A, then point A is negative with respect to ground. This means that point E must be _____ with respect to ground.

3·8 (positive) Point B is still on the "negative" side of the tap on R2, hence point B is negative with respect to ground. Thus, point D is _____ with respect to ground.

3·9 (positive) If we wanted to indicate the voltage at point
C with respect to ground, we would have to assign it a value of

_____ .

3·9 (zero)

Ohm's law

A simple relationship exists between the current that flows through a
resistance and the voltage applied across the resistance. This relationship,
called Ohm's law, may be most easily expressed this way:

$$I = \frac{E}{R}$$

where I = current, amp
  E = voltage or emf, volts
  R = resistance, ohms

The equation is valid *only for these units.*

Ohm's law contains three quantities that may be varied, hence there are
three variables present. Study of such a relationship is facilitated by hold-
ing one of these variables *constant* and observing how either one of the
two remaining variables affects the other. For example, suppose we hold
the resistance constant. This means that we are now going to vary the
voltage (in a circuit such as Fig. 3·1a) and observe how the current
changes as we do so.

Let us assume that $R = 10$ ohms and that this will not change. We
could now prepare a table showing how I varies with E, assuming different
values for E at will. If $R = 10$ ohms, then

  $I = 1$ amp when $E = 10$ volts
  $I = 2$ amp when $E = 20$ volts
  $I = 3$ amp when $E = 30$ volts
  $I = 4$ amp when $E = 40$ volts

and so forth. This table shows that, starting with $I = 1$ amp when $E = 10$
volts, if we double E, I doubles; if we increase E by a factor of 3 to 30 volts,
then I increases by a factor of 3 to 3 amp; if E is quadrupled, I quadruples;
etc. Such a relationship is called a "direct proportion" and always follows
the same rule: <u>Whatever is done by multiplication or division to the independent variable (E in this case) results in the same multiplication or division
of the dependent variable (I in this case).</u> You must remember, however,
that the direct proportion can be handled this way only if the third variable is held constant.

Now let us hold the voltage E constant at, say, 120 volts and observe
how the current changes as we vary R in Ohm's law. We obtain this table:
If $E = 120$ volts, then

  $I = 12$ amp when $R = 10$ ohms
  $I = 6$ amp when $R = 20$ ohms
  $I = 4$ amp when $R = 30$ ohms
  $I = 3$ amp when $R = 40$ ohms

and so forth. This relationship is entirely different as you can see. Here, with $E = 120$ volts *constantly,* if we double R from 10 to 20 ohms, then the current halves from 12 to 6 amp; if we treble R from 10 to 30 ohms, then the current is reduced to one-third of its original value, i.e., from 12 to 4 amp; finally, if we quadruple R from 10 to 40 ohms, the current goes down to one-fourth of its initial value, i.e., from 12 to 3 amp. This relationship is called an "inverse proportion." Evidently, in an inverse proportion, anything you do (multiplication or division) to the independent variable—R in this case—you must do to the dependent variable, I, in a *reciprocal* fashion. That is, if you multiply the independent variable by 3, you must multiply the dependent variable by ⅓, the reciprocal of 3. Similarly, if you multiply the independent variable by 21, you must multiply the dependent variable by the reciprocal of 21, or 1/21. Again, if you divide the independent variable by 4, you must divide the dependent variable by ¼ which is the same thing as multiplying it by 4.

Returning to Ohm's law, the proportionality relationship may be summarized as follows:

I is directly proportional to E (with R constant).

I is inversely proportional to R (with E constant).

If *both* of the variables change value from one situation to another, then the problem of finding out what happens to the current is handled in two steps: **1,** first assume R constant and find current change for the change in E; **2,** working with the new current value obtained, assume E constant and determine how this current will change for the change in R. Let's take an example.

Example: In a certain circuit, the current $I = 4$ amp. The voltage is now increased *ten*fold while the resistance is decreased by a factor of 5. Find the new current.

Solution: Assuming $R =$ constant, an increase of E by a factor of 10 would cause the current to increase by the same factor (direct proportion). Thus, the current would tend to rise to 40 amp.

Assuming $E =$ constant, a *de*crease of resistance by a factor of 5 would tend to *in*crease the current (inverse proportion) by a factor of 5. Thus, the 40-amp current would now rise to $40 \times 5 = 200$ amp (*Answer*).

In a single step, we could say:

$$4 \text{ amp} \times \frac{10}{\frac{1}{5}} = 4 \times 10 \times 5 = 200 \text{ amp}$$

3·10 Ohm's law for electric circuits states, in part, that the current in amperes in an electric circuit is directly proportional to the applied emf in volts. For example, the current in a given circuit is 3 amp when the applied voltage is 6 volts. If the potential is raised to 12 volts, the current becomes 6 amp. If the potential is increased to 14 volts, the current rises to 7 amp. If the potential goes up to 24 volts, the current will be

———————— .

3·11 (12 amp) The current in a given circuit is ¼ amp when the voltage is 80 volts. Increasing the voltage to 160 volts causes the current to rise to ½ amp. Increasing the voltage to 240 volts would cause the current to become _____ _____ .

3·12 (¾ amp) The current flowing in a circuit is 0.1 amp with an applied potential of 40 volts. The current will be _____ _____ when the potential is raised to 120 volts.

3·13 (0.3 amp) When the applied potential across a given resistor is X volts, the current is 1.5 amp. If the voltage is now made $4X$ volts, the current will be _____ _____ .

3·14 (6.0 amp) The second part of Ohm's law states that the current in an electric circuit is inversely proportional to the resistance in ohms. For a given voltage, a current of 8 amp flows when the resistance is 1,000 ohms. If the resistance increases to 2,000 ohms, the current becomes 4 amp. If the resistance increases further to 4,000 ohms, the current goes down to 2 amp. Thus, if the resistance were made 8,000 ohms, the current would be _____ amp.

3·15 (1) In a circuit having a fixed potential, the current flowing through a 6-ohm resistor is 0.88 amp. If the resistance is increased to 12 ohms, the current will drop to 0.44 amp. If the resistance is increased to 24 ohms, the current will be

_____ _____ .

3·16 (0.22 amp) A circuit contains a battery of constant potential. The resistance of the circuit is 18 ohms and the current flowing in the resistance is 0.3 amp. If the resistance is now increased to 54 ohms, the current will then be _____ _____ .

3·17 (0.1 amp) The voltage in a certain circuit remains constant while the resistance is reduced from X to $X/8$ ohms. If the initial current is 2.5 amp, the new current will be $2.5 \times 1/\frac{1}{8} = 2.5 \times 8 =$ _____ _____ .

3·18 (20 amp) Both proportions may be combined into a single Ohm's law equation: amperes = volts/ohms. In symbols, this is written $I = E/R$, where I = current, amp; E = emf, volts; and R = resistance, ohms. A 10-volt battery connected across a 5-ohm resistance will produce a current of $I = E/R = 10/5 =$ _____ amp.

3·19 (2) An emf of 30 volts applied across a resistance of 5 ohms will produce a current of $I = E/R = 30/5 =$ _____ amp.

3·20 (6) An emf of 75 volts applied across a resistance of 25 ohms will result in a current of _____ amp.

3·21 (3) An emf of 60 volts applied across a resistance of 5 ohms will produce a current of $I = E/R = 60/5 =$ _____ amp.

3·22 (12) An emf of 75 volts applied across 50 ohms will result in a current of _____ amp.

3·23 (1.5) The current flowing in a 12.0-volt circuit containing 24 ohms of resistance is ½ amp. The current flowing in a 50-volt circuit containing 25 ohms of resistance is 2.0 amp. The current flowing in a 100-volt circuit containing 300 ohms of resistance is _____ _____ .

3·24 (⅓ amp) The current flowing in a 40-volt circuit containing 2 ohms of resistance is 20 amp. The current flowing in a 20-volt circuit containing 10 ohms of resistance is _____ _____ .

3·25 (2 amp) The current flowing in a 120-volt circuit containing 20 ohms of resistance is _____ _____ .

3·26 (6 amp) A current of Z amp flows in a circuit containing a battery of X volts and a resistance of Y ohms. If the circuit is changed to one having a battery of $3X$ volts and a resistance of $3Y$ ohms, the new current will be $I = 3X/3Y$. Obviously, the 3's will cancel so that the new current will be _____ _____ as it was before.

3·27 (the same) If the applied voltage is doubled while the resistance of the circuit is increased fourfold, the current will be _____ as great as its initial value.

3·27 (one-half)

Information Panel

Useful Prefixes

Prefix	Abbreviation	Multiplier	Prefix	Abbreviation	Multiplier
tera	T	10^{12}	milli	m	10^{-3}
giga	G	10^{9}	micro	μ	10^{-6}
mega	M or meg	10^{6}	nano	n	10^{-9}
kilo	K or k	10^{3}	pico	p	10^{-12}

Examples

$$1 \text{ megohm} = 1 \text{ M}\Omega = 10^6 \text{ ohms} = 1{,}000{,}000 \text{ ohms}$$
$$1 \text{ gigavolt} = 1 \text{ Gv} = 10^9 \text{ volts} = 1{,}000{,}000{,}000 \text{ volts}$$
$$10 \text{ kilovolts} = 10 \text{ kv} = 10 \times 10^3 \text{ volts} = 10{,}000 \text{ volts}$$
$$5 \text{ microamperes} = 5\mu a = 5 \times 10^{-6} \text{ amp} = 0.000005 \text{ amp}$$
$$2.56 \text{ nanovolts} = 2.56 \text{ nv} = 2.56 \times 10^{-9} \text{ volt} = 0.00000000256 \text{ volt}$$
$$100 \text{ picofarads} = 100 \text{ pf} = 100 \times 10^{-12} \text{ farad} = 0.0000000001 \text{ farad}$$

3·28 A resistance of 4,000,000 ohms may be written as 4 megohms; a resistance of 2,500,000 ohms may be written as 2.5 megohms; thus, 1 megohm may be said to contain _____ ohms.

3·29 (1,000,000) A current of 0.1 amp is equivalent to 100 milliamperes (abbrev. ma); a current of 0.04 amp is the same as 40 ma; thus, a current of 1 amp must contain _____ ma.

3·30 (1,000) If the resistance of a certain circuit is 0.1 megohm (or 100,000 ohms) and the applied voltage is 100 volts, the current will be 100/100,000 or _____ ma. (*Hint:* First determine the current in amperes, then convert it to milliamperes by multiplying by 1,000.)

3·31 (1) There are 1,000,000 μa in 1 amp. Thus, 0.1 amp is the equivalent of 100,000 μa, 0.01 amp is the equivalent of 10,000 μa, and 0.001 amp is the equivalent of _____ μa.

3·32 (1,000) One ampere equals 1,000 ma; 0.1 amp equals 100 ma, or 100,000 μa; 0.02 amp equals 20 ma, or 20,000 μa. Therefore, 400 μa must equal _____ ma.

3·33 (0.4) The current in a certain circuit is 0.00002 amp. This current in milliamperes is 0.00002 × 1,000 = 0.02 ma. The same current in microamperes is 0.00002 × 1,000,000 = _____ μa.

3·33 (20)

Exercises in the Ohm's law proportions

Here are some additional practice exercises in which you use your knowledge about the proportionalities contained in Ohm's law. '

3·34 If the voltage of a circuit doubles when the resistance remains the same, then the current must double. If the voltage is tripled with no change in resistance, then the current triples. Thus, if the voltage is increased by a factor of 10 with no change in resistance, the current must be increased by a factor of _____ .

3·35 (10) If the voltage across a constant resistance is increased five times, the current increases five times. Hence, if the voltage across a constant resistance is made one-half of its former value, then the current must decrease to _____ of its former value.

3·36 (one-half) If the voltage across a resistance in a fixed circuit is reduced to one-fifth of its former value, the current will decrease to _____ of its former value.

3·37 (one-fifth) In any electric circuit, resistance is considered as an independent variable since it is governed by factors (length, material, cross-sectional area, temperature) that do not change with circuit conditions. If the voltage across a fixed resistance is doubled, the resistance remains the same; if the voltage is tripled, the resistance still remains the same; hence, if the voltage is multiplied tenfold, the resistance _____ _____ _____ .

3·38 (remains the same) A voltage of 20 volts is applied to a resistance of 10 ohms. If the voltage is now increased to 30 volts, the resistance is still 10 ohms. Thus, if the voltage is reduced to 8 volts, the resistance of the circuit is _____ _____ .

3·39 (10 ohms or the same) A 500-ohm resistor is first connected across a voltage source of 125.7 volts. Then it is connected across a voltage source of 128.3 volts. In the second case, its resistance must be _____ _____ .

3·40 (500 ohms or the same) Under normal conditions, the voltage applied to a load by a source is generally considered an independent variable depending on the construction of the source and not upon circuit conditions. Thus, a voltage of 100 volts applied across a 100-ohm resistor remains 100 volts even when the resistance is increased to 110 ohms. Similarly, the voltage remains at the 100-volt level when the resistance is increased to 150 ohms. Thus, the voltage of this source will be _____ volts when the resistance is changed to 96.3 ohms.

3·41 (100) A storage battery applies 6.3 volts to a 500-ohm resistor; when this resistor is replaced by one of 450 ohms, the storage battery voltage is still 6.3 volts. Therefore, when the resistor is increased to 505 ohms, the battery voltage is

_____ _____ .

3·42 (6.3 volts) A high-output generator is connected across 1,000 ohms; a voltmeter across the generator reads 220 volts. Now the circuit resistance is changed to 2,500 ohms. In this case, the voltmeter will read _____ _____ .

3·42 (220 volts)

Circuit calculations

Frames 3·43 to 3·48 contain some exercises on circuit calculations involving Ohm's law.

3·43 See Fig. 3·43. The current in this circuit in amperes is

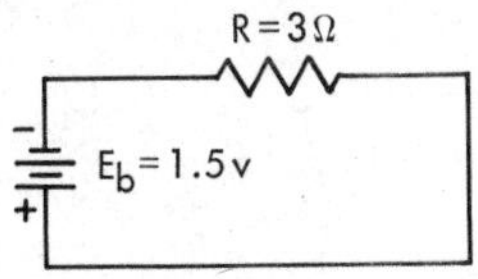

_____ _____ .

$R = 3\,\Omega$
$E_b = 1.5\,v$

Fig. 3·43

3·44 (0.5 amp) See Fig. 3·44. The current in this circuit in milliamperes is _____ _____ .

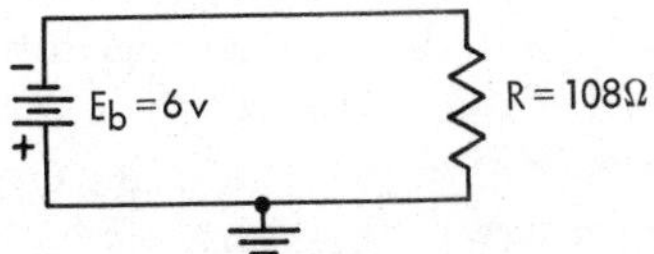

$E_b = 6\,v$
$R = 108\,\Omega$

Fig. 3·44

3·45 (55.5 ma) See Fig. 3·45. The applied voltage of the battery in this circuit must be _____ volts.

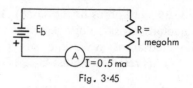

Fig. 3·45

3·46 (500) See Fig. 3·46. The battery voltage in this circuit is _____ _____ .

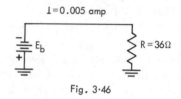

Fig. 3·46

3·47 (0.18 volt) See Fig. 3·47. The resistance through which the current of this circuit flows must have a value of

$$R = \frac{E}{I} = \frac{30 \text{ volts}}{0.5 \text{ ma}} = \frac{30 \text{ volts}}{0.0005 \text{ amp}} = \underline{\hspace{2cm}} \text{ ohms}$$

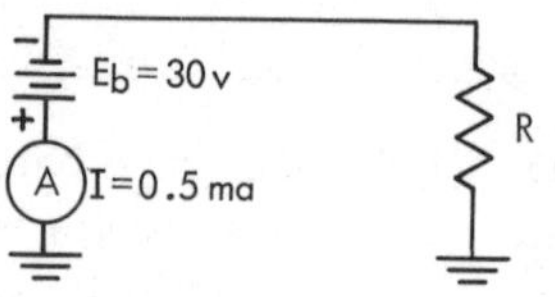

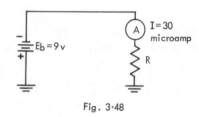

Fig. 3·47

3·48 (60,000) See Fig. 3·48. The resistance in this circuit must be

$$R = \frac{E}{I} = \frac{9 \text{ volts}}{30\mu a} = \frac{9 \text{ volts}}{0.00003 \text{ amp}} = \underline{\hspace{1.5cm}} \text{ megohms}$$

(*Hint:* First find the resistance in ohms, then multiply by 10^{-6} or divide by 10^6 to obtain it in megohms.)

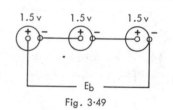

Fig. 3·48

3·48 (0.3)

Batteries in series and parallel

Electric cells may be connected in either series or parallel to form batteries. When cells are connected in series, the total emf obtainable is the sum of the individual cell emfs. The total emf obtainable from cells connected in parallel is that of any one of the cells. Normally, only cells having identical emfs are ever connected in parallel; cells having different emfs may be connected in series, however.

3·49 When electric cells are connected in series, the output voltage is the sum of the individual cell voltages. Thus, two dry cells (1.5 volts each) connected in series yield an output voltage of 3.0 volts. Similarly, four dry cells provide 6.0 volts. Three dry cells in series (Fig. 3·49) thus yield an output voltage of _____ volts.

1.5 v   1.5 v   1.5 v

Eb

Fig. 3·49

3·50 (4.5) Ten dry cells in series produce 15 volts. Thus, twenty dry cells in series would produce _____ volts.

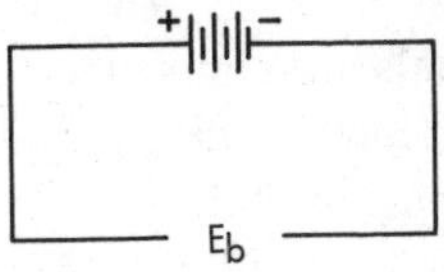

3·51 (30) Figure 3·51 shows a schematic diagram of three dry cells in series. The output voltage E_b therefore equals _____ _____.

Fig. 3·51

3·52 (4.5 volts) One Edison storage cell has an output voltage of approximately 1.2 volts. Two Edison cells in series produce 2.4 volts. Hence, three Edison cells in series would yield _____ volts.

3·53 (3.6) Ten Edison storage cells in series are capable of providing an output of 12 volts. Twenty such cells can yield _____ volts.

3·54 (24) Five Edison cells in series provide an output voltage of _____ _____.

3·55 (6 volts) A lead-acid storage cell yields about 2.0 volts when charged. Two such cells in series would therefore provide 4 volts. Ten storage cells in series would be expected to yield _____ volts.

3·56 (20) Five lead-acid storage cells in series have a total terminal voltage of 10 volts. Eight such cells in series would have a terminal voltage of _____ _____.

3·57 (16 volts) Six lead-acid storage cells in series would produce an output emf of _____ _____.

3·58 (12 volts) If a dry cell, an Edison cell, and a lead-acid storage cell are all connected in series, E_b will be _____ _____.

3·59 (4.7 volts) To set up a battery that delivers 45 volts using only dry cells, _____ such cells would be required in series.

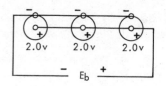

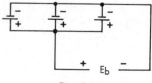

Fig. 3·60

3·60 (30) Three lead-acid storage cells are connected in parallel in Fig. 3·60. In this arrangement, all the positive terminals are connected together and all the negatives are likewise joined. Only similar-type cells are ever connected in parallel. The output voltage E_b of the parallel type of connection is equal to the output voltage of any one of the cells. Thus, the output voltage in Fig. 3·60 is _____ volts.

3·61 (2.0) Two dry cells connected in parallel yield an output voltage of 1.5 volts. Three dry cells connected in parallel yield an output voltage of _____ volts.

3·62 (1.5) Four Edison cells in parallel have a total output voltage of _____ _____ .

3·63 (1.2 volts) Six lead-acid storage cells in parallel produce an output voltage of _____ _____ .

3·63 (2 volts)

Voltages and currents from cell combinations

Cells in series comprise batteries wherein the output voltage is higher than that of any one of the single cells. However, by connecting cells in series, all their internal resistances add up too, thus placing a relatively high resistance in series with the *load,* or the device which uses the current. Such a high resistance has the effect of limiting the maximum current that can be obtained from the series combination.

The opposite effect is obtained when cells are connected in parallel. The voltage output is low; that is, it is equal to the voltage of one of the cells. As we shall see in forthcoming frames, however, the total resistance resulting from internal resistance is *decreased* when cells are connected in parallel. Hence, a parallel connection makes for low voltage at higher currents.

3·64 To obtain high voltages at low currents, cells should be connected in _____ .

3·65 (series) To obtain high circuit currents at low voltages, cells should be connected in _____ .

3·66 (parallel) Cells may be connected in series-parallel. Such an arrangement is shown in Fig. 3·66. The output voltage E_b is the same as either series group, but the output current capabilities are increased as compared with a single group in series. If the cells are dry cells, the output voltage would be 4.5 volts. If they are Edison cells, the output voltage would be _____ _____ .

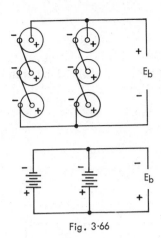

Fig. 3·66

3·67 (3.6 volts) If the cells are lead-acid storage cells, then E_b is _____ _____ .

3·68 (6 volts) Series-parallel is utilized when we have a load that demands both _____ voltage and _____ current.

3·68 (high, high)

Switches and fuses

A switch is a device used to render a circuit complete or open at the will of the operator. There are many types of switches of which but a few are shown. The individual switches in Figs. 3·69 to 3·96 consist of a single lever arm which either makes or breaks a contact when closed. Such switches are called single-pole, single-throw (abbrev. spst). The switch in Fig. 3·101b has two possible positions and therefore can close either one of two circuits; this is a single-pole, double-throw (abbrev. spdt) type, so called because it has one arm, hence single-pole, but can be moved into either one of two positions. In Fig. 3·101a we see a double-pole, single-throw (abbrev. dpst) type. This switch has only one position of closure but completes two contacts simultaneously. In Fig. 3·104 we have a double-pole, double-throw switch (abbrev. dpdt), so named for obvious reasons. (The crossed wires between switch contacts in this diagram are *not* part of the switch; they have been added for a specific purpose.)

A fuse may be considered as a type of switch. Fuses are fabricated of low-melting-point metallic alloys. Such alloys, when carrying currents that exceed predetermined safety limits, will melt and open the circuit in which this current is flowing.

3·69 In Fig. 3·69, current will flow through R if switch 1 (abbrev. SW1) is closed and the fuse is in good condition. When the switch is opened, the entire circuit must now be considered _____ .

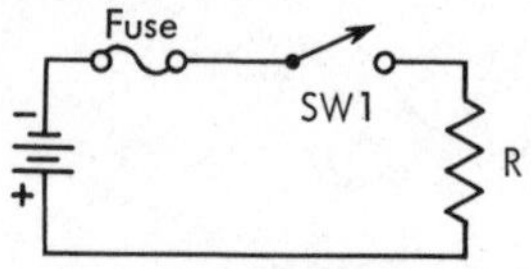

Fuse
SW1
R

Fig. 3·69

3·70 (open) In Fig. 3·69, assume that the fuse is rated at 5 amp. This means it will burn out if the current exceeds 5 amp. Thus, the fuse will not burn out with 4 amp. When the current rises to 10 amp, the fuse will _____ _____ .

3·71 (burn out) A fuse rated at 10 amp will carry 8 amp without burning out. If the current rises to 9 amp, the fuse will _____ _____ _____ .

3·72 (not burn out) A fuse rated at 25 amp will not burn out if the current is _____ amp or less.

3·73 (25) If the fuse in circuit 3·69 is rated at 5 amp maximum and the battery voltage is 10 volts, the minimum resistance R must have to keep the circuit complete is _____ _____ .

3·74 (2 ohms) If the resistance of R changes to ½ ohm, the fuse in circuit 3·69 will _____ _____ .

3·75 (burn out) The switches in Fig. 3·75 are said to be in series. If current is to flow through R, it is necessary to close _____ .

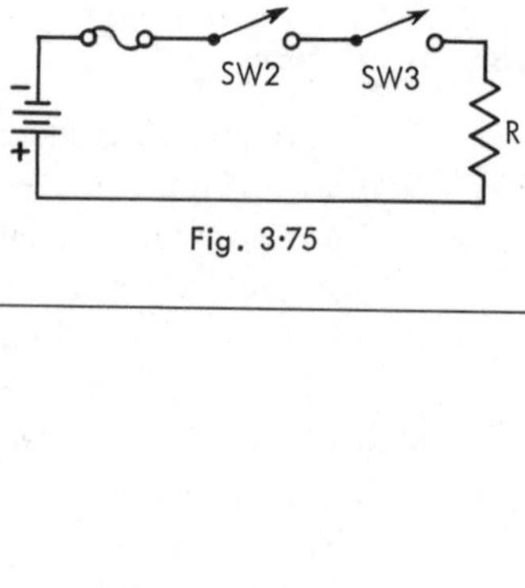

SW2   SW3
R

Fig. 3·75

3·76 (both) The battery voltage in 3·75 is 100 volts and R is 2 ohms. The fuse is rated at 2 amp maximum. If SW2 is closed and SW3 is open, the fuse will _____ _____ _____ .

3·77 (not burn out) The battery in Fig. 3·75 is changed to 1 volt, all other factors remaining the same. Both switches are now closed. The fuse will _____ _____ _____ .

3·78 (not burn out) If a third switch (SW2A not shown) were added in series with SW2 and SW3, the switches that would have to be closed to energize R would be _____ .

3·79 (all or SW2, SW3, SW2A) In Fig. 3·79, if SW4 were closed but SW5 were left open, current _____ flow through R from the negative terminal of the battery back to the positive terminal.

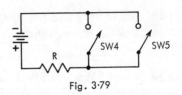

Fig. 3·79

3·80 (would) In Fig. 3·79 if SW5 were closed but SW4 were left open, current _____ flow through R in the same direction as before.

3·81 (would) In Fig. 3·79, if both switches were open, current _____ _____ flow through R.

3·82 (would not) In Fig. 3·79, if both switches were closed, current _____ flow through R.

3·83 (would) In Fig. 3·83, SW6 and SW7 are connected in exactly the same circuit and would have exactly the same effect as the switches in Fig. _____ .

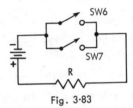

Fig. 3·83

3·84 (3·79) The switches in Fig. 3·79 are said to be connected in parallel. The switches in Fig. 3·83 are connected in _____ .

3·85 (parallel) The switches in Fig. 3·85 are connected thus: SW8 and SW9 are in parallel, while SW10 is in series with the parallel pair. The battery voltage = 100 volts, the resistance $R = 20$ ohms, and the fuse is rated at 10 amp maximum. If all the switches are open, the current flowing through the fuse is _____ amp.

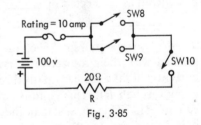

Fig. 3·85

3·86 (0) If SW8 is the only closed switch, the current in the fuse will be _____ amp.

3·87 (0) If SW10 is the only closed switch, the current flowing through R will be _____ amp.

3·88 (0) If both SW8 and SW9 are closed but SW10 is open, the current flowing through R will be _____ amp.

3·89 (0) If SW8 and SW10 are closed but SW9 is open, the current flowing through the fuse will be _____ amp.

3·90 (5) If SW9 and SW10 are closed but SW8 is open, the current flowing through the fuse will be _____ _____ .

3·91 (5 amp) If all three switches are closed, the current flowing through the fuse will be _____ amp.

3·92 (5) If you wish current to flow only through $R1$ in Fig. 3·92, this could be done by _____ _____ .

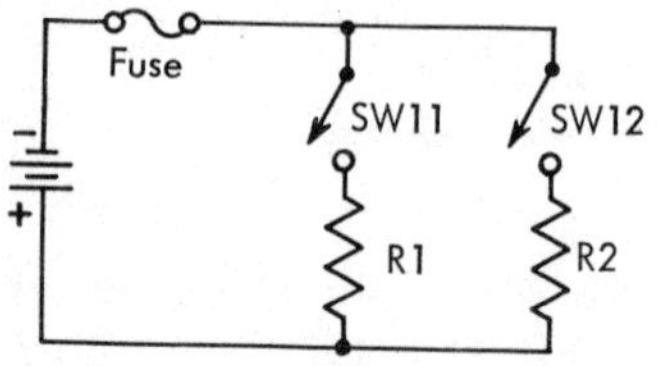

Fig. 3·92

3·93 (closing SW11) If you wished to have $R2$ energized by a flow of current, you would have to _____ _____ (Fig. 3·92).

3·94 (close SW12) In order for current to flow through $R1$ and $R2$ in Fig. 3·92, it would be necessary to _____ _____ _____ .

3·95 (close both switches) SW11 must be considered as connected in series with $R1$. This means that SW12 must be considered as connected in _____ with $R2$.

3·96 (series) In Fig. 3·96, the switches are connected in parallel with their respective resistors. If SW13 is closed, the current will take the easy path through this switch rather than going through $R1$. This condition is described as "a short circuit of $R1$." This means that the resistance of the SW13-$R1$ pair considered together is effectively zero. The same is, of course, true of the $R2$-SW14 pair. If both switches are open, the current will flow from the negative pole of the battery, through _____ and _____ , and back to the positive pole.

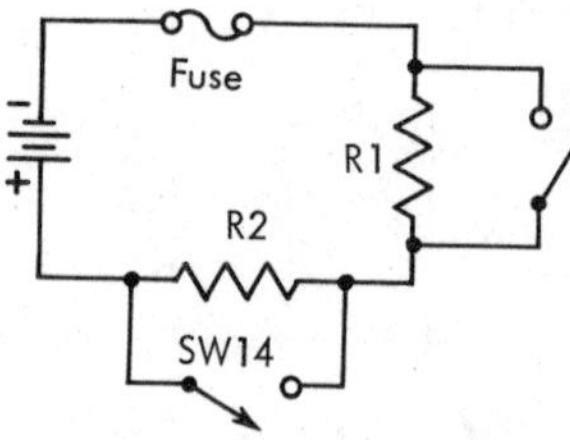

Fig. 3·96

3·97 ($R1$, $R2$) If SW13 is closed but SW14 is open, the only resistance greater than zero left in the circuit is that of _____ .

3·98 ($R2$) If SW14 is closed but SW13 is open, the resistance left in the circuit is equal to that of _____ .

3·99 (R1) If both switches SW13 and SW14 are closed, the total resistance left in the circuit is _____.

3·100 (zero) If both switches SW13 and SW14 are closed, we may be certain that the fuse will _____.

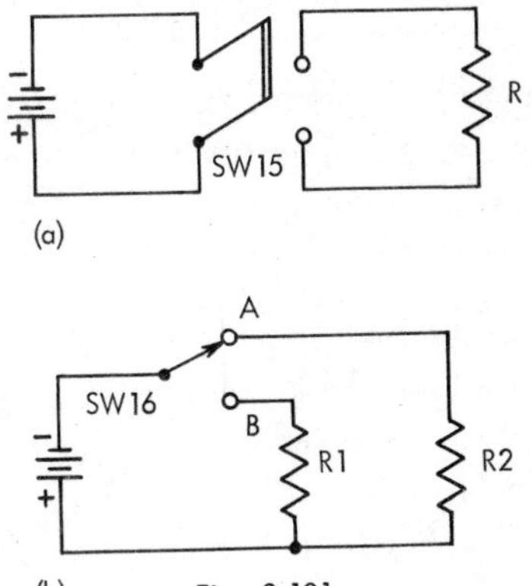

3·101 (blow) If the switch shown in this diagram (Fig. 3·101a) is a double-pole, single-throw type because it opens two lines or two legs of the same line and operates to close the circuit when thrown only in one direction, then switches SW1 through SW14 are all single-pole, single-throw switches because each can open only one line and can close a circuit when thrown only in one direction. SW16 in Fig. 3·101b is therefore a _____, _____ type because it can open one line but can close a circuit in either one of two directions.

(a)

(b)   Fig. 3·101

3·102 (single-pole, double-throw) In Fig. 3·101b, resistance _____ carries current when SW16 is in position A.

3·103 (R2) When SW16 is thrown to position B, the current in the circuit flows through resistance _____.

3·104 (R1) SW17 is a _____, _____ type of switch (Fig. 3·104).

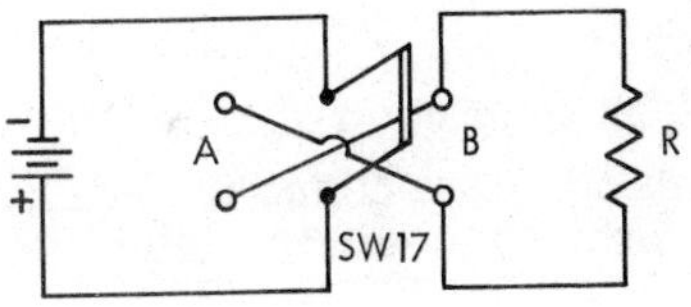

Fig. 3·104

3·105 (double-pole, double-throw) When moved to position A, SW17 closes the circuit in such a way that electrons flow *upward* through R. In position B (trace the electron flow), the circuit is closed in such a way that electrons flow _____ through R.

3·106 (downward) Thus, changing the position of SW17 causes the current through R1 to _____ direction.

3·107 (reverse or change) A doorbell located in the kitchen of a home is to be rung when either one of two switches is operated. The circuit diagram that shows a suitable system is Fig. _____.

3·108 (3·79 or 3·83) Two motors are to be operated from the same power source, each one to be controlled by its own individual spst switch. This requires that each motor be in series with its switch, with both series groups connected across the feed lines. The circuit diagram that shows this type of connection is that of Fig. _____ . (The motors are indicated as resistors in the proper circuit.)

3·109 (3·92) Two lights are to be operated by a single switch, one light being on while the other is off. A suitable system is shown in Fig. _____ .

3·110 (3·101b) SW17 in Fig. 3·104 is wired in the circuit in such a way that it becomes a *reversing switch,* since its function is to reverse the direction of the current through the load, R. Because this switch has two poles and two directions of throw, it is called a _____ , _____ type.

3·110   (double-pole, double-throw)

MEASURABLE BEHAVIORAL OBJECTIVES

Upon completion of a section, you should be able to achieve the objectives listed for it. The frame or frames that cover the related subject matter are indicated immediately following each objective.

Introduction to simple schematic diagrams

1   Draw electric circuits containing several components.   (3·1)
2   Discuss the use of ground as a return wire.   (3·2)

Ohm's law

1   State Ohm's law.   (Introduction)
2   Relate the following units: ohms, amperes, and volts.   (3·10, 3·14)
3   Discuss the direct and inverse proportionalities of Ohm's law.   (3·11, 3·15)
4   Formulate numerical examples for Ohm's law.   (3·21)
5   Depict some of the commonly used prefixes and their abbreviations when expressing the values of electric components.   (Information Panel)

Exercises in the Ohm's law proportions

Formulate numerical examples to demonstrate the proportionalities of Ohm's law.   (3·36)

Circuit calculations

1 Draw a simple series circuit with a d-c source and resistors. (3·43)
2 Determine the direction and the magnitude of current in simple circuits. (3·44)

Batteries in series and parallel

1 Determine the voltage of series connected batteries. (3·49)
2 Characterize the type of batteries we can connect in parallel. (3·60)
3 Find the voltage for parallel connected batteries. (3·61)

Voltages and currents from cell combinations

1 Determine the voltage across and the current through series and parallel connected batteries. (3·66)
2 Discuss the effect upon the total internal resistance of batteries connected in series or parallel. (Introduction)

Switches and fuses

1 Discuss the functions and uses of switches in electric circuits. (3·69)
2 Define and draw the schematic diagram symbol for spst, spdt, dpst, and dpdt switches. (3·85, 3·101, 3·104)
3 Discuss the functions and uses of fuses. (3·70)

chapter 4

power and series circuits

Electric power

Whenever an electric current flows through a resistance, heat is generated. Heat is a form of energy and, since energy cannot be created, the heat must be produced by a conversion of energy from the electric to the heat form.

It may be shown from basic considerations that the electric energy required to produce a given amount of heat H is the product of voltage, current, and time. That is

$$H = EIt$$

If E is in volts, I in amperes, and t in seconds, the heat unit in this case comes out to be the volt-amp-sec as you can see from the product form of the right side of the equation. But this is a cumbersome unit name; the volt-amp-sec, therefore, is renamed the *joule* after James Prescott Joule who first stated the law expressed by the above equation. It is a good idea to write the equation:

$$H \text{ (joules)} = E \text{ (volts)} \times I \text{ (amp)} \times t \text{ (sec)}$$

Thus, the joule is a unit of *energy* or *work*.

From basic physics, you know that *power* is the time rate of doing work or consuming energy. That is,

$$P = \frac{W}{t}$$

where P is power, W is work or energy, and t is time.

Since H in the equation above is *energy* (or work), let us divide both sides by t so that we can get the equation to read in terms of power. Thus:

$$\frac{H}{t} = P = \frac{EIt}{t}$$

or $P = EI$, since the t's cancel.

This result tells us that the *power* in a resistive circuit can be determined from the product of the voltage and current. The equation also tells us that the unit for power is the volt-amp. Here, again, we rename the unit to make it more concise. The volt-amp is called the watt, after James Watt, the inventor of the reciprocating steam engine.

In summary, electric power is measured in *watts* and may be determined from the equation $P = EI$. We can apply Ohm's law to this equation and obtain it in two other forms.

1. Since $I = E/R$, we can substitute E/R in place of I in the power equation. When we do this we obtain

$$P = EI = E \times \frac{E}{R} = \frac{E^2}{R}$$

2. Since $E = IR$, we can substitute IR in place of E and obtain:

$$P = EI = (IR)I = I^2R$$

Thus $\qquad P = EI \qquad P = \dfrac{E^2}{R} \qquad P = I^2R$

4•1 The electric power consumed in a circuit is measured in watts and is found by multiplying the applied voltage by the current in amperes. If $P =$ power, $E =$ applied voltage, and $I =$ current in amperes, the equation form of this definition is $P =$ _____ $\times$ _____ .

4•2 (E, I) If a source of 10 volts drives 2 amp through the circuit, the power is $P = EI = 10 \times 2 = 20$ watts. Similarly, if the source produces 14 volts and drives 7 amp through the load, the power is $P = EI =$ _____ watts.

4•3 (98) A source of 120 volts drives ½ amp through the load. The power dissipated in the load is _____ watts.

4•4 (60) A battery of 12.6 volts causes 1 amp to flow in a circuit. The power supplied is, therefore, 12.6 watts. Similarly, a battery of 6.3 volts which supplies 10 amp to a circuit is providing power at the rate of _____ watts.

4•5 (63) A generator of 240 volts that supplies 20 amp to a circuit provides _____ watts of power.

4•6 (4,800) The power dissipated by a resistor in a series circuit is also found by the product of the voltage drop across the resistor and the current through it. *Example:* If the voltage across a resistor is 10 volts and the current is 0.5 amp, the power dissipation is 5 watts. Also, if the voltage is raised to 20 volts and the current to 1 amp, the power dissipation is 20 watts. Thus, with a voltage of 100 volts across the resistor and a current of 2.5 amp through it, the power dissipated would be _____ watts.

4·7 (250) The voltage across a circuit is 120 volts and the current is 0.05 amp, making the power equal to 120 volts × 0.05 amp, or 6 watts. Also, if the voltage is 240 volts and the current remains the same, the power is 240 volts × 0.05 amp, or _____ watts.

4·8 (12) When the voltage is 18 volts and the current is 2 amp, the power dissipated is _____ watts.

4·9 (36) To find the current that will flow through a load having a known wattage rating at a given voltage, the power equation is solved for I. Thus $I = P/E$. *Example:* The normal current through a 60-watt lamp at 120 volts is $^{60}\!/_{120} = 0.5$ amp. The normal current through a 20-watt lamp at 120 volts is $^{20}\!/_{120} =$ _____ amp.

4·10 (⅙) The current flowing through a 5-watt lamp connected to a 10-volt battery is $I = P/E = 5/10 = 0.5$ amp. The current flowing through the 10-watt lamp when connected to a 20-volt battery is _____ amp.

4·11 (0.5) The current flowing through a 1,000-watt lamp at 120 volts is 8.33 amp. The current flowing through a 500-watt lamp at the same voltage is _____ amp.

4·12 (4.17 or 4⅙) The current flowing through a 50-watt lamp at 150 volts is _____ _____ .

4·13 (⅓ amp) The product IR can be substituted in place of E in the equation $P = EI$. This is true because Ohm's law tells us that $E =$ _____ .

4·14 (IR) When IR is substituted for E in the equation $P = EI$, we get the form $P = I \times R \times I$. Combining the two I's, this equation can then be written $P =$ _____ .

4·15 (I^2R) Using this form of the equation, we can calculate power dissipation if I and R are known. For example, the power dissipated in a 20-ohm resistor at 2 amp is $P = I^2R = 2^2 \times 20 = 4 \times 20 = 80$ watts. Similarly, the power used by a 40-ohm resistor at 2 amp is $P = I^2R = 2^2 \times 40 = 4 \times 40 =$ _____ watts.

4•16 (160) The power dissipated in a 12-ohm resistor carrying 0.5 amp is $(0.5)^2 \times 12 = 0.25 \times 12 = 3$ watts. The power dissipated in the same resistor when the current is 1 amp is $1^2 \times 12 = 1 \times 12 = $ _____ _____.

4•17 (12 watts) The power dissipated in a 120-ohm resistor carrying 3 amp is 1,080 watts. The power dissipated in a 120-ohm resistor carrying 2 amp is _____ _____.

4•18 (480 watts) The power consumed in a 25-ohm resistor through which a current of 0.11 amp flows is _____ _____.

4•19 (0.3025 watt) The power equation can be written in still a third form by substituting E/R for I (since Ohm's law says that $I = E/R$). The third form then is $P = E^2/R$. *Example:* The power used by a 12-ohm resistor across which 6 volts are applied is $P = E^2/R = 6^2/12 = 3$ watts. Thus, the power consumed by a 100-ohm resistor across which 30 volts is applied is $P = E^2/R = 30^2/100 = $ _____ _____.

4•20 (9 watts) The voltage applied across a 70-ohm resistor is 25 volts. The power consumed is $25^2/70 = 8.93$ watts. If the voltage is now raised to 50 volts, all other things equal, the power dissipation becomes $50^2/70 = $ _____ _____.

4•21 (35.7 watts) The power dissipated in an 80-ohm resistor across which 20 volts is applied is 5 watts. The power consumed by a 160-ohm resistor across which 40 volts is applied is _____ _____.

4•22 (10 watts) The power dissipated in a 25,000-ohm resistor across which a voltage of 500 volts is applied is _____ _____.

4•23 (10 watts) Total electric energy is the product of the power and the time over which the power is dissipated. That is, energy $= P \times t$. *Example:* A 100-watt lamp running for 10 hr consumes 1,000 watthours (abbrev. watt-hr) of energy or 1 kilowatthour (abbrev. kwhr) because energy $= Pt = 100$ watts $\times 10$ hr $= 1,000$ watt-hr. Thus, a 50-watt lamp operated for 100 hr uses an amount of energy $= Pt = 50$ watts $\times 100$ hr $= 5,000$ watt-hr or _____ kwhr.

4·24 (5) A 1,500-watt boiler running for 10 hr uses 1,500 watts × 10 hr = 15,000 watt-hr = 15 kwhr of energy. The same boiler running for 8 hr consumes _____ kwhr of energy.

4·25 (12) The energy consumed by a 600-watt toaster operated for 12 hr is 7.2 kwhr. The energy consumed by a 500-watt flatiron used for 2 hr is _____ kwhr.

4·26 (1) An electric motor uses 746 watt-hr for 8 hr each day for 1 week. At the end of the week, its energy consumption is _____ kwhr.

4·26   (41.8)

Current and resistance in series circuits

Figure 4·27 shows a *series* circuit, or a circuit in which the current must flow through each load (resistor) in turn before it can possibly return to the source. In such a circuit, the current in every component is exactly the same as in every other component. Also, the net or total resistance of the series circuit may be found by adding up the values of the individual resistances.

4·27 Figure 4·27 shows resistors connected in an end-to-end circuit or a series circuit. The current flowing in a series circuit is everywhere the same. If the current flowing in $R1$ is called $I1$ and the current flowing in $R2$ is called $I2$, then $I1 = I2$. By the same reasoning, the current flowing in $R3$ is called $I3$, and we may say that $I3 = I2 =$ _____ .

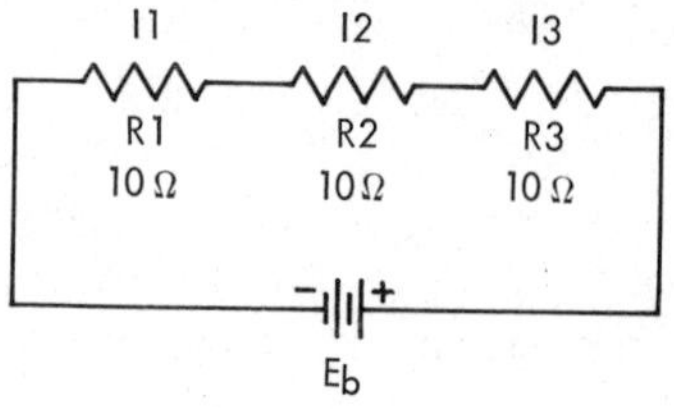

Fig. 4·27

4·28 ($I1$) In Fig. 4·27, if the current in $R1$ is 2 amp, then the current in $R2$ is also 2 amp. Therefore, the current in $R3$ must be _____ _____ .

4·29 (2 amp) If the current in $R2$ in Fig. 4·27 is 8.3 amp, then the current in $R1$ and $R3$ must be _____ _____ .

4·30 (8.3 amp) There are five unequal resistors in series. The current flowing in $R1$ is 0.3 amp. The current flowing in $R5 =$ _____ _____ .

4·31 (0.3 amp) The total resistance of a series circuit is the sum of the individual resistances. In Fig. 4·27, the total resistance R_t is equal to $R1 + R2 + R3$. The total resistance of this circuit, therefore, is _____ ohms.

4·32 (30) If each resistor in Fig. 4·27 is doubled in value, the total resistance of the circuit would then be _____ _____.

4·33 (60 ohms) To find the current in a series circuit, first determine the total resistance R_t and then apply Ohm's law. In Fig. 4·33, the total resistance is $10 + 10 + 10 = 30$ ohms. The current is, therefore, $I = E/R = 30/30 =$ _____ _____.

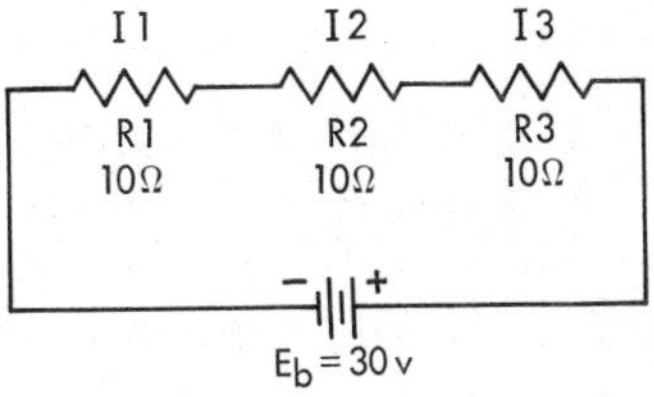

Fig. 4·33

4·34 (1 amp) If each resistance in the previous example had been 20 ohms instead of 10 ohms, the total resistance would then have been 60 ohms and the current in the circuit would have been _____ _____.

4·35 (½ amp) A series circuit contains one 10-ohm, one 30-ohm, and one 60-ohm resistor. The total resistance of this circuit is _____ ohms.

4·36 (100) A series circuit contains resistances as follows: $R1 = 0.42$ ohm, $R2 = 0.62$ ohm, and $R3 = 0.88$ ohm. The value of E_b is 0.64 volt. The current flowing in any resistor in this circuit is _____ _____.

4·37 (⅓ amp) The current flowing in resistor $R4$ in Fig. 4·37 is 0.6 amp. Thus, the current in $R1$ must be _____ _____.

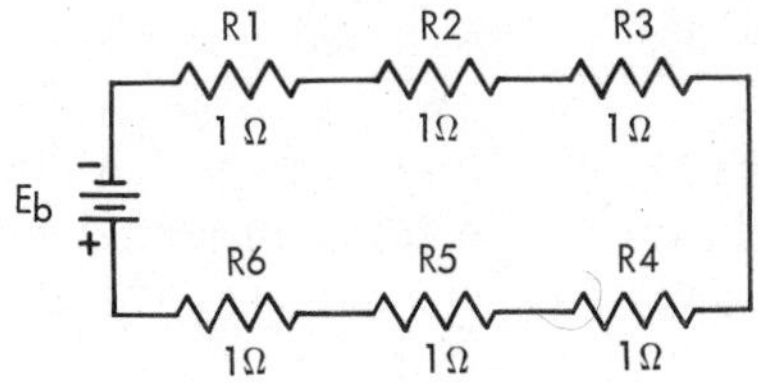

Fig. 4·37

4·38 (0.6 amp) The total resistance of the circuit in Fig. 4·37 is _____ _____.

4·39 (6 ohms) The battery voltage must, therefore, be _____ _____.

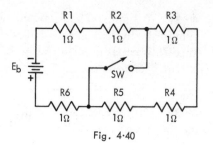

Fig. 4·40

4·40 (3.6 volts) A switch is connected in the previous circuit as shown in Fig. 4·40. If SW is open, the total circuit resistance is ＿＿＿＿ ＿＿＿＿ .

4·41 (6 ohms) When SW is closed, it produces what is known as a short-circuit path from the right end of *R2* to the right end of *R6*. Virtually all the electrons take this path, thus eliminating *R3*, *R4*, and *R5* from the circuit. Therefore, the total resistance now comprises *R1*, *R2*, and *R6* only in series. The total resistance now as seen by the battery is ＿＿＿＿ ＿＿＿＿ .

4·42 (3 ohms) When SW is closed, therefore, the circuit resistance is one-half of its value when SW is open. When SW is open, assume the current to be 0.6 amp. Now if SW is closed, the resistance drops to half its initial value, hence the new current will be ＿＿＿＿ ＿＿＿＿ .

4·42 (1.2 amp)

Voltages in series circuits

When a current flows through a group of series elements such as resistors, a *voltage drop* occurs across each of the elements. This is a condition in which a difference of potential between the two ends of the element is produced by the current flowing through the resistance of the element. The voltage drop is measured in volts and is found from Ohm's law: $E = IR$.

A voltage drop should not be confused with an emf. Although both are measured in volts, they have different directions, or better, different senses. An emf is a voltage *rise* produced by a battery or generator wherein chemical or mechanical energy is being converted into electric energy; a voltage drop is a *loss* of voltage caused by electric energy being converted into some other form, such as heat in a resistor.

In a series circuit, the sum of the individual voltage drops around the circuit is always numerically equal to the emf of the source.

4·43 When a series of ordinary stairway steps lead to a landing, the total height of the landing must be the sum of the individual step heights. For example, ten steps of 1 ft each in height must lead to a landing that is 10 ft above the lowermost step. Also, three steps of ½ ft each must lead to a point 1½ ft higher than the lowermost. Thus, eight steps each measuring ¾ ft in height must lead to a point _____ _____ higher.

4·44 (6 ft) Three stepped intervals (Fig. 4·44) of 3 ft, 4 ft, and 2 ft, respectively, lead to a point that is 9 ft high. Similarly, three stepped intervals of 1 ft, 8 ft, and 9 ft, respectively, must lead to a height of _____ ft.

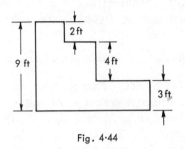

Fig. 4·44

4·45 (18) A height of 11 ft can be reached by a series of steps having heights of 2 ft, 6 ft, and _____ ft, respectively.

4·46 (3) The voltages across individual components of a series circuit are like steps on a stairway. That is, the sum of the individual voltage drops must equal the total applied voltage. Thus, in Fig. 4·46, voltage drops of 2, 4, and 3 volts must equal the source voltage of _____ volts.

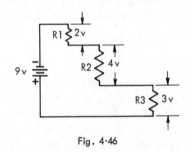

Fig. 4·46

4·47 (9) If the voltage drops were 4, 8, and 10 volts, respectively, the source voltage would have to be 22 volts. Similarly, if the voltage drops are 4, 5, and 9 volts, respectively, the source voltage must be _____ _____ .

4·48 (18 volts) Three resistors in a series circuit have voltage drops of 10, 20, and 30 volts across them, respectively. The source voltage must be 60 volts. Similarly, four resistors have drops of 45, 25, 15, and 15 volts, respectively. For this case the source voltage must be _____ _____ .

4·49 (100 volts) The voltage drops across five resistors in a series circuit are, respectively, 8, 9, 1, 2, and 5 volts. The source voltage must be _____ _____ .

4·50   (25 volts) The voltage drop across any resistor is found from this form of Ohm's law: $E = IR$. If 2 amp flow through a 5-ohm resistor, the voltage drop is $E = IR = 2 \times 5 = 10$ volts. If the second resistor in this series circuit is 10 ohms, the voltage drop would be $E = IR = 2 \times 10 =$ _____ volts.

4·51   (20) In the same series circuit, the current is the same throughout. Hence, if a third resistor in the circuit under discussion is 30 ohms, the voltage drop across it would be $E = IR =$ _____ volts.

4·52   (60) Two resistors, 8 and 4 ohms, respectively, are connected across a 24-volt source. The current flowing is $I = E/R = 24/(8 + 4) = 24/12 = 2$ amp. The voltage drop across $R1$ (8 ohms) is $E1 = IR1 = 2 \times 8 = 16$ volts. The voltage drop across $R2$ (4 ohms) $= E2 = IR2 = 2 \times 4 =$ _____ .

4·53   (8 volts) In the previous frame, the voltage drop across $R2$ might have been found from the "step" procedure by recognizing that if the total voltage is 24 volts and if the drop across $R1$ equals 16 volts, then the drop across $R2$ must equal _____ _____ .

4·54   (8 volts) If the battery voltage in Fig. 4·54 is given as 12 volts, then the current in the circuit is found by dividing 12 by the sum of the individual resistances or 24 ohms, giving a current of 0.5 amp. If the battery voltage were changed to 6 volts, the current would then be 6 volts divided by 24 ohms or _____ _____ .

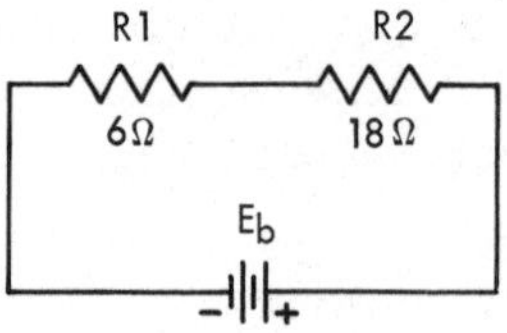

Fig. 4·54

4·55   (0.25 amp) If the battery voltage in Fig. 4·54 were changed to 3 volts, the current would be 3 volts divided by 24 ohms or _____ amp.

4·56   (0.125) If the battery voltage in Fig. 4·54 were changed to 24 volts, the current would be _____ amp.

4·57   (1) The voltage drop across the 6-ohm resistor with a battery voltage of 12 volts (Fig. 4·54) is $E1 = 0.5 \times 6 = 3$ volts. The voltage drop across the 18-ohm resistor must be the difference between the applied voltage ($E_b = 12$ volts) and the drop across $R1$ or _____ volts.

4·58 (9) The battery voltage is now changed to 6 volts, the current going down to 0.25 amp. Thus, the voltage drop across $R1$ is now $E1 = 0.25 \times 6 = $ _____ volts, and the drop across $R2$ must be _____ volts.

4·59 (1.5, 4.5) The battery voltage in Fig. 4·54 is now changed to 48 volts. The current in the circuit would be _____ amp; the voltage drop across $R1$ would be _____ volts; the voltage drop across $R2$ would be _____ volts.

4·60 (2, 12, 36) In the circuit of Fig. 4·60, the circuit values must be:

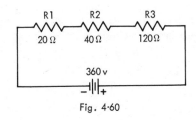

$$R_t = \text{_____} \text{ ohms}$$
$$I = \text{_____} \text{ amp}$$
$$E1 = \text{_____} \text{ volts}$$
$$E2 = \text{_____} \text{ volts}$$
$$E3 = \text{_____} \text{ volts}$$

Fig. 4·60

4·61 (180, 2, 40, 80, 240) These examples show that voltage drops are always proportional to the resistance across which the drop occurs. That is, $R1/E1 = 20/40 = 1/2$. Taking the second resistor-voltage ratio, $R2/E2 = 40/80 = 1/2$. By the same reasoning, $R3/E3 = 120/240 = $ _____ .

4·62 (1/2) This equality of resistor-voltage ratios makes it easy to find unknown voltage drops in series circuits. If a 10-ohm resistor in a certain series circuit has a 14-volt drop across it, then a 20-ohm resistor in the same series circuit would have twice the drop, or _____ volts.

4·63 (28) A series circuit contains a 10- and a 60-ohm resistor. The voltage drop across the 10-ohm resistor is 12 volts. Thus, the voltage drop across the 60-ohm resistor must be _____ volts.

4·64 (72) In Fig. 4·64, there is a 6-volt drop across the 100-ohm resistor, to give an $E1/R1$ ratio of 100/6. To find $E2$, we set up the ratio $300/E2$ which must be equal to 100/6. Thus $100/6 = 300/E2$ from which we find $E2 = $ _____ .

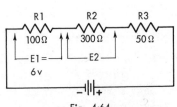

Fig. 4·64

73

4·65 (18) In Fig. 4·64, the voltage drop across $R3$ must be $E3 =$ _____ volts.

4·66 (3) In Fig. 4·64, the total voltage provided by the battery must be _____ volts.

4·67 (27) In Fig. 4·64, the current flowing in the circuit must be _____ amp.

4·67 (0.06)

Resistance-voltage relationships in series circuits

A very useful relationship may be set up between the emf applied to the whole series circuit and the individual voltage drops, using the ratio of total circuit resistance to individual element resistance. This relationship may be written in this manner:

$$\frac{R_x}{E_x} = \frac{R_t}{E_t}$$

where R_x = the resistance of the element under consideration
E_x = the voltage drop across this element
R_t = the total circuit resistance
E_t = the applied emf, or total circuit voltage

4·68 Any resistance in a series circuit is to the voltage drop across it as the total resistance of the circuit is to the total applied voltage. In equation form this is

$$\frac{R_x}{E_x} = \underline{\hspace{3cm}}$$

where R_x = given resistance, E_x = drop across R_x, and R_t and E_t are the total resistance and total voltage, respectively.

4·69 (R_t/E_t) In Fig. 4·69, $R1$ is 3 ohms and $E1$ is 9 volts. Thus, the ratio of $R1$ to $E1$ is 3:9 or _____ .

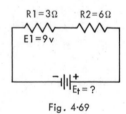

Fig. 4·69

4·70 (1:3) The total resistance of this circuit is $3 + 6$ ohms $= 9$ ohms. From our $R1/E1$ ratio we know that 1:3 must be equal to 9 ohms divided by the total source voltage. Hence, the total source voltage must be _____ volts.

4·71 (27) In Fig. 4·71, $R1 = 4$ ohms and $E1 = 24$ volts, so that the ratio of $R1$ to $E1$ is $4:24 = 1:6$. Since the total resistance is 5 ohms, the total voltage must be such that $5/E_t = 1/6$. Thus, the total voltage must be _____ _____ .

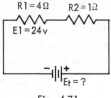

Fig. 4·71

4·72 (30 volts) In Fig. 4·72, the ratio of $R1$ to $E1$ is $80:240 = 1:3$. Thus, the total resistance of 100 ohms divided by the total voltage must also form a ratio of $1:3$. Hence, the total voltage is _____ _____ .

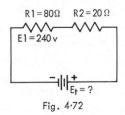

Fig. 4·72

4·73 (300 volts) In Fig. 4·73a, $R1$ and $E1$ form the ratio $1:12$. R_t and E_t must form the same ratio, and since $R_t = 30$ ohms, E_t must be 360 volts. In Fig. 4·73b, $R2$ is to $E2$ as $6:1$. Hence R_t which is 48 ohms to E_t must be $6:1$, so that E_t must be _____ _____ .

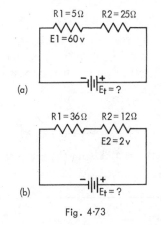

(a)

(b)

Fig. 4·73

4·74 (8 volts) To find the voltage of the source in Fig. 4·74, we set up the following ratio:

$$\frac{R_2}{E_2} = \frac{R_t}{E_t} \quad \text{or} \quad \frac{42}{3} = \frac{49}{E_t}$$

Then, solving for E_t we find the voltage of the source to be _____ volts.

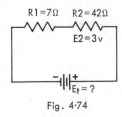

Fig. 4·74

4·75 (3.5) The total resistance in the circuit of Fig. 4·75 is _____ ohms. The current flowing in this circuit, from Ohm's law, is _____ _____ .

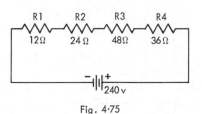

Fig. 4·75

4·76 (120, 2 amp) Using $E1 = IR1$, the voltage drop across $R1$ must be _____ volts.

75

4·77 (24) Using ratios of voltage drops and resistances, since $R2$ is twice as large as $R1$, then the voltage drop across $R2$ must be twice the voltage drop across $R1$, or _____ volts.

4·78 (48) Since $R3$ is four times greater than $R1$, the voltage drop across $R3$ must be _____ volts. The voltage drop across $R4$ must be _____ volts.

4·79 (96, 72) Using the relation $R_x/E_x = R_t/E_t$ we verify the drop across $R3$ by saying that since R_t is 120 ohms and E_t is 240 volts making a ratio of 120:240 or 1:2, then $R3/E3$ must be in the same ratio, making E_x equal to _____ volts.

4·80 (96) In Fig. 4·80, the voltage drop across $R1$ is found by saying that $R1$ is one-fifth of the total circuit resistance, hence the voltage drop across it must be one-fifth of the circuit voltage or _____ volts.

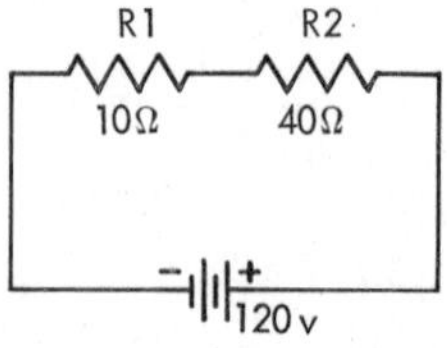

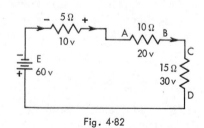

Fig. 4·80

4·81 (24) Using the same reasoning, the voltage drop across $R2$ is _____ _____.

4·81 (96 volts)

The polarity of a voltage drop

It is almost always necessary to determine the polarity of a voltage drop in a resistor due to the flow of current through it in analyzing d-c circuits. A very simple rule may always be employed if the circuit contains only one source of emf; this provision has been true thus far in all our circuits. The rule is this: Determine the direction of the electron flow, or current, in the resistor. Then assign a "$-$" sign to the end where the current enters the resistor and a "$+$" sign to the end where the current emerges.

4·82 When a voltage drop appears across a resistor carrying a current, the end of the resistor into which the electrons flow becomes more negative than the end from which they emerge. In Fig. 4·82, the left end of the 5-ohm resistor is negative and the right end positive according to this rule since the current enters the left and emerges from the right. Thus, end A of the 10-ohm resistor must be _____ and the right end _____ .

Fig. 4·82

4·83 (negative, positive) In the same figure, end C of the 15-ohm resistor must be _____ and the end labeled D must be _____.

4·84 (negative, positive) In Fig. 4·84, end A of resistor R1 must be _____ with respect to end B.

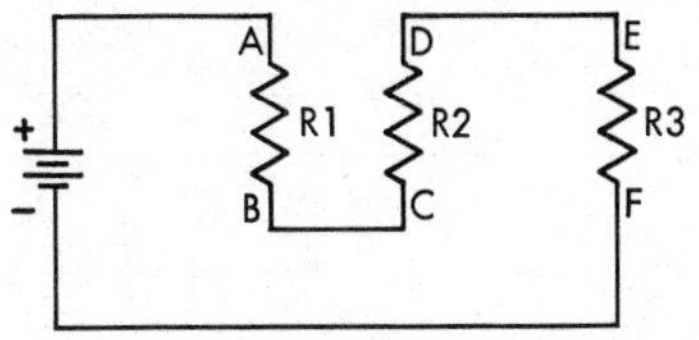

Fig. 4·84

4·85 (positive) In the same figure, end D of resistor R2 must be _____ while end C is _____.

4·86 (negative, positive) In the same figure, the negative end of resistor R3 is end _____.

4·87 (F) The series circuit of Fig. 4·87 uses ground as a common connection and a reference point for voltage measurement. Using Ohm's law, the current in this circuit is $I = E/R =$ $50/(100 + 100) = 50/200 = 0.25$ amp. The voltage drop across R1 equals $IR1 =$ _____ volts.

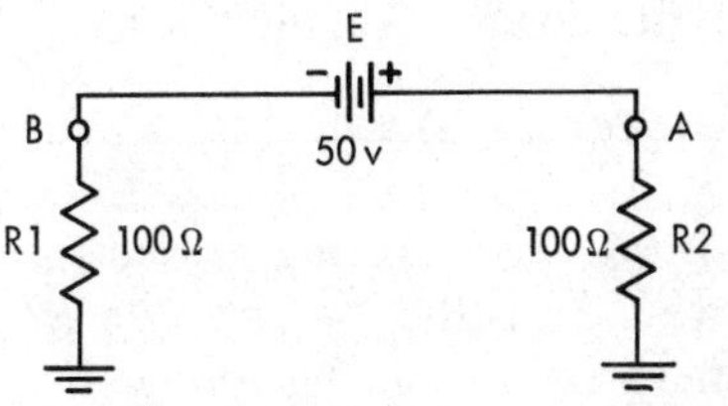

Fig. 4·87

4·88 (25) In Fig. 4·87, the voltage drop across R2 is _____ _____.

4·89 (25 volts) Current flows from the negative end of the battery through point B, through R1, through ground, up through R2, through point A, and back to the positive end of the battery. Thus, point B is _____ in polarity with respect to ground.

4·90 (negative) On the same basis, point A must be _____ with respect to ground.

4·90 (positive)

Kirchhoff's voltage law states that in tracing the voltage drops around a series loop, the *algebraic* sum of the emfs and voltage drops must be equal to zero. Since an emf is a voltage *rise,* we assign a "+" sign to all emfs. A voltage *drop,* however, has the opposite sense and is assigned a "−" sign. The rules for so doing are given in the text that follows.

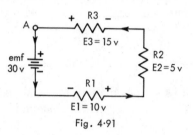

4·91   In tracing voltage drops around a circuit, we always start at a junction nearest the "+" side of the source. Thus, in Fig. 4·91, we would start at the point labeled _____, since this is the junction nearest the "+" side of the battery.

Fig. 4·91

4·92   (*A*) Starting at point *A*, we now traverse the circuit in the direction of the *electron flow.* The first algebraic sign we meet is a _____ sign at the top of the battery. We therefore write down +30 volts for the battery emf.

4·93   (+) Having passed through the battery, the next sign we meet is the "−" sign on *R*1. This means we must assign a negative sign to the voltage *drop* across *R*1. Thus, for the voltage drop *E*1 we would write _____ volts rather than +10 volts.

4·94   (−10) Since we next meet a "−" sign on *R*2, we can say that *E*2 (the drop across *R*2) is _____ volts.

4·95   (−5) Finally, we encounter a "−" sign on *R*3. Thus, *E*3 is _____ volts.

4·96   (−15) In Fig. 4·96, we start at *A* and trace the electron flow. The first sign encountered is the "+" of the battery, hence the emf is called +100 volts. Next we meet the "−" sign of *R*2, thus *E*2 = −40 volts. Next we come to the "−" sign of *R*1, hence *E*1 = _____ _____ .

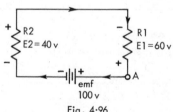

Fig. 4·96

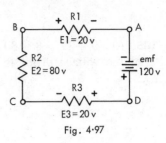

Fig. 4·97

4·97 (−60 volts) Remember that we always start our traversal of the circuit at a point *nearest the plus end of the source*. In Fig. 4·97, we have four labeled points: *A*, *B*, *C*, and *D*. The proper place to begin the traversal is at point _____ .

4·98 (*D*) In Fig. 4·97, the first sign encountered from a proper start at point *D* is the _____ sign of the battery.

4·99 (+) Thus, the battery voltage should be called _____
_____ .

4·100 (+120 volts) The next sign encountered in Fig. 4·97 is the "−" sign of *R*1, making *E*1 = _____ _____ .

4·101 (−20 volts) Thus, in Fig. 4·97, *E*2 = _____ _____ .

4·102 (−80 volts) Also, in Fig. 4·97, *E*3 = _____ _____ .

4·103 (−20 volts) Kirchhoff's second law states that the algebraic sum of the emfs and voltage drops around any closed circuit is zero. In an algebraic sum, consideration must be given to each algebraic sign as in the previous questions. Thus, in Fig. 4·91, Kirchhoff's second law has us write for the algebraic sum $+ 30 - 10 - 5 - 15 = 0$. In Fig. 4·96, we write $+ 100 - 40 - 60 = 0$. Similarly, in Fig. 4·97 we must write $+ 120 - 20 - 80 - 20 =$ _____ .

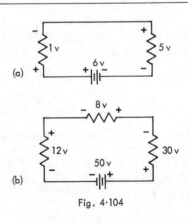

Fig. 4·104

4·104 (0) In Fig. 4·104*a*, the expression of Kirchhoff's second law would be $+ 6 - 5 - 1 = 0$. Similarly, in Fig. 4·104*b*, the expression of Kirchhoff's second law would be

_____ .

4·105 $(+50 - 12 - 8 - 30 = 0)$ In Fig. 4·105, the algebraic sum of the voltage drops is zero and is proved by writing _____ .

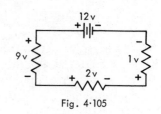

Fig. 4·105

4·106 $(+12 - 1 - 2 - 9 = 0)$ The best place to start tracing in the circuit of Fig. 4·106 is at point _____, since this is the junction nearest the "+" side of the source.

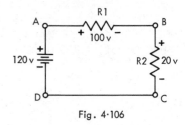

Fig. 4·106

4·107 (A) The emf of the battery is written down, according to Kirchhoff's second law, as _____ _____ .

4·108 $(+120$ volts$)$ The voltage drop across $R2$ is written as _____ _____ .

4·109 $(-20$ volts$)$ The voltage drop across $R1$ is written as _____ _____ .

4·110 $(-100$ volts$)$ The sum of the voltage drops and emf of this circuit is written as _____ .

4·111 $(+120 - 20 - 100 = 0)$ In Fig. 4·111, a good place to start the tracing of emfs and voltage drops would be point _____ .

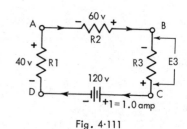

Fig. 4·111

4·112 (C) We want to find the value of $R3$. First set up the Kirchhoff's second law equation which reads like this: _____ (Fig. 4·111).

4·113 $(+ 120 - 40 - 60 - E3 = 0)$ Solving this equation for $E3$ tells us that $E3$ must be _____ volts.

4·114 (20) Applying Ohm's law $(E = IR)$ to $R3$, we find that the value of this resistor must be $R = E/I =$ _____ _____.

4·114 (20 ohms)

Using Kirchhoff's voltage law

A problem in Kirchhoff's voltage law is solved in the same way as any simple algebraic equation. The substitutions are made, with close attention being paid to the algebraic signs; terms are then transposed from one side to the other (signs are changed as this is done), leaving the unknown on the left side of the equation in the final step.

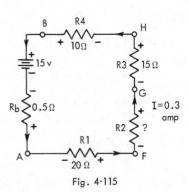

Fig. 4·115

4·115 In Fig. 4·115, a 15-volt battery with an internal resistance R_b of 0.5 ohms feeds a series circuit containing $R1$, $R2$, $R3$, and $R4$. All resistors except $R2$ are known. The problem is to find $R2$ when the current in the circuit is given as 0.3 amp. The best place to start tracing this circuit is point _____.

4·116 (B) Since the voltage drop across each resistor is the product of I times that resistance, we might write the Kirchhoff equation as $0 = + 15 - 0.5 \times 0.3 - 20 \times 0.3 - 0.3 \times R2 - 15 \times 0.3 - 10 \times 0.3$. When all products are taken, this equation becomes _____.

4·117 $(0 = + 15 - 0.15 - 6 - 0.3R2 - 4.5 - 3)$ Moving the term containing $R2$ to the left side of the equation and changing the sign, we have _____.

4·118 $(0.3R2 = + 15 - 0.15 - 6 - 4.5 - 3)$ Combining terms on the right side, this equation becomes _____.

4·119 $(0.3R2 = 1.35)$ Solving for $R2$, we then obtain

_____ .

4·120 $(R2 = 4.5 \text{ ohms})$ In Fig. 4·120, the value of $R4$ is to be found by the Kirchhoff method. The emf and voltage drop equation is _____ .

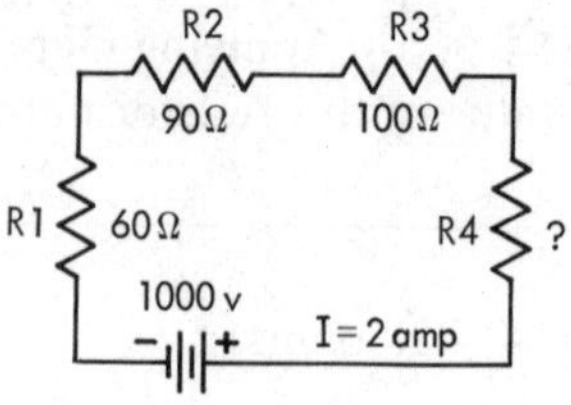

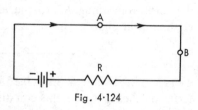

Fig. 4·120

4·121 $(0 = 1,000 - 60 \times 2 - 90 \times 2 - 100 \times 2 - R4 \times 2)$ With products taken, the equation is _____ .

4·122 $(0 = 1,000 - 120 - 180 - 200 - 2R4)$ Solved for $2R4$, the equation will then read (when terms are collected)

_____ .

4·123 $(2R4 = 500)$ Hence, the unknown resistor is _____ ohms.

4·123 $(R4 = 250)$

Kirchhoff's current law

Kirchhoff's current law (Gustav R. Kirchhoff, 1847) states that the current approaching a given electrical junction in a circuit loop equals the current leaving this junction. This law is almost self-evident, for consider what would happen if this were not true. If the current approaching a junction were to exceed the current leaving it, then electrons would quickly pile up at the junction until the voltage at this point would become excessive. This does not occur. On the other hand, if the current leaving the junction were to exceed the current approaching it, the junction would soon "run dry" of electrons and be unable to support the current in the conductors after the junction. This does not occur, either. Hence, we must conclude that the approaching and retreating currents must be equal.

4·124 Kirchhoff's current law states that the current approaching a given electrical junction must equal the current leaving this junction. In Fig. 4·124, the current flowing into junction A is equal to the current flowing out of junction A according to Kirchhoff's first law. Similarly, the current flowing into junction B is _____ to the current flowing out of junction B.

Fig. 4·124

4·125 (equal) In Fig. 4·125, the total current flowing away from junction A must be equal to the current flowing into junction A. Therefore, the sum of the currents in $R1$ and $R2$ must equal the current flowing away from junction _____ .

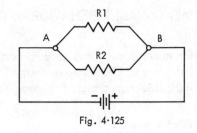

Fig. 4·125

4·126 (A or B) In Fig. 4·125, the sum of the currents in $R1$ and $R2$ must equal the current flowing into junction _____ .

4·127 (B or A) In Fig. 4·127, the current flowing in $R1$ is 36 amp. It divides evenly between $R2$, $R3$, and $R4$. Thus, the current flowing in $R2$ must equal _____ amp.

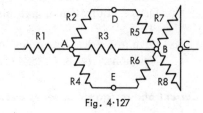

Fig. 4·127

4·128 (12) The current flowing into junction E is the same current that just passed through $R4$ since junction E is part of the series circuit containing $R4$. The current in $R4$ is 12 amp, hence the current flowing through junction E is _____ amp.

4·129 (12) In Fig. 4·127, the current flowing into junction B must be _____ _____ .

4·130 (36 amp) In Fig. 4·127, if $R7$ and $R8$ have equal resistance, the current in each resistor must be _____ amp.

4·131 (18) The current flowing out of junction C is _____ amp.

4·131 (36)

MEASURABLE BEHAVIORAL OBJECTIVES

Upon completion of a section, you should be able to achieve the objectives listed for it. The frame or frames that cover the related subject matter are indicated immediately following each objective.

Electric power

1 Discuss the conversion of electric energy to heat.   (Introduction)
2 Define the joule as a unit of energy.   (Introduction)
3 Relate power to energy.   (4·23)
4 Derive an equation for power in an electric circuit.   (4·1)
   a Define the watt as a unit of power.   (4·1)
   b Derive equivalent equations for power by applying Ohm's law. (4·15, 4·19)
   c Give numerical examples to illustrate the use of the above power equations.   (4·8, 4·18, 4·22)

Current and resistance in series circuits

1 Discuss the properties of series circuits in relation to voltages and resistance.   (4·27, 4·31)
2 Calculate the total resistance and current in a series circuit.   (4·35, 4·36)
3 Draw schematic diagrams for series circuits.   (4·33)

Voltages in series circuits

1 Define voltage drop.   (Introduction)
2 Differentiate between voltage drop and emf.   (Introduction)
3 Calculate the voltage drops across the resistors in a series circuit. (4·50)
4 Relate the sum of the voltage drops around a circuit and the emf of the source.   (4·46)

Resistance-voltage relationships in series circuits

1 Relate the voltage drop across any one of the series resistors to the applied emf.   (4·68)
2 Give a mathematical equation expressing the ratio of the voltage drop to other values in the circuit.   (4·74)
3 Demonstrate the usefulness of the above equation with numerical values.   (4·80)

The polarity of a voltage drop

1 State the rule for determining the polarity of voltage drop in a series circuit with a single battery.   (4·82)
2 Discuss the meaning of a "−" or a "+" sign in relation to electron flow.   (4·82, 4·83)
3 Draw series circuits and assign voltage polarities to each element. (4·87)

Kirchhoff's voltage law

1 State Kirchhoff's voltage law for a series circuit. (4·103)
2 Demonstrate the validity of Kirchhoff's voltage law for a series circuit. (4·104)

Using Kirchhoff's voltage law

1 Formulate algebraic equations to determine the value of an unknown resistance in a series circuit. (4·115, 4·116)
2 Write Kirchhoff's voltage law and use it to calculate the unknown resistance in a series circuit. (4·115)

Kirchhoff's current law

1 State Kirchhoff's current law. (Introduction)
2 Discuss what would happen if the above law did not hold. (4·124)
3 Demonstrate the validity of Kirchhoff's current law by performing calculations on a parallel circuit. (4·127)

chapter 5

parallel circuits

Parallel circuits

A parallel circuit is a *branched* arrangement in which two or more elements, such as resistors, are connected across a single source of emf as in Fig. 5·1. The characteristics of a parallel circuit may be listed as follows:

1. The branches are independent of one another. That is, the current that flows and the power consumed in branch $R1$ (Fig. 5·1) are not influenced by the values of the resistors in the other branches. Each branch may be treated, in the ideal case, as though the other branches do not exist.

2. All connecting wires are considered to have zero resistance. Therefore, the voltage applied (emf) by the source to each resistor in a parallel circuit is the same as the source voltage, and the same as every other resistor in the parallel circuit

$$E_t = E1 = E2, \text{etc.}$$

3. The total current supplied by the source equals the sum of the individual branch currents

$$I_t = I1 + I2 + I3, \text{etc.}$$

4. The *reciprocal* of the total resistance (or net resistance) of the circuit equals the sum of the reciprocals of the individual resistances. That is

$$1/R_t = 1/R1 + 1/R2 + 1/R3, \text{etc.}$$

5·1 A parallel circuit is a circuit in which two or more resistors are connected across the same source of voltage by "resistanceless" wires. In Fig. 5·1, the wires are to be considered resistanceless. Since $R1$, $R2$, and $R3$ are all connected across the same battery, this must be a _____ circuit.

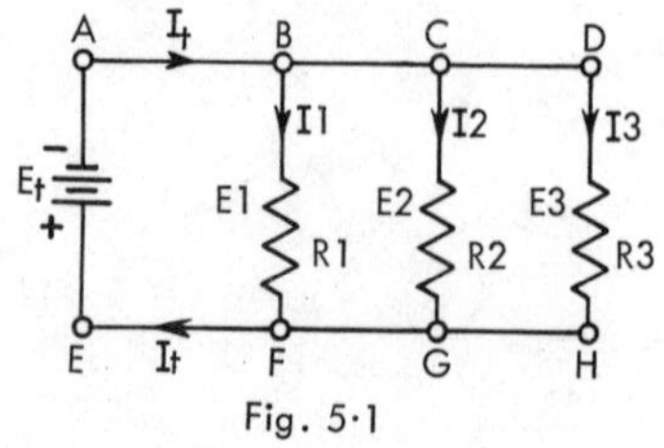

Fig. 5·1

5·2 (parallel) In Fig. 5·1, the wires are resistanceless. If a resistance is zero, no voltage drop can appear across it. This is stated by the equation $E = IR$, since if $R = 0$, then _____ must also be zero.

5·3 (E) In Fig. 5·1, if no voltage drop can develop across the wires AB, BC, and CD, then point A must have the same potential as point B; and finally, point D must have the same potential as point _____.

5·4 (C) In Fig. 5·1, the voltage at D must be the same as the voltage at A, B, and _____.

5·5 (C) In Fig. 5·1, the voltage at H must be the same as the voltage at _____, _____, and _____.

5·6 (E, F, G) The potential difference between A and E is that of the battery E_t. Since B is at the same voltage as A, and F at the same voltage as E, then the voltage across B and F must be equal to _____.

5·7 (E_t) By the same reasoning the voltage across C and G and the voltage across D and H must be equal to _____.

5·8 (E_t) Thus, a parallel circuit may be defined as a circuit in which $E_t = E1 = E2 = E3$. This is the same as saying that in a parallel circuit, the voltage across any branch is equal to the _____ voltage.

5·9 (source or applied) In Fig. 5·1, the total current I_t splits up into three branch currents $I1$, $I2$, and $I3$. From Kirchhoff's first law, if the current approaching point B is called I_t, then the current leaving point F is _____.

5·10 (I_t) In Fig. 5·1, $I1 + I2 + I3$ must be equal to _____.

5·11 (I_t) This is the same as saying that the total current flowing in and out of the source must be equal to the _____ of the individual branch currents.

5·12 (sum) The voltage across B and F is E_t, hence the current in $R1$ (that is, $I1$) must be $I1 = E_t/R1$. Also, the current in $R2$ (that is, $I2$) must be $I2 = E_t/R2$. Thus, the current $I3$ must be given by the equation _____.

5·13 ($I3 = E_t/R3$) In Fig. 5·1, the total current flowing in the circuit, given in terms of E_t and the resistances, must equal the total voltage divided by the total resistance. Thus, if R_t is the total resistance, then I_t must be given by the equation $I_t = E_t/R_t$. Since $I_t = I1 + I2 + I3$, then we can say that $E_t/R_t = E_t/R1 + E_t/R2 +$ _____.

5·14 ($E_t/R3$) In Fig. 5·1, since E_t is the same in each term of the equation, we may divide through by E_t and obtain the following expression for total resistance: $1/R_t = 1/R1 + 1/R2 +$ _____.

5·15 ($1/R3$) This expression may be read off as follows: The _____ of the total resistance of a parallel circuit is equal to the sum of the reciprocals of the individual resistances.

5·16 (reciprocal) In summary, the voltage law for parallel circuits states that the voltage across each individual branch equals the _____ _____.

5·17 (source voltage) In summary, the current law for parallel circuits states that the total current is the _____ of the individual branch currents.

5·18 (sum) In summary, the resistance law for parallel circuits states that the reciprocal of the total resistance is the _____ of the reciprocals of the branch resistances.

5·19 (sum) In Fig. 5·19, the voltage across $E3$ is 10 volts; hence, the voltage across $E2$ is 10 volts; thus, the source voltage must be _____ _____.

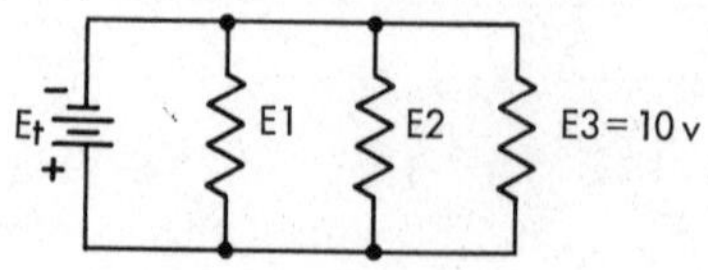

Fig. 5·19

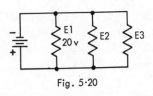

Fig. 5·20

5·20 (10 volts) In Fig. 5·20, the voltage $E1 = 20$ volts, hence the voltage $E3$ must equal _____ _____ .

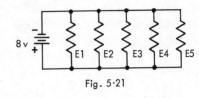

Fig. 5·21

5·21 (20 volts) In Fig. 5·21, the source voltage is 8 volts, hence $E4 =$ _____ _____ .

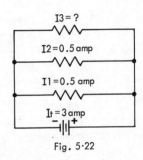

Fig. 5·22

5·22 (8 volts) Since the sum of the branch current must equal the total current in a parallel circuit, the current $I3$ in Fig. 5·22 must add to $I2$ and $I1$ in order to total up to I_t. If $I_t = 3$ amp, then $I3 =$ _____ _____ .

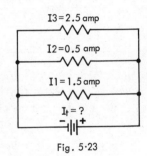

Fig. 5·23

5·23 (2 amp) Since $I1 + I2 + I3 = I_t$, then in Fig. 5·23, the total current must be _____ amp.

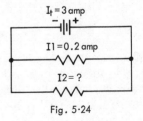

Fig. 5·24

5·24 (4.5) In Fig. 5·24, the current $I2 =$ _____ _____ .

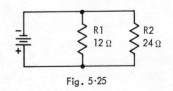

Fig. 5·25

5·25 (2.8 amp) In Fig. 5·25, the total resistance of the circuit is obtained by substituting in the equation $1/R_t = 1/R1 + 1/R2$. This gives a value for R_t obtained from $1/R_t = 1/12 + 1/24$ which in turn yields $1/R_t =$ _____ .

89

5·26 (3/24) In Fig. 5·25, the total resistance of the circuit is then obtained by inverting both fractions and reducing to lowest terms. Thus, $R_t = 24/3 =$ _____ ohms.

5·27 (8) In Fig. 5·27, the total resistance is obtained by taking the sum of the reciprocals of the individual resistances and inverting the final fraction obtained; thus, the total resistance is $R_t =$ _____ ohms.

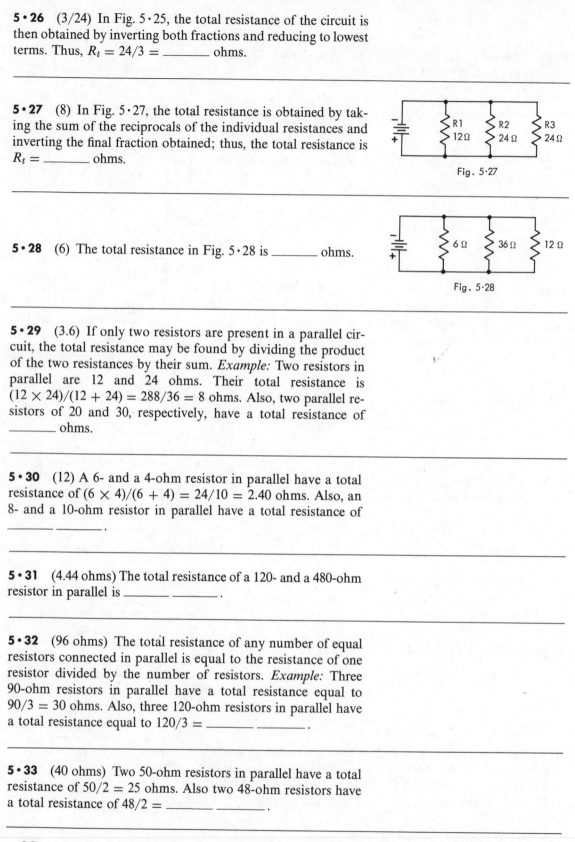

Fig. 5·27

5·28 (6) The total resistance in Fig. 5·28 is _____ ohms.

Fig. 5·28

5·29 (3.6) If only two resistors are present in a parallel circuit, the total resistance may be found by dividing the product of the two resistances by their sum. *Example:* Two resistors in parallel are 12 and 24 ohms. Their total resistance is $(12 \times 24)/(12 + 24) = 288/36 = 8$ ohms. Also, two parallel resistors of 20 and 30, respectively, have a total resistance of _____ ohms.

5·30 (12) A 6- and a 4-ohm resistor in parallel have a total resistance of $(6 \times 4)/(6 + 4) = 24/10 = 2.40$ ohms. Also, an 8- and a 10-ohm resistor in parallel have a total resistance of _____ _____ .

5·31 (4.44 ohms) The total resistance of a 120- and a 480-ohm resistor in parallel is _____ _____ .

5·32 (96 ohms) The total resistance of any number of equal resistors connected in parallel is equal to the resistance of one resistor divided by the number of resistors. *Example:* Three 90-ohm resistors in parallel have a total resistance equal to $90/3 = 30$ ohms. Also, three 120-ohm resistors in parallel have a total resistance equal to $120/3 =$ _____ _____ .

5·33 (40 ohms) Two 50-ohm resistors in parallel have a total resistance of $50/2 = 25$ ohms. Also two 48-ohm resistors have a total resistance of $48/2 =$ _____ _____ .

5•34 (24 ohms) Four 80-ohm resistors in parallel have a total resistance of 20 ohms. Five 250-ohm resistors in parallel have a total resistance of _____ ohms.

5•35 (50) Eight lamps each having a resistance of 240 ohms are connected in parallel. The total resistance of this circuit is _____ _____.

5•36 (30 ohms) Draw a circuit to illustrate the conditions given in the following problem, then determine the answers required for each part. Three resistors are connected in parallel across a 24-volt battery. The values of the resistors are 30, 60, and 20 ohms. The equivalent total resistance of this circuit is _____ _____.

5•37 (10 ohms) The current through the 30-ohm resistor is _____ _____.

5•38 (0.8 amp) The current through the 60-ohm resistor is _____ _____.

5•39 (0.4 amp) The current through the 20-ohm resistor is _____ _____.

5•40 (1.2 amp) The total circuit current is _____ _____.

5•41 (2.4 amp) The power dissipated in the 30-ohm resistor is _____ _____.

5•42 (19.2 watts) The power dissipated in the 60-ohm resistor is _____ _____.

5•43 (9.6 watts) The power dissipated in the 20-ohm resistor is _____ _____.

5•44 (28.8 watts) The total power dissipated in any circuit is the sum of the powers dissipated in each component. In the problem just solved, the total power is 19.2 + 9.6 + 28.8 watts = _____ _____.

5•44 (57.6 watts)

MEASURABLE BEHAVIORAL OBJECTIVES

Upon completion of a section, you should be able to achieve the objectives listed for it. The frame or frames that cover the related subject matter are indicated immediately following each objective.

Parallel circuits

1 State the rule for finding the net resistance for parallel resistors. (5·14)
2 Demonstrate the above rule with numerical examples. (5·25)
3 Show that the total resistance of a parallel circuit is always less than that of any of the single resistors. (5·27)
4 Discuss for an ideal case the relationship between the applied voltage and the number of parallel resistive elements in an electric circuit. (5·21)
5 Describe a method for finding the current in each branch of a parallel circuit. (5·13)
6 Give an equation relating the current from the source to the current in the individual branches. (5·23)
7 Analyze a parallel circuit by drawing a schematic diagram. Then, determine the magnitudes and polarities of voltages and magnitudes and directions of currents. (5·23)
8 Give equations for determining the power supplied by the source and the power dissipated in the branches. (5·41)

chapter 6

series-parallel circuits

Basic considerations for series-parallel combinations

Series and parallel circuits may be combined to form series-parallel combinations. The fundamental rules developed for series and parallel circuits independently apply equally well to combinations. You are afforded some practice on such combinations in Frames 6·1 to 6·14.

6·1 Resistors may be connected in combination circuits in which some parts are in series and others in parallel. This combination is called a series-parallel circuit. The first step in series-parallel circuit analysis is to recognize which parts are the series groups and which are the parallel groups. In Fig. 6·1, R1 is in series with R2. Also, R3 is in series with _____.

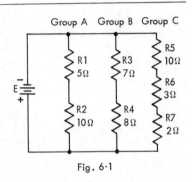

Fig. 6·1

6·2 (R4) In Fig. 6·1, R5 is in series with R6 and _____.

6·3 (R7) In Fig. 6·1, the combination of R1-R2 is in parallel with the combination R3-R4. Also, the combination of R3-R4 is in parallel with the combination R6-R7-_____.

6·4 (R5) One parallel group in Fig. 6·4 is composed of resistors _____ and _____.

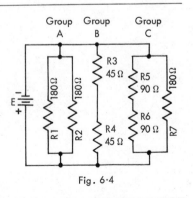

Fig. 6·4

6·5 (R1, R2) Resistors R3 and R4 are in _____
(Fig. 6·4).

6·6 (series) Resistors R5 and R6 are in _____
(Fig. 6·4).

6·7 (series) The series group comprising R5 and R6 is in
parallel with R7. The resistors R5 and R6 may be combined to
form an equivalent resistance of 90 + 90 Ω = 180 Ω. This
equivalent resistance would still be in _____ with R7.

6·8 (parallel) If each group is combined (A, B, and C) within
itself to form a single equivalent resistance per group, then all the
groups could be considered to be connected in _____
(Fig. 6·4).

6·9 (parallel) A parallel circuit is simplified by combining
resistors within each group to form equivalent resistors. *Example:* In Fig. 6·1, R1 and R2 are in series and may be combined to form an equivalent resistance of 15 ohms. Also, R3
and R4 are in series and can be combined to form an equivalent resistance of _____ _____ .

6·10 (15 ohms) Resistors R5 and R6 and R7 in Fig. 6·1 can
be combined to form an equivalent resistance of _____ _____ .

6·11 (15 ohms) Thus, the total equivalent resistance of the
entire circuit in Fig. 6·1 is _____ _____ .

6·12 (5 ohms) In Fig. 6·4, R1 and R2 can be combined to
give a group-A resistance of 90 ohms. Also, R3 and R4 give an
equivalent group-B resistance of _____ _____ .

6·13 (90 ohms) In Fig. 6·13, we have three groups of
resistors (A, B, and C) all in series with each other. The equivalent resistance of group B is 6 ohms. The equivalent resistance
of C is _____ _____ .

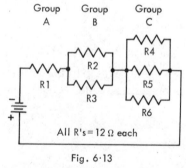

Fig. 6·13

6·14   (4 ohms) The total equivalent resistance of the circuit in Fig. 6·13 is _____ .

6·14   (22 ohms)

Simplifying series-parallel combinations

Frames 6·15 to 6·30 provide some practice in the simplification of parallel and series groups into equivalent resistances for the solution of complex series-parallel circuits.

6·15   Solving series-parallel circuits is greatly simplified if all parallel and series groups are first reduced to single equivalent resistances and the circuit redrawn in simplified form. In Fig. 6·15, the parallel groups are first reduced to equivalent resistances. *Example: R2* and *R3* reduce to 10 ohms of equivalent resistance. Also, *R4* and *R5* reduce to _____ ohms of equivalent resistance.

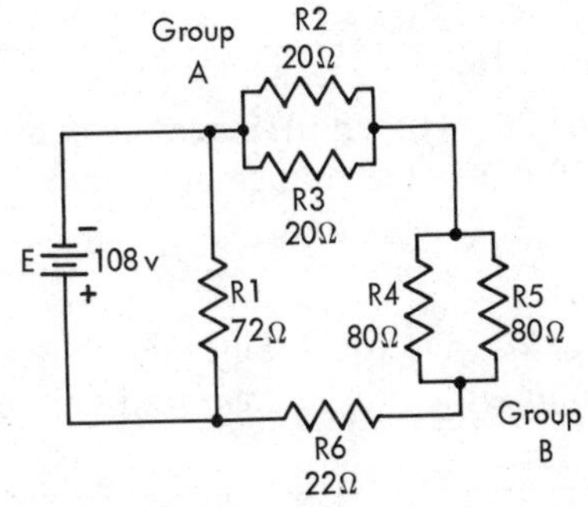

Fig. 6·15

6·16   (40) In Fig. 6·15, *R6* and the equivalent resistances of group *A* and group *B* are all in _____ .

6·17   (series) The total equivalent resistance of *R6* combined with group *A* and group *B* is _____ (Fig. 6·15).

6·18   (72 ohms) In Fig. 6·15, resistor *R1* as connected with the equivalent resistance of *R6*, group *A*, and group *B* taken together, is in _____ with the combined groups.

6·19   (parallel) Thus we have *R1* (72 ohms) in parallel with an equivalent resistance of 72 ohms made up of the simplification of *R2*, *R3*, *R4*, *R5*, and *R6*. Two 72-ohm resistances in parallel then give us a net circuit resistance in Fig. 6·15 of _____ ohms.

6·20   (36) In Fig. 6·15, the total current in the circuit is equal to the total voltage divided by the total equivalent resistance. The total current is therefore _____ .

6·21 (3 amp) The voltage drop across $R1$ is _____ _____ .

_____

6·22 (108 volts) The voltage drop across the entire series set consisting of $R6$, group A, and group B is ____ _____ .

_____

6·23 (108 volts) The current flowing in $R1$ is ____ _____ .

_____

6·24 (1.5 amp) The current flowing through the series set consisting of $R6$, group A, and group B is ____ _____ .

_____

6·25 (1.5 amp) Since the equivalent resistance of group A is 10 ohms, the voltage drop across either $R2$ or $R3$ is ____ ____ .

_____

6·26 (15 volts) Since the equivalent resistance of group B is 40 ohms, the voltage drop across either $R4$ or $R5$ is ____ _____ .

_____

6·27 (60 volts) The voltage drop across $R6$ is ____ _____ .

_____

6·28 (33 volts) The sum of the voltage drops around the entire circuit is _____ volts and is equal to the _____ voltage.

_____

6·29 (108, source) The current flowing in $R2$ must be half the current in group A, hence it must be 0.75 amp. The current flowing in $R5$ must be half the current in group B. This current is _____ .

_____

6·30 (0.75 amp) The current flowing in $R6$ is ____ _____ .

_____

6·30 (1.5 amp)

_____

MEASURABLE BEHAVIORAL OBJECTIVES

Upon completion of a section, you should be able to achieve the objectives listed for it. The frame or frames that cover the related subject matter are indicated immediately following each objective.

Basic considerations for series-parallel combinations

1 State the rule for combining series resistors. $(6 \cdot 1, 6 \cdot 2)$
2 State the rule for combining parallel resistors. $(6 \cdot 7)$
3 State the rule for combining series-parallel resistors. $(6 \cdot 1, 6 \cdot 9)$
4 Demonstrate the use of the above rules on a simple series-parallel circuit. $(6 \cdot 13)$

Simplifying series-parallel combinations

1 Give a step-by-step generalized method for simplifying a series-parallel resistive circuit. $(6 \cdot 15)$
2 Analyze a series-parallel circuit. $(6 \cdot 15)$

chapter 7

voltage dividers

Introduction to voltage dividers

A simple *voltage divider* consists of two or more resistors connected across a source of emf. Current flowing through the series resistors gives rise to voltage drops across them. Junctions between resistors, therefore, are at different potentials than the ends connected to the source. These voltage drops may now be used as seats of emf to operate loads which require lower voltages than that provided by the "undiluted" source of emf (Fig. 7·1).

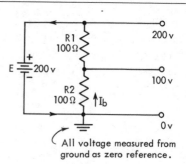

Fig. 7·1

7·1 A simple voltage divider is shown in Fig. 7·1. Since the source voltage $E = 200$ volts, and $R1$ and $R2$ are equal resistors—100 ohms apiece—the voltage drop across $R1$ must be 100 volts, and the voltage drop across $R2$ must be _____ volts.

7·2 (100) In Fig. 7·1, the current flowing through the voltage divider consisting of $R1$ and $R2$ is calculated from Ohm's law and is called the bleeder current I_b. The bleeder current in this circuit is _____ amp.

7·3 (1) In Fig. 7·1, the voltages appearing across the output terminals of this voltage divider are all measured from one common point. This common point is _____ .

7·4 (ground) In Fig. 7·1, since no external loads are shown connected to the voltage divider, the total current supplied by the source must be _____ _____ .

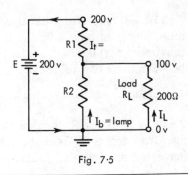

Fig. 7·5

7·5 (1 amp) In Fig. 7·5, an external load has been added to the 100-volt terminal of the voltage divider. Assume that this load is to be operated at exactly 100 volts and that its resistance is 200 ohms. Thus, the load current I_L must be specified as

_____ .

7·6 (0.5 amp) The bleeder current was originally 1 amp before connection of the load. Assuming that the source is still to provide a bleeder current of the same value as before the addition of the load, the current in $R2$ and $R1$ due *only* to bleeder action is _____ amp.

7·7 (1) In Fig. 7·5, resistor $R1$ must, therefore, carry the sum of the bleeder current and the load current. Hence, the current in $R1$ is the total current I_t and is _____ amp.

7·8 (1.5) The voltage drop across $R1$ must be 100 volts if the voltage drop across $R2$ is 100 volts as the load demands. Hence, the resistance of $R1$ as found from Ohm's law must be $R = E/I = 100/1.5 =$ _____ ohms.

7·9 (66.6) Only the bleeder current of 1.0 amp flows through $R2$. Since the voltage drop across this resistor must be 100 volts to satisfy the load, its resistance from Ohm's law must be $R2 =$

_____ .

7·9 (100 ohms)

Simple voltage-divider calculations

All voltage-divider problems are solved by application of Ohm's law. Care must be exercised, however, in determining currents flowing in the voltage-divider parts as a result of both bleeder and load effects. This sample calculation will clarify these methods.

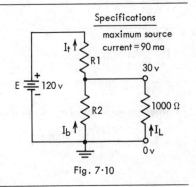

Fig. 7·10

7·10 In Fig. 7·10, the load resistor R_L is 1,000 ohms and the voltage applied to the load resistor is to be 30 volts. This means that the load current will be _____. (Note that this is to be in milliamperes, not amperes.)

7·11 (30 ma) Note that the specifications call for a maximum source current of 90 ma. If the load takes 30 ma, then the maximum permissible bleeder current must be the difference between these two values, or _____ ma.

7·12 (60) Since R_L is in parallel with $R2$, and since the voltage drop across R_L is to be 30 volts, then the voltage drop across $R2$ must be _____ _____ .

7·13 (30 volts) Since the bleeder current is to be 60 ma and the voltage across $R2$ is to be 30 volts, then using $R = E/I$, the resistance of $R2$ must be _____ ohms. (Remember to convert the current from milliamperes to amperes!)

7·14 (500) The current in $R1$ must be $I_b + I_L$. Hence, the current in $R1$ must be _____ _____ .

7·15 (90 ma) Since the sum of the voltage drops across the series elements must be equal to the source voltage, and since the drop across R_L (or $R2$) = 30 volts, the drop across $R1$ must be _____ _____ .

7·16 (90 volts) Hence, the resistance of $R1$ carrying a current of 90 ma with a voltage drop of 90 volts must be _____ _____ .

7·17 (1,000 ohms) The required power rating for $R2$, from $P = I^2R$, is $(0.06)^2 \times 500 =$ _____ _____ .

7·18 (1.8 watts) The required power rating for $R1$, from $P = I^2R$, is _____ _____ .

7·18 (8.1 watts)

Another voltage-divider calculation

Here is another useful exercise in calculating the resistive components and the power dissipations of a voltage divider.

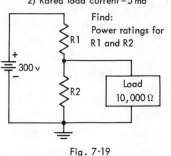

Specifications
1) Maximum source current = 45 ma
2) Rated load current = 5 ma

Find:
Power ratings for R1 and R2

Fig. 7·19

7·19 Figure 7·19 illustrates another voltage-divider problem. The maximum source current is given as 45 ma. Expressed in amperes, the maximum source current is _____ _____ .

7·20 (0.045 amp) The rated load current as shown is 5 ma or 0.005 amp. The source current may not be allowed to exceed 0.045 amp. Therefore, the maximum allowable bleeder current (the difference between maximum source current and load current) is _____ amp .

7·21 (0.040) The load resistance is specified as 10,000 ohms. The rated load current is 0.005 amp (5 ma). From Ohm's law, the rated load voltage should then be _____ _____ .

7·22 (50 volts) R2 is in parallel with the load, hence the voltage drop across R2 must be _____ _____ .

7·23 (50 volts) The current through R2 is the bleeder current of 0.04 amp. For a 50-volt drop with a current of 0.04 amp the resistance of R2 must be _____ _____ .

7·24 (1,250 ohms) To produce a sum of voltage drops equal to the source voltage, the drop across R1 must be _____ _____ .

7·25 (250 volts) Since R1 carries the total circuit current of 0.045 amp and has a voltage drop of 250 volts across it, its resistance must be _____ _____ .

7·26 (5555.5 ohms) Using any one of the three power equations, the power dissipation rating required for R2 is ___ _____ .

7·27 (2 watts) Using the power equation $P = EI$, the simplest for this case, the power dissipation rating required for R1 is _____ _____ .

7·27 (11.25 watts)

Figure 7·28 illustrates a practical relay problem involving the use of a voltage divider. The relay should be viewed merely as a load; the fact that relays have not been discussed makes no difference whatever in the solution of the problem. Equations (a) and (b) given below facilitate the solution of this type of problem. These equations have been derived from considerations similar to those described in prior sections.

$$R1 = \frac{E_t - I_L R_L}{I_t} \qquad\qquad (a)$$

$$R2 = R_L \left(\frac{I_t}{I_t - I_L} - 1 \right) \qquad\qquad (b)$$

where E_t = available source voltage
I_L = load current
R_L = load resistance
I_t = maximum source current

The student should make use of these equations in the solution of the problem that follows.

7·28 Study the specifications given in Fig. 7·28. To simplify your calculations, find $R1$ from Eq. (a). The value of $R1$ as determined from Eq. (a) is found by substituting the specifications thus:

$$R1 = \frac{200 - (0.01 \times 5,000)}{0.015}$$

The answer for $R1$ is _____ ohms.

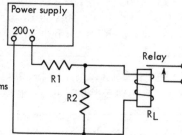

SPECIFICATIONS

E_t = Available operating voltage   200 v
I_t = Maximum available current   15 ma
R_L = Load resistance (relay coil resistance)   5,000 ohms
I_L = Load current (current relay needs to operate) 10 ma

FIND

Values of R1 and R2 in ohms
Required power ratings of R1 and R2 in watts

Fig. 7·28

7·29 (10,000) The value of $R2$ may be determined from Eq. (b). The values substituted in this equation are also obtained from the specifications shown in Fig. 7·28. The substitutions are

$$R2 = 5,000 \left(\frac{0.015}{0.015 - 0.01} - 1 \right)$$

and the answer for $R2$ is _____ ohms.

7·30 (10,000) The minimum power rating required for $R1$ is obtained from Eq. (c):

$$P1 = I_t^2 R1 \qquad (c)$$

Substituting, we have $P1 = (0.015)^2 \times 10,000$

so that the answer for $P1$ is ____ _____ .

7·31 (2.25 watts) The minimum power rating required for $R2$ is obtained from Eq. (d):

$$P2 = (I_t - I_L)^2 R2 \qquad (d)$$

Substituting, we have $P2 = (0.015 - 0.01)^2 \times 10,000$

so that the answer for $P2$ is ____ _____ .

7·32 (0.25 watt) The validity of Eqs. (a) and (b) should be checked by a sequential analysis. We start first by obtaining the rated load voltage. Since the resistance is 5,000 ohms and the current 0.01 amp, the voltage drop across the load is ____ _____ .

7·33 (50 volts) $R2$ is in parallel with the load, hence the voltage drop across $R2$ must be ____ _____ .

7·34 (50 volts) The current through $R2$ is the bleeder current. Since $I_t = 0.015$ amp and $I_L = 0.01$ amp, the bleeder current must be ____ _____ .

7·35 (0.005 amp or 5 ma) Hence, with a 50-volt drop across $R2$ at a current of 0.005 amp, the resistance of $R2$ must be ____ _____ .

7·36 (10,000 ohms) There is a 50-volt drop across $R2$. The source voltage is 200 volts. The voltage drop across $R1$ must, therefore, be the difference between the source voltage and the drop across $R2$, or ____ _____ .

7·37 (150 volts) Since $R1$ carries the total circuit current $I_t = 0.015$ amp and has a voltage drop of 150 volts across it, its resistance must be ____ _____ .

7·37 (10,000 ohms)

MEASURABLE BEHAVIORAL OBJECTIVES

Upon completion of a section, you should be able to achieve the objectives listed for it. The frame or frames that cover the related subject matter are indicated immediately following each objective.

Introduction to voltage dividers

1 Draw a simple voltage divider. (7·1)
2 Discuss a method for determining the voltage across each resistor in a series resistive circuit. (7·5)
3 Give an example of the use of a voltage divider. (7·5)

Simple voltage-divider calculations

1 Illustrate the use of Ohm's law as it applies to voltage-division problems. (7·10)
2 Draw a schematic diagram for a voltage divider and indicate the voltage polarities and current direction. (7·10)
3 Discuss the effects of a load resistor on voltage dividers. (7·13)

Another voltage-divider calculation

1 Illustrate the design procedure for determining the values of the voltage-divider resistors with source emf, rated current, and load resistor given. (7·19 to 7·21)
2 Discuss the importance of power rating of resistors. (7·26)
3 Find the power developed in each of the resistors of a voltage divider. (7·27)

Useful voltage-divider equations

1 Derive equations to simplify the design of a voltage divider. (7·29)
2 Demonstrate the use of the above equations. (7·37)

chapter 8
magnetism

Magnets

At this point we leave the subject of direct current temporarily to learn some fundamental facts about magnetism. One of the important outcomes of the frames that follow is the student's familiarization with certain new words that appear for the first time.

8·1 A magnet is an object that can attract certain materials to itself. Such materials, known as magnetic materials, are pure or alloyed iron, nickel, and cobalt. A "tin" can is really iron coated with a thin layer of tin, hence such a can is attracted to a _____ .

8·2 (magnet) A magnet made of iron is a *temporary* one and has *low retentivity,* or short-term ability to retain its magnetism. Silicon steel also has low retentivity, hence this material forms temporary magnets, too. Permalloy has very low retentivity, hence forms _____ magnets.

8·3 (temporary) Hard steels have *high retentivity,* hence form *permanent magnets.* Alnico, an alloy of aluminum, iron, nickel, and cobalt, also has high retentivity. Therefore, alnico would be suitable for making _____ magnets.

8·4 (permanent) Nickel-steel has high retentivity. This material is therefore suitable for manufacture of _____ magnets.

8·5 (permanent) When the magnetizing force is removed from a bar of alnico, the *residual magnetism* is high. When the magnetizing force is removed from a bar of permalloy, the residual magnetism is _____ .

8·6 (low or small) All common magnets have two poles, one at each end. When the magnet is freely suspended, the pole which points approximately north is called the N-pole. The other pole, therefore, is the _____ .

8·7 (S-pole) The first law of magnetism is that like poles repel each other and unlike poles attract each other. If an N-pole is placed near an N-pole, the force between them is one of _____ .

8·8 (repulsion) If an N-pole is placed near an S-pole, the force between them is one of _____ .

8·9 (attraction) If an S-pole is placed near an S-pole, the force between them is one of _____ .

8·9 (repulsion)

Law of magnetic poles

The force of attraction between unlike magnetic poles, and the force of repulsion between like poles, may be calculated from the law of poles given below. Note that this law has a form similar to that of Coulomb's law for electric charges. *It is easy to confuse these two laws.* To avoid confusion, remember that:

1. The word "charge" belongs to electricity and is identified by a "+" or "−" sign.

2. The word "pole" belongs to magnetism and is identified by an N or an S.

8·10 The law governing magnetic attraction and repulsion is:

$$\text{Magnetic force} = \frac{\text{pole strength 1} \times \text{pole strength 2}}{(\text{distance between poles})^2}$$

If each pole has unit strength, and the distance between poles is unit distance, then the force equals _____ unit(s).

8·11 (1) If two magnets have pole strengths of 10 and 20 units, respectively, and a separation distance of 2 units, then the force is 10×20 over $2^2 = {}^{20\%} = 50$ units. If the pole strengths are 3 and 12 units with a separation of 3 units, the force is 3×12 over 3^2 or _____ units.

8·12 (4) If two bodies have charges of 4 and 25 units, respectively, and if the distance between them is 2 units, then the force is _____ units.

8·13 (25) Two unlike poles of 6 units each are separated by 3 units of distance. The force of attraction is 6×6 divided by $9 = \frac{36}{9} = 4$ units. Similarly, if two unlike poles have strengths of 20 units each and are separated by 10 units of distance, the force of attraction between them is _____ units.

8·14 (4) Two N-poles of 25 and 10 units of strength, respectively, are separated by 5 units of distance. The force of repulsion is _____ units.

8·15 (10) If we double the strength of pole 1, the magnetic force doubles; if we triple the strength of pole 1, the magnetic force triples; if we quadruple the strength of pole 1, the magnetic force _____ .

8·16 (quadruples) If the strength of pole 1 is doubled while that of pole 2 is halved, the force remains unchanged. If the strength of pole 1 is tripled, then the strength of pole 2 would have to be cut to _____ of its initial value if the force is to remain unchanged.

8·17 (one-third) When the strengths of both poles are raised, it is noted that the force rises to twenty times its original size. If pole 1 was strengthened by a factor of 4, then pole 2 must have been strengthened by a factor of _____ .

8·18 (5) If the strength of each pole is increased by a factor of 10, the magnetic force must increase by a factor of _____ .

8·19 (100) Doubling the distance between poles reduces the magnetic force to one-fourth of its initial value. Thus, tripling the distance between poles reduces the magnetic force to _____ of its initial value.

8·20 (one-ninth) If pole 1 is strengthened by a factor of 4 and pole 2 is reduced in strength to one-half of its former value while the distance is doubled, the force will change by a factor of _____ .

8·21 (one-half) If both pole 1 and pole 2 are doubled in strength, it would be possible to keep the magnetic force the same by increasing the distance by a factor of _____ .

8·21 (2)

The magnetic field

The concept of a magnetic field is similar in many respects to that of an electric field. Lines of force have no real existence but are helpful in constructing a mechanical visualization of the field. Lines of force do not move in magnetism any more than they do in electrostatics. But, as we found in the latter subject, we must assign a direction to each line of force in order to account for the effects they produce in other activities. The choice is entirely arbitrary. We agree that any line of force is assumed to emanate from an N-pole and enter a magnet via the S-pole (Fig. 8·22).

8·22 A magnet is capable of acting over a distance on another magnet, or on an unmagnetized magnetic material, by virtue of its magnetic field. A magnetic field consists of lines of force. According to the drawing in Fig. 8·22, all lines of force are said to leave a magnet via the N-pole and reenter the same or a nearby separate magnet via the _____ .

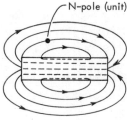

Fig. 8·22

8·23 (S-pole) Figure 8·22 shows an isolated N-pole moving along a line of force. By convention, the direction assigned to a magnetic field is the direction along which a unit N-pole would move if free to do so. Thus, the direction of a magnetic field outside a magnet must be from _____ to _____ .

8·24 (N, S) The lines of force at the center of the pole faces between unlike poles are almost _____ lines (Fig. 8·24).

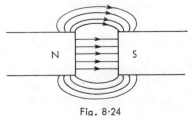

Fig. 8·24

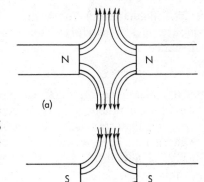

(a)

8·25 (straight) The lines of force coming from or entering adjacent like poles appear to _____ each other (Fig. 8·25a and b).

(b)

Fig. 8·25

8·26 (repel) As shown in Fig. 8·26, magnetic lines of force appear to prefer the path through the iron rather than the path through the air. Substances which offer good paths for lines of force are said to be permeable substances. The permeable substance in Fig. 8·26 is made of _____ .

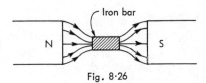

Fig. 8·26

8·27 (iron) In Fig. 8·27, pole A is the _____ pole and pole B is the _____ pole.

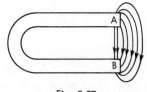

Fig. 8·27

8·27 (N, S)

Magnetic materials

A substance is called a magnetic material if, when placed in a magnetic field, sensible forces are exerted on it. As defined in Frames 8·28 to 8·42 below, *diamagnetic* and *paramagnetic* substances are of little interest to us. However, the *ferromagnetic* substances are very important and are therefore to be emphasized.

8·28 Some materials are slightly repelled by a strong magnetic field. Such substances are called diamagnetic. Copper is repelled by a strong magnetic field, hence is a diamagnetic substance. Bismuth undergoes a similar repulsion, hence is a _____ substance.

8·29 (diamagnetic) Pure water is slightly repelled by a strong magnetic field. Therefore, water may be classed as a _____ substance.

8·30 (diamagnetic) Materials that are very slightly attracted by a strong magnetic field are called paramagnetic. Aluminum is very slightly attracted by strong fields, hence is paramagnetic in character. The element erbium is slightly attracted by a strong magnetic field and is, therefore, classed as a _____ substance.

8·31 (paramagnetic) Pure oxygen in its liquid form is slightly attracted by a strong magnet, hence oxygen is a _____ substance.

8·32 (paramagnetic) Those materials that are strongly affected by magnets are called ferromagnetic. Thus, iron is ferromagnetic since it is a prime magnetic material. Nickel is strongly attracted by a magnetic pole, hence nickel is _____ .

8·33 (ferromagnetic) Cobalt is strongly affected by a magnet, hence is a _____ material.

8·34 (ferromagnetic) The permeability of a substance is a number which tells how strongly the substance reacts in a magnetic field. A vacuum is assigned a permeability of unity (1). Diamagnetic substances have permeabilities of less than 1. Since the permeability of copper is 0.9999, it is diamagnetic. The permeability of bismuth is 0.9998, hence bismuth is

_____ .

8·35 (diamagnetic) Paramagnetic substances have permeabilities slightly greater than 1. Aluminum, a paramagnetic substance, has a permeability of 1.000022. The permeability of erbium is 1.00289, hence this element is classed as _____ .

8·36 (paramagnetic) Ferromagnetic substances have large permeability figures. For example, iron has a permeability of about 7,000 because it is ferromagnetic. The permeability of cobalt is 170, hence cobalt is _____ .

8·37 (ferromagnetic) The alloy perminvar has a permeability of 2,000. Perminvar is, therefore, a _____ material.

8·38   (ferromagnetic) The permeability of oxygen is 1.0000019. Hence oxygen may be classified as _____ .

8·39   (paramagnetic) The permeability of nickel is 1,000; thus, nickel may be classified as _____ .

8·40   (ferromagnetic) The permeability of water is 0.9999992. Hence, water may be classified as _____ .

8·41   (diamagnetic) The permeability of air is so close to that of a vacuum that it is generally taken to be the same. Thus, the permeability of air for practical purposes may be considered to be _____ .

8·42   (1) Pure iron has a permeability of about 7,000, while an alloy called permalloy has a permeability of close to 1,000,000. Hence the material with more intense ferromagnetic properties must be _____ .

8·42   (permalloy)

Magnetic field around a current-carrying conductor

The connection between electricity and magnetism was discovered by Hans Oersted, in 1820. He found that a wire carrying an electric current was surrounded by a magnetic field and that the direction of the lines of force of this field was determined by the direction of the current flow (Fig. 8·43a and b). We make use of a rule called the "left-hand rule for conductors" to determine the direction of the field when the direction of the current is known, or vice versa. This rule may be stated as follows: Using the left hand with the thumb extended at right angles to the other fingers in the same plane as the palm, wrap the fingers around the conductor in the direction of the lines of force. The extended thumb will then point in the direction of the electron flow.

8·43   A magnetic field is always associated with a current flowing through a wire. In Fig. 8·43a, the current is shown flowing downward into the platform of cardboard and the lines of force are seen to have a counterclockwise direction. When the current is reversed, as in Fig. 8·43b, the lines of force appear to be headed in a direction that could be called _____ .

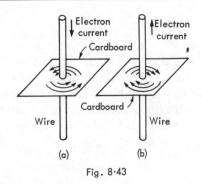

Fig. 8·43

8·44 (clockwise) A reasonable assumption that could be made at this time is that a reversal of current direction in a wire will produce a _____ of the direction of the associated magnetic field.

8·45 (reversal) An experiment is performed in which it is noted that a current flowing from north to south in a wire produces a magnetic field that is clockwise around the wire as viewed by a certain observer. When the wire is rotated so that the current flows from south to north, the same observer will see a _____ magnetic field.

8·46 (counterclockwise) The left-hand rule for single conductors is illustrated in Fig. 8·46. Note how the extended thumb points in the direction of the current. The encircling fingers now show the direction of the _____ of force caused by this current.

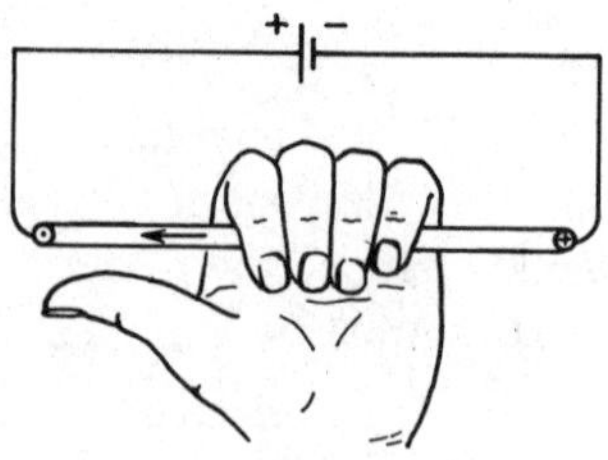

Fig. 8·46

8·47 (lines) Applying this rule to Fig. 8·43a, the fingers will encircle the wire in the counterclockwise direction (corresponding to the lines of force) provided that the thumb is pointed downward. In Fig. 8·43b, the fingers will go round the wire in a clockwise direction if the thumb is pointed _____ .

8·48 (upward) In Fig. 8·46, the fingers go up behind the wire and down in front of the wire when the current flows to the left; if the current were flowing to the right, the fingers would have to go up _____ of the wire.

8·49 (in front) To avoid perspective drawings, we might look straight down on the Oersted surface as in Fig. 8·49. The cross section of the conductor appears as a tiny centered circle. The cross inside the circle indicates the direction of the current flow and symbolizes the tail of an arrow going into the page away from the observer. Using the left-hand rule, the lines of force should show a _____ direction.

Fig. 8·49

8·50 (counterclockwise) In Fig. 8·50, the lines of force are clockwise. This indicates that the point in the center of the conductor cross section represents the point of an arrow and symbolizes the current going _____ the observer.

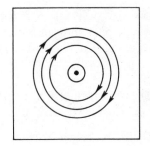

Fig. 8·50

8·51 (toward) In Fig. 8·51, use of the left-hand rule indicates that the current in this conductor must be flowing from _____ to _____ .

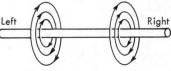

Fig. 8·51

8·51 (left, right)

Magnetic field of a solenoid

The solenoid shown in Fig. 8·52a and b consists of many single conductors wound around the form so that they are adjacent to each other. In this section, we shall apply the Oersted analysis (left-hand rule) to determine the direction of the *net* magnetic field. Before doing this, it is necessary to study the drawings in Figs. 8·52 to 8·70 in conjunction with the frames that describe them. It is important to note that we make free use of the convention which indicates current direction in the cross section of a conductor: a "×" means that the current is moving into the page away from the observer; a "•" means that the current is moving out of the page, toward the observer.

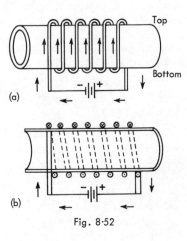

Fig. 8·52

8·52 Figure 8·52a and b illustrate two different views of a coil wound around a hollow cardboard cylinder. In Fig. 8·52a, the current is shown going up in front of the coil and down behind it. This means that the current is coming out of the page at the bottom of the coil and going into the page at the _____ of the coil.

8·53 (top) In Fig. 8·52b, the dots in the centers of the lower row of circles indicate that the current is flowing *out of* the page, _____ the observer.

8·54 (toward) In Fig. 8·52b, the crosses in the centers of the upper row of circles indicate that the current is flowing _____ the page at these points.

8·55 (into) If each of the cut wires in Fig. 8·52b is treated as a single Oersted conductor, applying the left-hand rule shows that the lines of force around each of these conductors in the lower row must be going in a _____ direction.

8·56 (clockwise) If each of the cut wires in the upper row in the diagram of Fig. 8·52b is treated as a single Oersted conductor, the left-hand rule shows that the lines of force around each of these must be going in a _____ direction.

8·57 (counterclockwise) Figure 8·57 is an enlarged view of part of the coil in Fig. 8·52b. From this view, the lines of force around the individual upper conductors are counterclockwise. The lines of force around the individual lower conductors are _____ in direction.

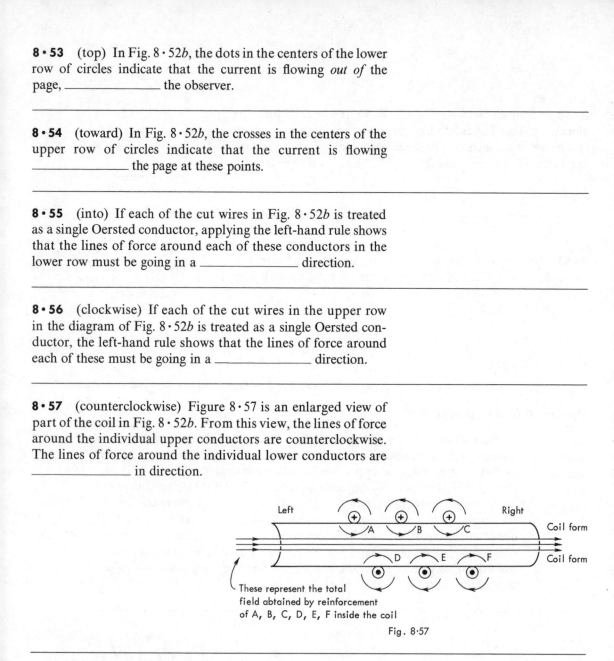

Fig. 8·57

8·58 (clockwise) Inside the coil of Fig. 8·57, all the lines labeled *A*, *B*, and *C* are directed to the right. Since these lines reinforce and add to each other, the net magnetic field inside the coil form may be said to be directed to the _____ side of the diagram.

8·59 (right) The lines labeled *D*, *E*, and *F* *inside* also reinforce each other. Note that all these lines are also directed toward the right side of the coil. Thus, the net magnetic field is directed toward the _____ side of the coil.

8·60 (right) Thus, in the example of Fig. 8·57, the total magnetic field produced by all the turns in the coil must be considered to emerge from the _____ side of the coil and enter into the _____ side of the coil.

8·61 (right, left) Since lines of force are always considered as emerging from the N-pole of a magnet, the N-pole of this electromagnet must be on the _____ side (Fig. 8·57).

8·62 (right) By similar reasoning, the S-pole must be on the _____ side of the electromagnet (Fig. 8·57).

8·63 (left) In Fig. 8·63a, the left hand is shown encircling the coil in the direction of the flow of current. For this condition the extended thumb is pointing toward the N-pole. Note that this manipulation gives the same answer as the Oersted analysis of the previous questions. Similarly, in Fig. 8·63b, the direction of the current is reversed, but if the fingers of the left hand encircle the coil in the new current direction, the thumb still points toward the _____ pole.

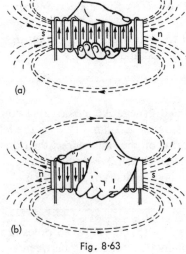

(a)

(b)

Fig. 8·63

8·64 (N) The general rule, called the "left-hand rule for solenoids," may thus be stated: If the fingers of the _____ hand encircle the coil in the direction of the _____ flow, the extended thumb will point toward the _____ pole of the electromagnet thus formed.

8·65 (left, current, N) In Fig. 8·65, the current is flowing down in front of the coil and up behind it as indicated by the battery polarity shown. Using the left-hand solenoid rule, we find that the pole at the left must become the _____ pole.

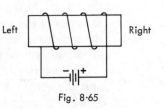

Left   Right

Fig. 8·65

8·66 (N) Let us apply the left-hand rule to the coil of Fig. 8·66 to find the polarity of the source. Since the N-pole of the resulting electromagnet points to the left, we first extend the thumb of the left hand and point it toward the _____ side of the coil.

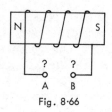

Fig. 8·66

8·67 (left) When we encircle the coil in Fig. 8·66 with the fingers, we find that they go down in front of the coil and _____ behind the coil.

8·68 (up) Hence, the electrons must be moving down in the lead that goes to point A of the source and up out of the lead that comes from point _____ of the source.

8·69 (B) Since electrons always flow from the "−" to the "+" terminal, and since electrons in Fig. 8·66 are flowing from B to A through the coil, then B must be the _____ terminal and A the _____ terminal.

8·70 (negative, positive) Two coils are shown in Fig. 8·70. Using the left-hand rule on the left coil, we find that an S-pole forms on the side nearest the other coil. Using the same rule on the right coil, we find that an _____-pole forms on the side facing the first coil.

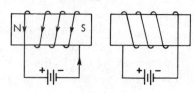

Fig. 8·70

8·71 (S) Thus, two S-poles are adjacent to each other. The magnetic force acting between the coils, therefore, must be one of _____ since like poles are adjacent.

8·71 (repulsion)

Lenz's law

When a conductor moves through a magnetic field so that it cuts through the lines of force at any angle *other than zero degrees,* an emf appears across the ends of the conductor. This emf is called an *"induced emf."* If the conductor moves parallel to the lines of force (angle of zero degrees), there is zero emf induced.

The polarity of the induced emf depends upon the direction of motion and the direction of the magnetic field lines. A length of wire moving through a given field, say downward, will develop a specific emf polarity; should the wire now be moved upward through the same field, the polarity

116

of the induced emf will reverse. Similarly, if the direction of the field is reversed for a given motion, there will be a consequent reversal of polarity.

Lenz's law presents a method of attack on the determination of induced polarity; it is a general statement based upon conservation of energy principles which applies to all variations and combinations of motion and field direction. It may be stated as follows:

The direction of an induced emf is such that the current produced by this emf in a closed circuit will produce a magnetic field which *opposes* the motion that caused the induced emf to appear.

The key word in Lenz's law is *opposition*. Induction produces an emf. A current will flow as a result of an induced emf *only* if the emf appears at the termini of a closed circuit. This current produces a magnetic field having a definite direction. The direction of the field must be such as to produce a force that opposes the original motion. This is Lenz's law in essence.

8·72 If a wire moving downward through a given field induces a "+" potential at its right end and a "−" potential at its left end, then the same conductor moving upward through the same field will induce a "+" potential at its ___*left*___ end and a "−" potential at its ___*right*___ end.

8·73 (left, right) If the conductor passed through the field as described above is a closed loop (thus making a complete "circuit"), then the emf induced in the wire will cause a ___*current*___ to flow.

8·74 (current) If the conductor is formed into several loops to make a solenoid, the current that flows due to induced emf will cause the solenoid to develop its own ___*magnetic*___ field.

8·75 (magnetic) Refer to Fig. 8·75. The arrow shows the N-pole of the permanent magnet approaching the coil. Since the induced current that flows in the coil must produce a magnetic field that *opposes* the approaching N-pole, then the coil must form an ___*N*___-pole on the side near the approaching magnet.

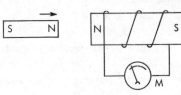

Fig. 8·75

8·76 (N) The newly formed N-pole will oppose the approaching N-pole as required by Lenz's law. To form an N-pole on the left side of the coil, the current must flow ___*downward*___ in front of the coil and upward behind the coil.

8·77 (downward) In Fig. 8·77, an S-pole is approaching the coil. The induced current in the coil must oppose the approaching S-pole, hence an S-pole must form on the left side of the coil to repel the approaching pole. To form an S-pole on the left side, the current must be induced in such a direction that it will flow _____ in front of the coil and _____ behind the coil.

8·78 (upward, downward) In Fig. 8·78, an N-pole is shown moving away from the coil. The induced current in the coil must, therefore, flow in a direction such that an __S__-pole forms on the left side of the coil to oppose the retreat of the N-pole by a force of attraction.

8·79 (S) In Fig. 8·78, therefore, the direction of the induced current must be such as to flow _____ in front of the coil and _____ behind the coil.

8·80 (upward, downward) In Fig. 8·80, according to Lenz's law, the current induced in the coil must form an __N__-pole on the left side.

8·81 (N) In Fig. 8·80, the induced current must flow _____ in front of the coil and _____ behind the coil.

8·82 (downward, upward) In Fig. 8·82, a magnet is shown approaching a coil; the current is induced in the coil in a direction such that the current flows upward in front of the coil and downward behind it. Using the left-hand rule for solenoids, you can find that the electromagnetic pole formed on the right end of the coil is an N-pole. Hence, by Lenz's law, the approaching pole on the moving magnet must be an _____-pole.

8·83 (N) In Fig. 8·83, the induced current flows upward in front of the coil and downward behind it as shown. The polarity of the induced magnetism must form an _____-pole on the right side of the coil.

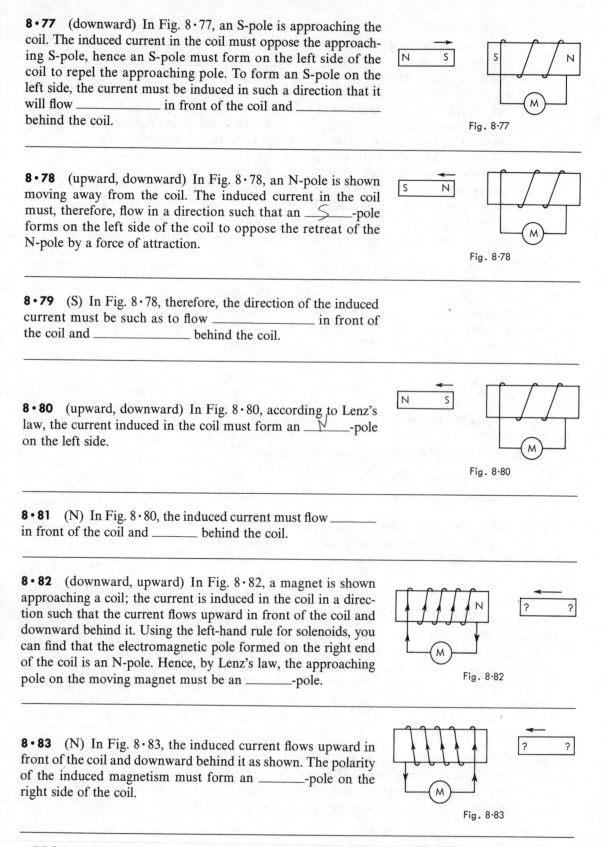

Fig. 8·77

Fig. 8·78

Fig. 8·80

Fig. 8·82

Fig. 8·83

8·84 (N) In Fig. 8·83, therefore, the approaching pole must be an _____-pole.

8·85 (N) In Fig 8·85, the moving magnet produces the current direction shown by the arrows on the coil. Using the left-hand rule, we find that the end nearest the moving magnet becomes an S-pole. To account for the S-pole forming on the coil, the magnet's S-pole must be moving _____ the coil according to Lenz's law.

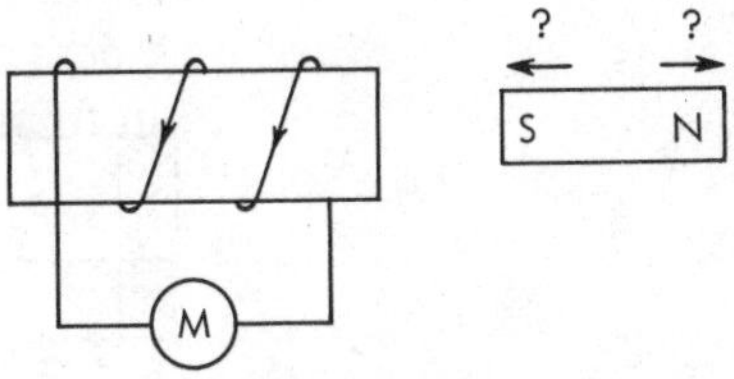

Fig. 8·85

8·86 (toward) In Fig. 8·86, an S-pole is shown moving away from the coil. To oppose this motion, the coil must *attract* the retreating S-pole. Hence, an _____-pole must form on the end of the coil nearer the moving magnet.

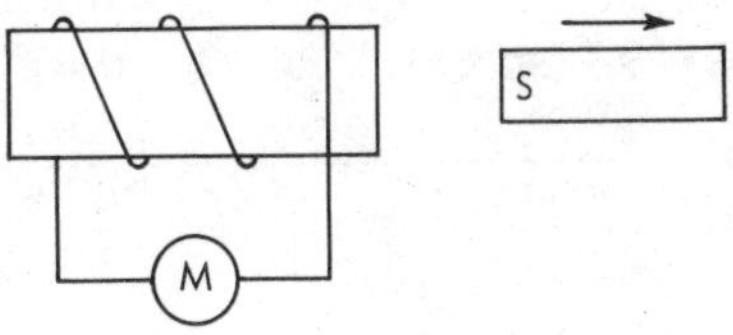

Fig. 8·86

8·86 (N)

Magnitude of the induced emf

The magnitude of the emf induced in a conductor moving through a magnetic field is determined by several factors. These factors are illustrated pictorially in Frames 8·87 to 8·89.

8·87 In Fig. 8·87a, a single approaching magnet induces a voltage of 5 volts across the coil. When another identical magnet is added to the first, as shown in Fig. 8·87b, the voltage becomes 10 volts. Thus, the magnitude of the induced emf must depend upon the _____ of the magnetic field that causes the induction.

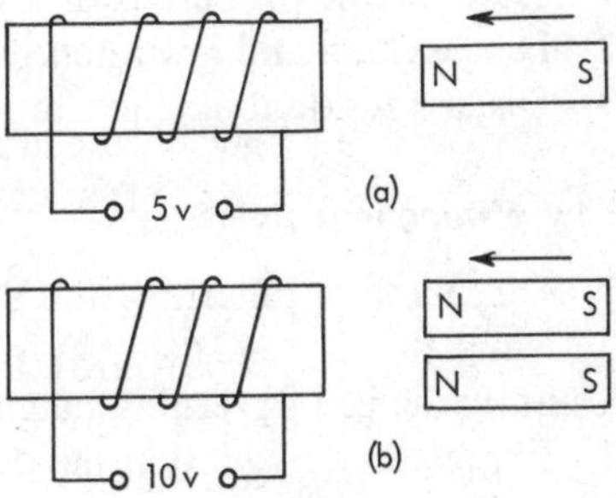

Fig. 8·87

8·88 (strength) In Fig. 8·88, a greater emf is shown induced in the lower drawing. From the information given in the drawing, it is evident that the magnitude of the induced emf must also depend upon the _____ _____ _____ in the coil.

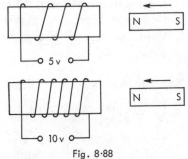

Fig. 8·88

8·89 (number of turns) From the information given in Fig. 8·89, another factor that controls the magnitude of the induced emf is the _____ of motion.

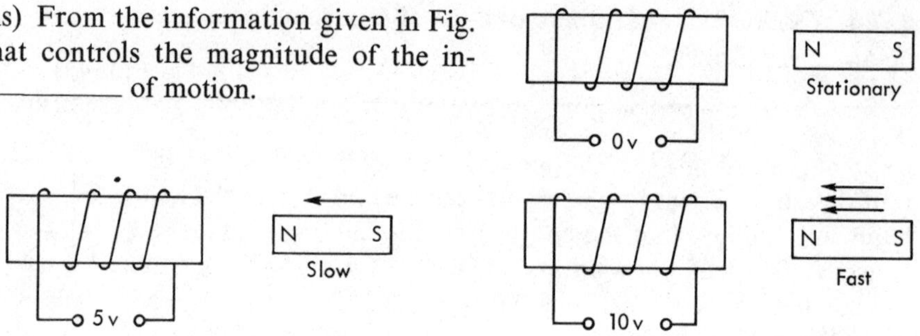

Fig. 8·89

8·89 (speed)

MEASURABLE BEHAVIORAL OBJECTIVES

Upon completion of a section, you should be able to achieve the objectives listed for it. The frame or frames that cover the related subject matter are indicated immediately following each objective.

Magnets

1 Describe the properties of a magnet. (8·1)
2 Discuss high and low retentivity as it applies to magnetism. (8·2, 8·3)
3 Discuss residual magnetism. (8·5)

Law of magnetic poles

1 Discuss the similarities and differences between electricity and magnetism. (8·12, 8·13)
2 State the law governing magnetic attraction or repulsion. (8·10)
3 Express in an equation the dependence of magnetic force. (8·10)

The magnetic field

1 Discuss the existence of the magnetic lines of force. (8·22)
2 Define the direction of magnetic lines. (8·22, 8·23)
3 Depict some examples of the formation of magnetic lines of force. (8·24, 8·25)

Magnetic materials

Define diamagnetic, paramagnetic, and ferromagnetic substances. (8·28, 8·32)
  a Give examples of the above substances. (8·30)
  b Discuss the permeability property of the above substances. (8·34, 8·35)

Magnetic field around a current-carrying conductor

1 Discuss the connection between electricity and magnetism. $(8 \cdot 43)$
2 State and demonstrate the "left-hand rule" as it applies to magnetism. $(8 \cdot 46)$

Magnetic field of a solenoid

1 Describe a solenoid. $(8 \cdot 52)$
2 Illustrate the direction of the current and magnetic field in a solenoid. $(8 \cdot 52, 8 \cdot 57)$
3 Illustrate the use of the "left-hand rule" as it applies to solenoids. $(8 \cdot 63)$

Lenz's law

1 Describe a way to produce an induced emf. $(8 \cdot 72)$
2 Determine the polarity of the induced emf. $(8 \cdot 72)$
3 State Lenz's law. $(8 \cdot 82)$

Magnitude of induced emf

List several factors that determine the magnitude of an induced emf. $(8 \cdot 87, 8 \cdot 88)$

chapter 9

further principles of electromagnetic induction

Electromagnetic induction by current changes

A coil has certain electrical characteristics which make it necessary for a finite time interval to elapse between the closing of the switch that applies emf to a coil and the establishment of the final magnetic field that permeates the space around the coil. That is, the magnetic field does not come into existence instantaneously upon a switch closure. The time required for completion of the sequence depends on several factors which will not be discussed here, but we must recognize that it exists.

As a result of this required time interval, a magnetic field is said to *grow* from its zero magnitude state to its final state. Once a magnetic field has been established by a current in a coil, it is said to have reached a *steady state*. Now if the circuit is opened, the magnetic field *collapses*, again requiring a finite time interval. The growth and collapse of a field must be viewed as a *dynamic process;* that is, the induction effects of growth and collapse are very much the same as those obtained from actual motion of a permanent magnet as these frames describe. On the other hand, a steady-state field does not cause induction effects; it resembles a stationary magnet in this regard.

9·1 If a current is suddenly made to flow in a coil, a magnetic field grows quickly in and around the coil; should the circuit be opened suddenly, the magnetic field quickly collapses. A growing or collapsing magnetic field can induce an emf in a nearby coil. As evident from Fig. 9·1, the coil containing the battery in its circuit is called the _____ coil.

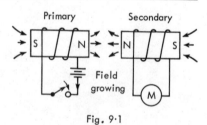

Fig. 9·1

9·2 (primary) As evident from Fig. 9·1, the coil in which the induced current appears is called the _____ coil.

9·3 (secondary) When the switch in the primary circuit of Fig. 9·1 is closed, a magnetic field grows in the primary coil. When the switch is suddenly opened, the magnetic field _____ .

9·4 (collapses) In Fig. 9·1, a primary coil in series with a switch and battery is placed near a secondary coil. When the switch is closed, a surge of current flows in the primary winding. The direction of this current is _____ in front of the coil and _____ in back of the coil.

9·5 (upward, downward) This surge of current causes the rapid growth of a magnetic field around the primary coil. According to the left-hand rule, the right end of the coil must form an _____-pole.

9·6 (N) Since a field is considered to have a direction so that the lines emerge from the N-pole, then the lines must be growing out of the _____ side of the coil.

9·7 (right) This growing field cuts through the turns of the secondary coil. A current is induced in the secondary coil; thus, a magnetic field now forms in the secondary coil. The direction of this field must _____ the growth of the primary field according to Lenz's law.

9·8 (oppose) The only way the new field can oppose the growing field is for the new field to have a polarity that forms lines which go opposite to the growing primary lines. Thus, the lines of force from the secondary field must emerge from the _____ side of the coil.

9·9 (left) If the lines of force of the secondary coil emerge from the left side of the coil, then the left side of the coil must become an _____-pole.

9·10 (N) Thus, using the left-hand rule, we find that the induced current in the secondary coil must flow _____ in front of the coil and _____ in back of the coil.

9·11 (downward, upward) See Fig. 9·11. Assume that the switch in the primary circuit is closed, thus establishing a steady-state field (no induction). Upon opening the switch, the field collapses back into the primary, cutting through the secondary, and inducing a current therein. This induced current produces a magnetic _____ of its own.

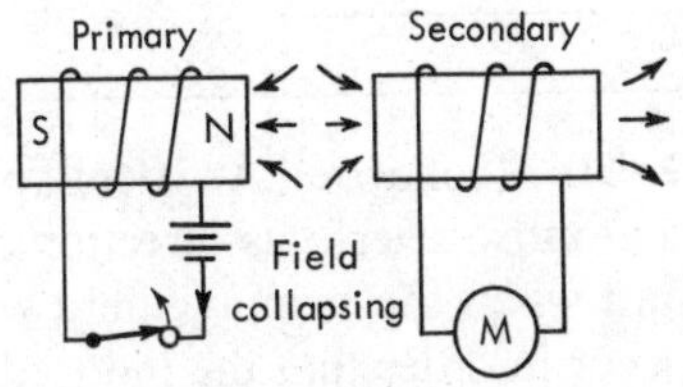

Fig. 9·11

9·12 (field) The field thus produced in the secondary must act upon the collapsing field in the primary in such a way as to *oppose* its collapse, according to _____ law.

9·13 (Lenz's) In the primary, the lines are *retreating* into the N-pole end as the field collapses. To oppose the collapse, the field in the secondary must head the other way. That is, lines must grow to the right in the secondary coil. But, lines of force going into the end of the secondary must form an _____-pole at this end.

9·14 (S) In Fig. 9·14, a quiescent arrangement is illustrated consisting of a primary coil, a secondary coil, a source of primary emf, and a meter to indicate secondary induced current. When the switch is first closed, the current surge into the primary causes an _____-pole to build up at the right end of the primary.

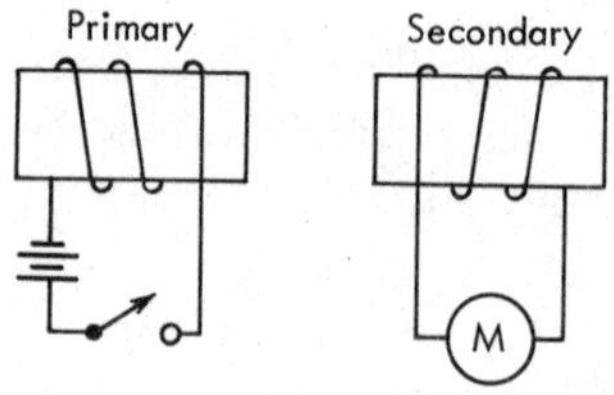

Fig. 9·14

9·15 (S) In Fig. 9·14, as this growing primary field cuts through the secondary turns, the induced current in the secondary must take on a direction which _____ the growing primary field.

9·16 (opposes) In Fig. 9·14, the pole that forms on the left side of the secondary must be an _____-pole.

9·17 (S) In Fig. 9·14, the current direction in the secondary to form such a pole must be _____ in front and _____ behind the coil.

9·18 (upward, downward) In Fig. 9·14, the magnitude of the induced emf becomes equal to _____ after the primary current has reached a steady state.

9·19 (zero) In Fig. 9·14, when the switch is now opened the primary current ceases to flow and the primary field begins to _____ .

9·20 (collapse) As it collapses, the induced secondary current must reverse its direction as compared with the direction it had when the primary field was growing. This reversal must occur in order that the induced field have such a direction as to _____ the collapse of the primary field.

9·21 (oppose) Therefore, in Fig. 9·14, as the primary field collapses, an _____-pole must form on the left side of the secondary coil.

9·22 (N) Hence, in Fig. 9·14, as the primary field collapses, the current in the secondary induced by this collapse must flow _____ in front and _____ behind the coil.

9·22 (downward, upward)

Mutual inductance

Two adjacent coils are said to have *mutual inductance* if a changing magnetic flux (flow of magnetic lines of force) from one of them causes an induced emf in the other. The situations described in Frames 9·1 to 9·22 may be discussed in terms of mutual inductance; in these cases, the change of magnetic flux was the result of the opening or closing of a switch which controlled the current in the primary coil. But a switch is not the only agency whereby current magnitude, hence magnetic flux, may be changed.

At this time, we introduce a few rather simple notions pertaining to *alternating current.* The emf from a battery is unchanging in direction, that is, it is representative of *direct* potential, or potential with fixed polarity. The current caused by such a seat of emf is direct current whose characteristic is *unidirectional, steady* flow. When a switch in a d-c circuit is periodically opened and closed, the current remains unidirectional but it is no longer steady. Such d-c is generally called *pulsating;* this word refers to changing magnitude, but not changing direction.

Alternating current is the result of an emf which periodically changes its polarity. Thus, a-c is current that is constant *neither in direction nor magnitude.* An a-c flows first one way through a conductor, then the other way. Clearly, for a current to change its direction with regularity, the electrons that constitute it must also come to rest periodically.

A-C theory will be discussed separately later in detail. But we require some fundamental concepts in a-c in order to complete the study of d-c. At this point, it is sufficient to remember that a-c is a kind of current that rises to a maximum value in a short time interval, drops back to zero, then reverses its direction of flow, reaching a maximum value in the other direction in an equal time interval.

As shown in Fig. 9·23, an a-c generator will be symbolized with a circle containing a short wavy line.

9·23 In Fig. 9·23, an alternating-current generator causes the magnetic polarity of the primary winding to reverse each time the _____ changes its direction.

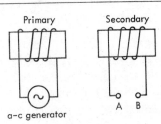

Primary   Secondary

a-c generator

A   B

Fig. 9·23

9·24 (current) Each time the current reverses in the primary, the magnetic field grows and collapses, cutting through the turns of the secondary coil. As this changing flux cuts through the secondary wires, an _____ emf must appear across the secondary terminals *A* and *B*.

9·25 (induced) Since the emf induced in the secondary is the result of an alternating primary field, then the secondary induced emf must also be _____ rather than direct.

9·26 (alternating) Thus, an a-c in the primary of Fig. 9·23 causes an alternating emf to appear across terminals *A* and *B* of the secondary. If *A* and *B* are now connected to complete the circuit, an _____ induced current will flow in this circuit.

9·27 (alternating) Because flux changes in the primary in Fig. 9·23 cause induced voltages across the secondary, these two coils have a mutual _____ with respect to one another.

9·28 (inductance) Induction may also occur between two coils placed side by side as in Fig. 9·28. Thus, two coils placed this way also have _____ _____ with respect to one another.

a-c generator

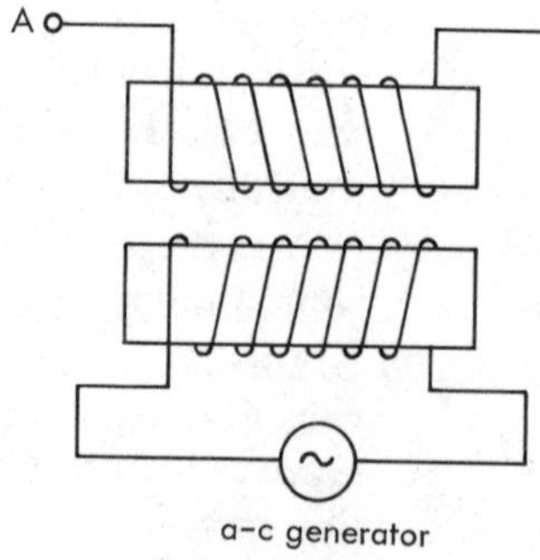

Fig. 9·28

9·29 (mutual inductance) In Fig. 9·29, the voltmeter will show a reading because there is _____ _____ between the two coils.

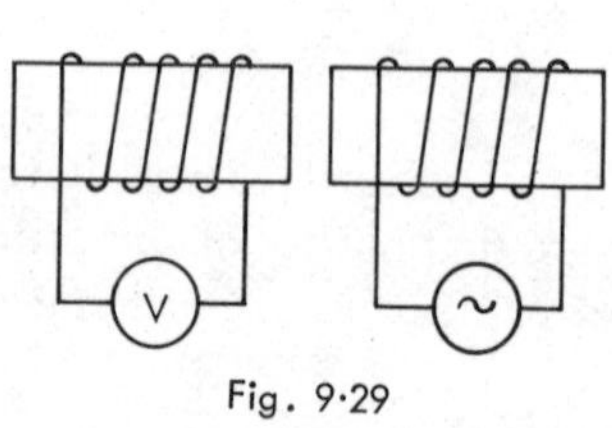

Fig. 9·29

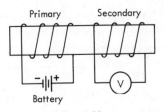

Fig. 9·30

9·30 (mutual inductance) In Fig. 9·30, mutual inductance exists between the two coils, yet the voltmeter will not show a steady deflection. This is explained by the fact that a battery source is used, hence the _____ flux is not changing.

9·30 (magnetic)

Mutual inductance is measured in a unit called the *henry* (plural: *henrys*). *Two coils have a mutual inductance of one henry if a change of current of one ampere/second in one coil induces one volt in the other coil.*

Assume that we have a primary coil in which the current is changing at the rate of 1 amp/sec as in the definition of the henry. Assume further that we place a secondary coil adjacent to primary but separated from it just enough to cause 1 volt of induced a-c emf to appear across the secondary terminals. In this case, the mutual inductance M is exactly 1 henry. Now let us move the secondary coil closer until 2 volts of induced emf are obtained *for the same primary current*. The value of M is now 2 henrys. Similarly, if we can get 10 volts of induced a-c emf from the same primary current by reorienting the coils, M would then be 10 henrys.

Thus we see that the induced emf is proportional to M. In addition, we shall see that the induced emf is also proportional to the *rate of change of current*. Rate of change of current means *time* rate of change. That is, a small current change divided by the time required to cause this change is what we mean by rate of change of current. This quantity is symbolized by

$$\frac{di}{dt} \quad \text{or} \quad \frac{\text{a small difference in current } i}{\text{the small time required for change } t}$$

Whenever we wish to speak of rate of change of current particularly in a-c circuits, we shall use the symbol di/dt in amperes per second.

Since the induced emf is directly proportional to M and to di/dt, we can write the equation: $E = M\, di/dt$ where E is in volts, M is in henrys, and di/dt is in amperes per second.

9·31 The mutual inductance between two coils is 1 henry if a di/dt of 1 amp/sec causes an induction of 1 volt. The M is 2 henrys if a di/dt of 1 amp/sec induces 2 volts. The M is 4 henrys if a di/dt of 1 amp/sec induces _____ volts.

9·32 (4) If the rate of change of primary current is 1 amp/sec and the induced voltage is 5 volts, the mutual inductance is 5 henrys. If the induced voltage is 10 volts for the same rate of change of current, the mutual inductance is _____ henrys.

9·33   (10) If a rate of change of 1 amp/sec causes an induced voltage of 100 volts across the secondary terminals, the mutual inductance must be _____ henrys.

9·34   (100) With a faster rate of change of current, a greater voltage is induced for a given mutual inductance. For example, if the mutual inductance is assumed to be 1 henry, then a rate of change of 2 amp/sec will induce 2 volts across the secondary. Thus, a rate of change of 5 amp/sec will induce _____ volts across the secondary.

9·35   (5) When the mutual inductance between two coils is 1 henry, and the rate of change of current is 7.3 amp/sec, the induced voltage will be _____ volts.

9·36   (7.3) Using the equation $E = M \, di/dt$, we see that if $M = 3$ henrys and $di/dt = 2$ amp/sec, the induced voltage is 6 volts. Similarly, if $M = 2.5$ henrys and $di/dt = 1.2$ amp/sec, the induced voltage is _____ volts.

9·37   (3) Two coils are coupled with a mutual inductance of 8 henrys. If $di/dt = 0.5$ amp/sec, the induced voltage is

_____ _____ .

9·38   (4 volts) Two coils are coupled with $M = 6$ henrys. An induced voltage of 12 volts appears across the secondary winding. The rate of change of current must be _____ _____ .

9·39   (2 amp/sec) The voltage appearing across the secondary of a two-coil system is 22 volts. If the rate of change of current in the primary is 0.11 amp/sec, the mutual inductance between coils must be _____ _____ .

9·39   (200 henrys)

Self-induction

A coil carrying a changing current can induce an emf in its own turns and thereby develop a correspondingly large emf across its own terminals. Alternating current flowing through the turns of a coil gives rise to an alternating field which cuts through the turns of the coil and causes induction. This process is called "self-induction."

The direction of this self-induced emf is determined from Lenz's law in exactly the same way, and for the same reasons, as in the case of primary and secondary coils. The induced emf always has such a polarity as to give rise to a current which opposes the changing magnetic flux. Such an emf is called a "back emf" or "counter emf" and always has a direction opposite to that of the applied emf that produces the original coil current. The property of self-induction is measured in henrys. A coil of one henry self-inductance will develop a back emf of one volt when the current in it changes at the rate of one ampere/second.

We might point out at this time that the self-inductance of a coil depends primarily upon the *number of turns* and the *character of the core material*. Self-inductance increases as the number of turns is increased; also, self-inductance can be increased tremendously by inserting a core of high permeability and low retentivity. Soft-iron and silicon steel have these characteristics. Thus, if we wanted to build a coil of very high self-inductance, we would plan to wind the wire around a soft-iron or silicon steel core.

9·40 A coil has a self-inductance of 1 henry if 1 volt of back emf is induced in it for a di/dt of 1 amp/sec. When an iron core is inserted, without changing di/dt, the self-inductance becomes 20 henrys. The back emf in this case would be _____ volts.

9·41 (20) In Fig. 9·41, the switch has just been closed and the current has begun to flow in the direction shown. The lines of force have begun to build up as indicated, causing end B of the coil to begin to develop an _____-pole.

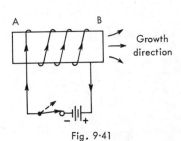

Fig. 9·41

9·42 (N) According to Lenz's law, the self-induced emf across the coil in Fig. 9·41 must therefore have such a direction as to _____ the growth of the current.

9·43 (oppose) Since the current is going up in the turns in front of the coil in Fig. 9·41, the self-induced emf must tend to produce a current that goes _____ in the turns in front of the coil.

9·44 (down) The net effect of an applied voltage that creates a current in one direction and a self-induced emf that tends to cause a current in the opposite direction, is to _____ the net emf acting on the coil.

9·45 (reduce) In Fig. 9·45, the switch has just been opened. The decaying current has, therefore, caused the field to begin to collapse back into end *B*. As the field collapses, it cuts through the conductors of the coil, inducing an emf that tends to _____ the collapse of the field.

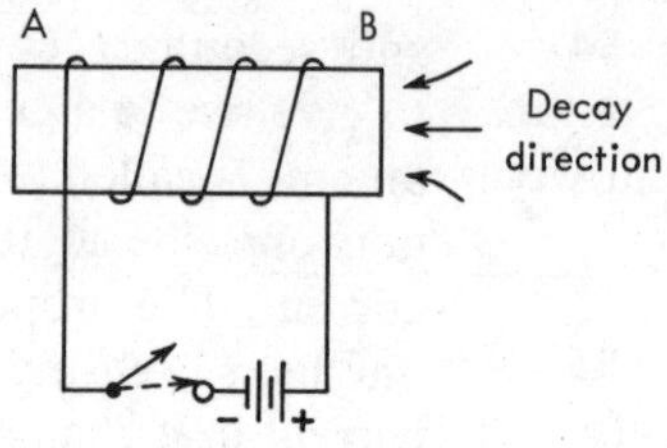

Fig. 9·45

9·46 (oppose) Such an emf can only produce a current which flows in the *same* direction as the original current. Only by flowing in the same direction can the induced current _____ the decay of the original current.

9·47 (oppose) To test your understanding of Lenz's law as applied to self-induction, refer to Fig. 9·47, and answer the following group of questions. The switch has just been closed; therefore, the current must be building up in a direction such that the electrons are flowing _____ in front of the coil.

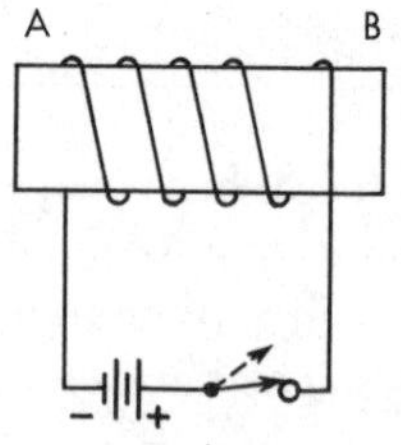

Fig. 9·47

9·48 (down) Thus, an N-pole must be in the process of forming at end _____ .

9·49 (*A*) The growing magnetic field must be emerging from end _____ .

9·50 (*A*) The self-induced emf must have such a direction as to _____ the growth of this field.

9·51 (oppose) Hence, the emf must have a direction such that the current it tends to produce will flow _____ in front of the coil.

9·52 (up) Since the self-induced emf bucks the applied emf, the net emf acting on the coil is _____ than it would be if self-induction were not occurring.

9·53 (less) If the current in the coil were made to change at the rate of 1 amp/sec, the self-induced emf would be 1 volt provided that the inductance of the coil were 1 henry. If the inductance were changed to 2 henrys with no change in current rate of growth or decay, the induced emf would be ___ _____ .

9·54 (2 volts) If the current changed at the rate of 3 amp/sec, and if the inductance of the coil were 10 henrys, the self-induced emf would be _____ _____ .

9·55 (30 volts) If the rate of current growth were 0.5 amp/sec, and if the induced voltage were 10 volts, this would mean that the inductance of the coil must be _____ henrys.

9·56 (20) If a coil of 4 henrys develops a counter emf of 12 volts, the current must be changing at the rate of _____ _____ .

9·57 (3 amp/sec) The inductance of a coil may be increased by improving the permeability of the core or by _____ the number of turns.

9·57 (increasing)

Dependence of induced emf on angle of cutting

Consider a single conductor moving through a magnetic field. Maximum induced emf is obtained in this conductor when it moves through the field at right angles to the lines of force; zero emf is obtained when the motion of the conductor is parallel to the lines of force (zero degrees). Angles intermediate between 0 and 90° yield intermediate values of emf.

9·58 In Fig. 9·58, a conductor in cross section is shown moving through a magnetic field in several different directions. If the conductor moves in either direction E or _____, the induced emf will be zero.

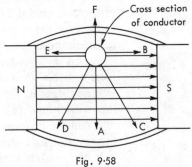

Fig. 9·58

9·59 (B) In Fig. 9·58, if the conductor moves in either direction D or _____, the emf will be larger than zero but less than maximum.

9·60 (C) In Fig. 9·58, maximum emf is induced when the conductor moves in either direction F or _____ .

9·61 ' (A) In Fig. 9·61, a conductor is seen rotating around center C in a circular path. The conductor is shown in cross section as before. The direction of rotation is clockwise as indicated. In position 1, the conductor is instantaneously moving parallel to the lines of force (0° angle). The induced emf is, therefore, _____ .

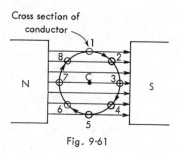

Fig. 9·61

9·62 (zero) In Fig. 9·61, the induced emf when the conductor is in position 3 is a maximum because the angle of cutting is now _____°. The induced emf is again maximum when the conductor reaches position _____ .

9·63 (90, 7) The induced emf in Fig. 9·61 is between zero and maximum when the conductor is in position 2, 6, 8, and _____ . The induced emf is _____ when the conductor is in position 5.

9·63 (4, zero)

Introduction to generator action

A single conductor moving through a magnetic field develops an induced emf across its ends. If the ends are connected in a complete circuit, an induced current flows which then gives rise to circular (Oersted) lines of force around the conductor. Now we have two magnetic fields: one due to the external magnets that produce the original field, and the second due to the induced current.

We know from Lenz's law that the field due to the induced current will have a direction such that the motion of the conductor through the field will be opposed. That is, the induced current *must* flow in the direction that will ultimately cause opposition to motion. This opposition in the case of a conductor moving through a field must result from the *interaction* of the two magnetic fields mentioned above.

It can be shown experimentally that a force of repulsion exists between lines of force that have the same direction. Referring for the moment to Fig. 9·65, we show a conductor moving downward through the field; the field has a left-to-right direction. An induced current flows in the conductor, and this current produces its own circular field. Below the conductor, the lines of both fields are pointed in the same direction; this may be viewed as a condition in which the field is *intensified* by the cooperation of lines from two different sources. In any case, the wire in moving downward would experience a repulsion which opposes its downward motion owing to the repulsion between its field and that of the external magnets.

9·64 When lines of force induced around a conductor moving through a magnetic field have the same direction as the magnetic field, a force of _____ exists causing opposition to the motion.

9·65 (repulsion) In Fig. 9·65, the lines of force *under* the wire are in the same direction as those of the external field. Hence, as this wire moves downward, it must experience a force of _____ .

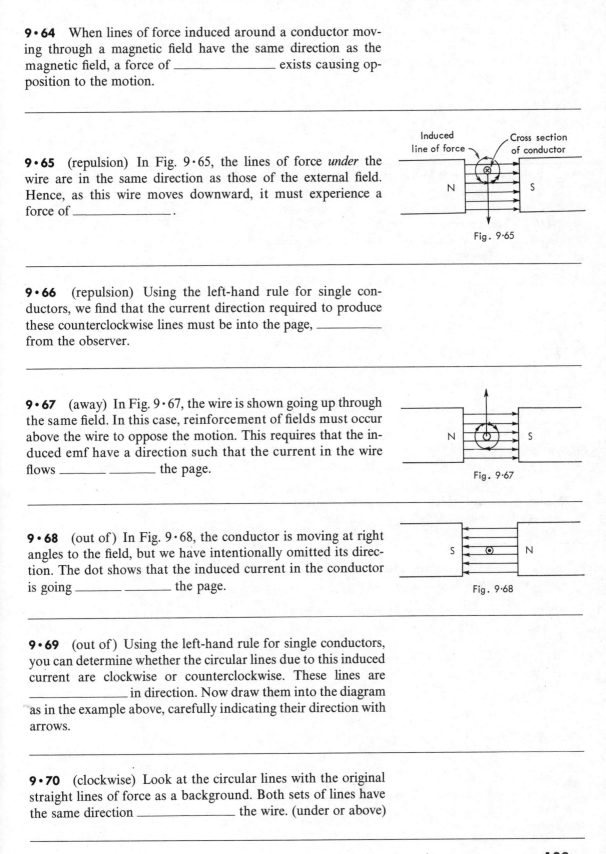

Fig. 9·65

9·66 (repulsion) Using the left-hand rule for single conductors, we find that the current direction required to produce these counterclockwise lines must be into the page, _____ from the observer.

9·67 (away) In Fig. 9·67, the wire is shown going up through the same field. In this case, reinforcement of fields must occur above the wire to oppose the motion. This requires that the induced emf have a direction such that the current in the wire flows _____ _____ the page.

Fig. 9·67

9·68 (out of) In Fig. 9·68, the conductor is moving at right angles to the field, but we have intentionally omitted its direction. The dot shows that the induced current in the conductor is going _____ _____ the page.

Fig. 9·68

9·69 (out of) Using the left-hand rule for single conductors, you can determine whether the circular lines due to this induced current are clockwise or counterclockwise. These lines are _____ in direction. Now draw them into the diagram as in the example above, carefully indicating their direction with arrows.

9·70 (clockwise) Look at the circular lines with the original straight lines of force as a background. Both sets of lines have the same direction _____ the wire. (under or above)

9·71 (under) Since the lines have the same direction under the wire, then the field is intensified under the wire and opposition would be produced if the wire were moving in a _____ direction.

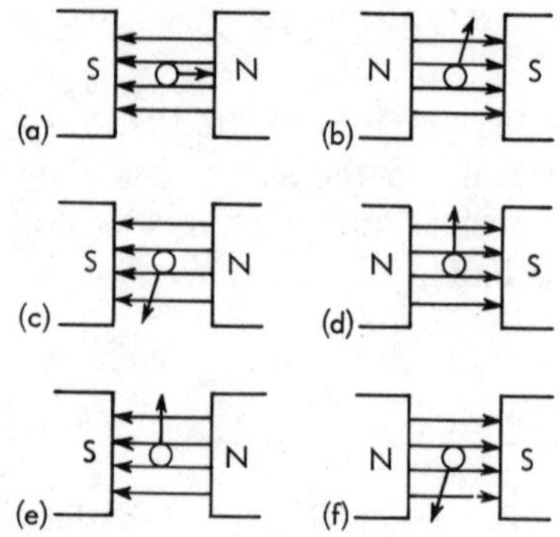

9·72 (downward) Refer to the six different situations in Fig. 9·72. Identify the letter of the situation which shows maximum induced emf (right-angle cutting) with current direction into the page. (*Hint:* The current direction would have to produce a circular line which has the same direction as the external field *above* the wire.) The letter is _____ .

Fig. 9·72

9·73 (*e*) The letters which identify the two situations in which an emf between zero and maximum is being induced, with current direction out of the page, are _____ .

9·74 (*b* and *c*) The letter which identifies zero emf of induction is _____ .

9·75 (*a*) The letter which identifies maximum induced emf with current direction out of the page is _____ .

9·76 (*d*) The letter which identifies emf between zero and maximum with current direction into the page is _____ .

9·76 (*f*)

MEASURABLE BEHAVIORAL OBJECTIVES

Upon completion of a section, you should be able to achieve the objectives listed for it. The frame or frames that cover the related subject matter are indicated immediately following each objective.

Electromagnetic induction by current changes

1   Discuss how a growing or collapsing magnetic field can induce an emf in a nearby coil.   (9·1)
2   Differentiate between the primary and secondary of an inductive coil.   (9·1, 9·2)
3   Exemplify the way Lenz's law applies to the two-coil situation.   (9·7)
4   Discuss the steady-state operation of two coils.   (9·11)

Mutual inductance

1   Discuss what will happen when an a-c generator is connected to the primary of: (9·23 to 9·26)
    a   A mutual inductor.   (9·28, 9·29)
    b   Illustrate several mutual inductance configurations.   (9·28 to 9·30)
2   Define the mutual inductance of 1 henry.   (9·31)
3   Give an equation relating the induced emf and mutual inductance.   (9·36)

Self-induction

1   Define a self-inductance of 1 henry.   (9·40)
2   Describe two methods for increasing or decreasing self-inductance.   (9·40, 9·57)
3   Use Lenz's law to describe self-inductance.   (9·42, 9·47)

Dependence of induced emf on angle of cutting

1   Discuss what will happen when a conductor is moved through a stationary magnetic field.   (9·58)
2   Relate the direction of magnetic field and the direction of motion of the conductor to the induced emf.   (9·58, 9·60)

Introduction to generator action

1   Discuss the forces acting upon a conductor moving in a magnetic field.   (9·64, 9·67)
2   Illustrate the direction of induced current in a conductor moving through a magnetic field.   (9·68)

chapter 10

introduction to generators

The basic generator

Refer to Fig. 10·1. This is a diagram of a basic generator. A single loop of wire is to be imagined rotating between the poles of the *field magnets* in a counterclockwise direction as indicated. The end wires (*CB* and *DA*) are always parallel to the field during rotation, hence cannot contribute to the induced emf. We ignore these. As wire *AB* moves around, it will sometimes be cutting through the lines of force at right angles, sometimes at 0°, and most of the time at some angle between 0 and 90°. In Frames 10·1 to 10·8, we study the induced emfs obtained by the sequence of cuttings at various angles.

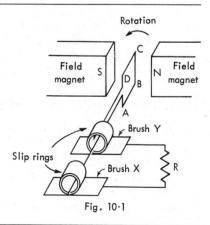

Fig. 10·1

10·1   Figure 10·1 shows a single generator. As the one-turn coil rotates about an axis perpendicular to the magnetic field, it cuts lines of force and induces a voltage. In the position shown, the emf is _____ because the conductors *AB* and *CD* are moving parallel to the field and no lines of force are being cut.

10·2   (zero) As *AB* moves upward, it cuts through lines of force going from right to left (from N to S). According to Lenz's law, the induced current in *AB* must produce a magnetic field that opposes the motion. Thus, the induced field must reinforce the lines of the original field _____ the wire *AB* in order to cause opposition to the motion.

10·3   (above) Using the left-hand rule to fit the direction of the field about *AB*, we find that the induced current must flow from _____ to _____ in this piece of wire.

10·4 (*A, B*) As *DC* moves downward, it cuts through the same magnetic field as *AB*, the field going from right to left. Since *DC* is moving downward, however, the reinforcements of fields to produce the Lenz's law opposition must occur _____ the wire *DC*.

10·5 (below) Thus, the left-hand rule tells us that the induced current in *DC* must flow from _____ to _____ .

10·6 (*C, D*) Tracing the circuit of Fig. 10·1, we find that the current in *DC* flows out through brush _____ to the resistor *R*.

10·7 (*Y*) The electrons reenter the system through brush _____ .

10·8 (*X*) The electrons then flow from *A* to *B*, thence to _____ , thus completing the circuit.

10·8 (*CD*)

Analysis of a generator cycle

The rotating portion of a generator is known as the *armature*. In these frames, a single-turn armature is studied with a view to learning how the induced emf depends upon the angle of cutting. When the various emfs obtained at different armature positions are plotted with respect to time, a *sine curve* such as that shown in Fig. 10·10 is obtained. In our study of a-c, we shall have to analyze this curve in detail.

10·9 Figure 10·9 shows the same generator as in Fig. 10·1, except that this is a cross-sectional view. *A* is the cross section of wire *DC* in Fig. 10·1, and *E* is the cross section of wire *AB* in Fig. 10·1. Since the conductors in position *AE* are moving parallel to the lines of force, the induced emf is _____ .

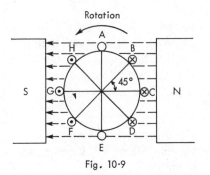

Fig. 10·9

10·10 (zero) This is the starting position; therfore, we call the angle of rotation 0°. Since the voltage is zero at 0°, we can mark off these coordinates on the graph of Fig. 10·10. These coordinates give us the position numbered _____ on the graph.

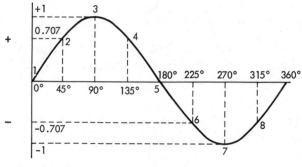

Fig. 10·10

10·11 (1) With the armature in position H (considering only the upper wire DC, since the lower conductor merely adds to the current induced in the same direction), the armature has rotated through 45° and is now cutting the lines of force at a slant. An induced current, therefore, flows out of the page (from Lenz's law and the left-hand rule) at H. The magnitude of this induced current, however, is between zero and _____ .

10·12 (maximum) It turns out that the magnitude of the induced current is 0.707 of its value at maximum. Calling the maximum value 1 volt for convenience, then the voltage obtained at 45° mark must be _____ volt.

10·13 (0.707) The voltage induced at 45° rotation point (point H) must, therefore, be shown in Fig. 10·10 as the point numbered _____ .

10·14 (2) After a rotation of an additional 45° for a total of 90° from the starting position, the upper wire reaches the lettered point G. Since it is still moving downward, the induced current direction is still out of the page. At this point the magnitude of the induced emf is at a _____ value.

10·15 (maximum) The voltage induced at point G is shown as the point numbered _____ on the graph in Fig. 10·10.

10·16 (3) At point F, the rotation completed is now 135°. The conductor is again moving at a slant through the field. Since the angle of cutting is the same as it was at point H, the induced voltage must now be _____ volt.

10·17 (0.707) The point on the graph that corresponds to point F is numbered _____ .

10·18 (4) The voltage developed at point E is _____ volts.

10·19 (zero) The completed angle of rotation at point E is _____° .

10·20 (180) The point on the graph that corresponds to rotation at point E is numbered _____ .

10·21 (5) At point D, the conductor has begun to move upward through the field. This causes the induced current to _____ in direction.

10·22 (reverse) The angle of cutting is now the same as it was at points H and _____ earlier in the same rotation.

10·23 (F) Hence, the induced voltage is again 0.707 volt, but _____ in direction as compared with the induced voltage of the same magnitude obtained earlier in the rotation.

10·24 (opposite) On the graph, the voltage induced at point D is numbered _____ .

10·25 (6) A voltage of -0.707 will again be obtained at point _____ in the rotation.

10·26 (B) The induced voltage will again be a maximum at point _____ in the rotation.

10·27 (C) At point B in the rotation, the total angle covered since the start is _____° .

10·28 (315) The voltage drops to zero after a total of _____°
of rotation.

10·28 (360)

Characteristics of the sine curve

The sine curve as derived from the analysis of a single loop generator is actually a plot of this equation:

$$E_i = E_{max} \sin \theta$$

in which E_i = the instantaneous voltage induced when the generator is at some angle θ (Greek *theta*) with reference to its starting position, E_{max} = the maximum voltage induced when the generator is at its 90 and 270° positions, and $\sin \theta$ is the sine function of the angle for which the instantaneous voltage is being obtained.

The sine function varies between values of $+1$ and -1 for a complete rotation. It has a value of zero for $\theta = 0$ and 180°, a value of $+1$ for 90°, and a value of -1 for 270°. Thus, for all angles between 0 and 180°, the sine of θ is positive; and for all angles between 180 and 360°, it is negative.

10·29 The graph shown in Fig. 10·10 is a plot of

$$E_i = E_{max} \sin \theta$$

where E_{max} = maximum induced emf occurring at 90 and
_____°.

10·30 (270) E_i is the instantaneous induced emf at any angle, and θ is the instantaneous angle of rotation for a given value of E_i. The sine of this angle can never exceed unity and attains this value when $\theta = 90$ or _____°.

10·31 (270) Assume $E_{max} = 100$ volts; assume, also, that the start of rotation occurs at position AE of Fig. 10·9 and is 0°. Assume further that all angles are measured counterclockwise from AE. At position AE, the induced emf is _____ volts because the sine of 0° is zero.

10·32 (zero) The instantaneous voltage induced in the armature of the generator at 45° rotation (position HD) is $E_i = E_{max} \sin 45° = 100 \times 0.707 =$ _____ volts. (Sin 45° = 0.707.)

10·33 (70.7) The instantaneous voltage developed by the generator at 90° rotation is $E_i = E_{max} \sin \theta = 100 \times 1 = $ _____ volts. (Sin 90° = 1.)

10·34 (100) The instantaneous voltage developed by the generator at 135° rotation is $100 \times 0.707 = $ _____ volts. (Sin 135° = 0.707.)

10·35 (70.7) The instantaneous voltage developed by the generator at 270° rotation position is _____ volts.

10·36 (−100) The instantaneous emf developed at the 315° position is _____ volts.

10·37 (−70.7) The instantaneous emf induced in a generator at a point reached after it has rotated through 450° is _____ volts.

10·38 (100) For angles between 0 and 180°, the sine of the angle is positive; for angles between _____ and _____°, the sine is negative.

10·39 (180, 360) Since a rotating armature must cut the magnetic field first one way and then the other in each rotation, the output of such an armature must always be a(n) _____ voltage.

10·40 (alternating) Slip rings merely take the voltage from the armature and lead it without change to the load circuit. Thus, for this generator, the current flowing in the load would be _____ current.

10·41 (alternating) One complete rotation of the armature produces one complete sine wave cycle as shown in Fig. 10·10. Two armature rotations would produce two cycles. Ten armature rotations would produce _____ cycles.

10·42 (ten) If the armature rotates 10 times per second, the a-c produced contains 10 hertz (abbrev. Hz), or has a frequency of 10 Hz. If the armature rotates 20 times per second, the frequency of the output would be _____ Hz.

10·43 (20) If the armature rotates 60 times per second, the frequency of the a-c in the load would be _____ _____ .

10·44 (60 Hz) Each cycle of a sine wave has two peaks, a positive one and a negative one (Fig. 10·10). The total number of peaks in a 10-Hz wave is 20. The total number of peaks in a 60-Hz wave is _____ .

10·45 (120) A 40-Hz a-c has 80 peaks per second. A 120-Hz sine wave has _____ peaks per second.

10·46 (240) The a-c frequency of a certain generator is 400 Hz. In 1 sec, _____ peaks would be produced.

10·47 (800) A single cycle contains two reversals of emf direction. One occurs at the 180° phase where the curve sweeps from the "+" quadrant down into the "−" quadrant. The other occurs at the 360° phase where the wave sweeps back up from the "−" to the "+" quadrant. Thus, the number of emf reversals in a 10-Hz wave is 20. Similarly, the number of reversals in a 20-Hz wave is _____ .

10·48 (40) A 30-Hz wave contains 60 reversals in 1 sec. A 60-Hz wave contains _____ reversals in 1 sec.

10·49 (120) A 400-Hz wave reverses its polarity _____ times per second.

10·49 (800)

The action of a commutator

The a-c generated by the generator discussed in Frames 10·29 to 10·49 may be converted to d-c by replacing the slip rings (Fig. 10·1) with a *commutator*. A commutator is a split cylinder in which the two halves are electrically insulated from each other. Each half is known as a *segment*. The commutator is fixed to the armature. As the latter turns, the commutator segments interchange the brushes against which they make contact. That is, one segment touches one brush and the other segment, the other brush at a given instant in time; after a fraction of a rotation, the first segment switches to the second brush and vice versa. This interchange of contacts *rectifies* the a-c, or converts it to d-c.

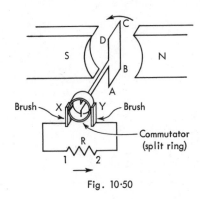

Fig. 10·50

10·50 Figure 10·50 illustrates a simple d-c generator. In the position shown, induced current flows in wire *CD* toward the reader into the top segment of the commutator and out of brush *X*. From here it flows into the load going from 1 to 2. The current returns to the armature coil through brush _____ and the lower segment of the commutator.

10·51 (*Y*) The current continues in this direction until wire *CD* passes the S-pole at the 180° cutting angle where *CD* is now at the bottom of the rotation. At this point, *CD* begins to cut upward through the field. From 180 to 360°, the direction of flow in *CD* is _____ _____ the reader.

10·52 (away from) At the 180° position, however, the commutator segment originally in contact with *X* has now shifted over to brush _____ .

10·53 (*Y*) With *BA* at the top of the rotation at this time, current will flow in *BA* toward the reader. Thus, the current will emerge from the armature again through brush _____ .

10·54 (*X*) Hence, the current will flow in the load from point _____ to point _____ .

10·55 (1, 2) Since current in the load is always toward the right, the shifting commutator segments have succeeded in changing the a-c of the armature to _____ in the load.

10·56 (d-c) Although the current in the load never reverses direction, it does grow and decay with the same waveform as the original sine wave as shown in Fig. 10·56. Referring to this waveform, the first cycle of the original a-c is labeled as *A, B, C, D', E*. The second cycle of the original a-c waveform is labeled as *E, F, G,* _____ , *I*.

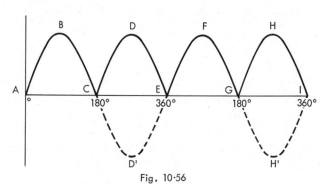

Fig. 10·56

10·57 (*H'*) As a result of the reversal caused by the commutator, half-cycle *CD'E* becomes half-cycle *CDE*. Likewise, half-cycle *GH'I* becomes half-cycle _____ .

10·58 (*GHI*) For the two cycles, the current in the load is shown by the waveform labeled *A, B,* ___, ___, ___, ___, ___, ___, *I*.

10·59 (*C, D, E, F, G, H*) The pulsations or ripples in this current consist of peaks *B, D, F, H*, that rise to E_{max}, and hollows *C, E, G, I*, that fall to _____ .

10·60 (zero) A 60-Hz sine wave when converted to d-c by this method contains _____ peaks in 1 sec.

10·61 (120) The ripple frequency of the converted wave is, therefore, _____ Hz.

10·62 (120) Commercial d-c generators have many coils rather than just two; each coil must have a pair of commutator segments. By connecting these coils in series, the ripples are not allowed to drop to _____ , since each hollow is filled in by one or more other coil inductions.

10·63 (zero) More coils in the armature result in higher ripple frequency. For example, two coils in a 60-Hz generator produce a ripple frequency of 120 Hz. Four coils produce 240 Hz. Thus, eight coils would produce a ripple frequency of _____ Hz.

10·64 (480) A d-c generator with 12 coils would have a ripple frequency of 720 Hz. A d-c generator with 10 coils would have a ripple frequency of _____ Hz.

10·65 (600) A 60-Hz a-c generator when equipped with 20 coils, 20 pairs of commutator segments, becomes a d-c generator with a ripple frequency of _____ Hz.

10·65 (1,200)

MEASURABLE BEHAVIORAL OBJECTIVES

Upon completion of a section, you should be able to achieve the objectives listed for it. The frame or frames that cover the related subject matter are indicated immediately following each objective.

The basic generator

Demonstrate the functioning of a generator by the use of a simplified diagram. (10·1)
a Determine the direction of current in the above generator by the use of Lenz's law. (10·2)
b Determine the direction of current in the above generator by the use of the left-hand rule. (10·3)

Analysis of a generator cycle

1 Discuss the action of an armature of a generator. (10·9)
2 Illustrate the formation of a sinusoidal voltage of a generator by the application of the left-hand rule. (10·11)

Characteristics of the sine curve

Describe a sine wave mathematically and indicate where the maxima and minima occur. (10·30, 10·31)

The action of a commutator

D-c generator (10·50)
a Discuss the functioning of the commutator. (10·51)
b Draw a rectified sine wave. (10·56)
c Differentiate between any a-c and a d-c generator. (10·59, 10·60)

chapter 11
electrical meters

The d'Arsonval meter movement (construction)

Electrical meters are the "eyes" of the scientist or technician who works with electricity in any form. They are indispensable for design work, repair and service, and for monitoring any type of electrical equipment while in operation. Ammeters, voltmeters, ohmmeters, wattmeters, etc., are usually built around the moving-coil design, originally called the d'Arsonval meter movement.

11·1 Electrical meters are used to determine various quantities present in electric circuits. For example, a voltmeter measures emf or potential difference. An ammeter, on the other hand, measures current intensity in units called _____ .

11·2 (amperes) As its name implies an ohmmeter measures ohms. Thus, an ohmmeter is used to determine the _____ of a circuit or a circuit component.

11·3 (resistance) Refer to Fig. 11·3. In this movement, a magnetic field is supplied by the part labeled *permanent magnet.* Two ends of the coil shaft are used for *needle bearings;* the current to be measured is made to flow through the part labeled _____ which is shown wound on an aluminum frame.

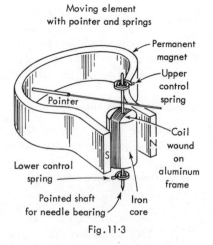

Moving element with pointer and springs

Permanent magnet

Upper control spring

Pointer

Coil wound on aluminum frame

Lower control spring

Pointed shaft for needle bearing

Iron core

Fig. 11·3

11·4 (coil) A scale reading in volts, amperes, or ohms would be placed beneath the part labeled *pointer* in the finished instrument. The magnetic field produced by the current to be measured would appear in and around the part labeled *iron* _____ .

11·5 (core) When no current flows through the instrument, the pointer is brought back to the left by a pair of control _____ .

11·6 (springs) The fixed element of the meter movement is the permanent magnet; the restoring elements are the control springs; the moving element that reacts with the permanent magnet field is the _____ that is shown wound on an aluminum frame.

11·7 (coil) Free turning action is provided by a pair of pivots into which the needle bearings fit; magnitude indications are provided by the _____ .

11·8 (pointer) The control springs expand and contract with temperature variations. To counteract this effect, the springs are wound in _____ directions. (same/opposite)

11·9 (opposite) The bearings of a meter movement must have virtually zero friction. Sapphires make good bearings because they are extremely hard; glass is often used for bearings for the same reason; synthetic jewels are also used because they have very little _____ (Fig. 11·9).

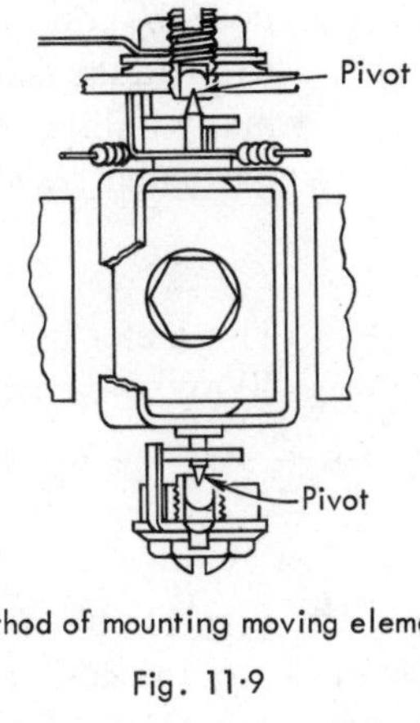

Method of mounting moving elements

Fig. 11·9

11·10 (friction) The upper needle of the shaft fits into the upper bearing; the lower needle of the shaft fits into the lower _____ .

11·11 (bearing) Each bearing is set in a threaded nut to allow adjustment. The number of threaded adjusting nuts shown in Fig. 11·9 is _____ .

11·12 (two) d'Arsonval meter movements are always housed in a case for mechanical protection. Such a case must have a transparent window which permits the user to see the scale and _____ .

11·13 (pointer) The terminals of the meter are available on the outside of the case. The terminals conduct the required current into and away from the _____ of the meter.

11·13 (coil)

The d'Arsonval meter movement (operation)

The d'Arsonval movement depends for its operation on magnetic forces produced by the interaction of fixed-field magnets and electromagnetism in the moving coil. The coil and its frame are extremely light in weight necessitating very small forces to cause rotation. All the parts of the movement are delicate; great care must be taken to ensure trouble-free operation.

The sensitivity of a meter movement may be expressed in either one of two ways:

1. It can be expressed in terms of the current required to give a full-scale deflection. For example, a very sensitive meter will deflect full scale with only 25 μa, while a less sensitive meter might require 10 ma.

2. Or it can be expressed in terms of the number of millivolts (thousandths of a volt—abbrev. mv) across the coil when full-scale current flows. Suppose the coil resistance of a movement is 50 ohms and that 1 ma is required to produce full-scale deflection. Using Ohm's law, we can find out how many millivolts are needed to produce full-scale deflection (1 ma) for that particular resistance.

$$E = IR = 0.001 \times 50 = 0.05 \text{ volt} = 50 \text{ mv}$$

The meter in the example would then be rated as having a sensitivity of 50 mv, 0–1 ma.

11·14 In Fig. 11·14, a moving coil on an axis is shown. In this drawing, the coil can rotate clockwise as indicated by the curved arrow. In the position shown, the control springs have brought the coil back to "zero" position. The straight arrows from N to S give the direction of the permanent _____ field.

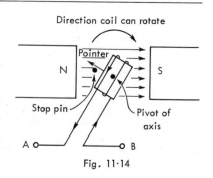

Fig. 11·14

11·15 (magnetic) The arrows on the coil wires show the direction of current that will produce a clockwise rotation. To obtain this current direction, the terminal labeled *A* would have to be connected to the _____ end of the source to be measured, while *B* would be connected to the opposite polarity.

11·16 (positive) With the current direction shown, the left end of the coil (end nearest the N-pole) must take on the characteristics of an _____-pole, while the right end of the coil takes on opposite polarity.

11·17 (N) When this coil polarity reacts with the poles of the permanent magnet, the coil is repelled at both ends and tends, therefore, to rotate in a _____ direction.

11·18 (clockwise) If the current is fed to the coil in the wrong direction, the coil will tend to rotate in a _____ direction.

11·19 (counterclockwise) This may cause the pointer to bend against the stop pin in the case, causing _____ to the meter.

11·20 (damage) Since a d'Arsonval movement can safely accept current in only one direction, this instrument is used only for measuring _____ current.

11·21 (direct) When the amount of pointer deflection is proportional to the coil current, the scale beneath the pointer is uniform or linear. A d'Arsonval meter movement when used for current and voltage measurements produces a pointer deflection proportional to the coil current, hence the scale of a d'Arsonval ammeter or voltmeter is _____ .

11·22 (linear) The pointer deflection of an ohmmeter, however, is not proportional to the resistance being measured. Thus, when a d'Arsonval movement is used to make an ohmmeter, the scale of the instrument is _____ .

11·23 (nonlinear) On a certain d'Arsonval ammeter, full-scale reading is 10 amp; since the scale is linear, half-scale reading would be 5 amp; also one-tenth of the scale reading would indicate _____ amp.

11·24 (1) On the same instrument, this time used as a 0–12 volt voltmeter, full-scale reading is 12 volts. Hence, one-fourth scale reading would be _____ volts.

11·25 (3) Quarter-scale reading on a certain linear voltmeter is 8 volts. Full-scale reading would, therefore, be _____ volts.

11·26 (32) A meter that deflects full scale for 1 ma flowing through its coil may be rated for sensitivity as a 1-ma meter. A meter that deflects full scale for a coil current of 5 ma is a 5-ma meter. Thus, a meter rated at 10 ma requires _____ ma of coil current for full-scale deflection.

11·27 (10) A 50-μa rating means that 50 μa is needed for full-scale deflection. Therefore, an instrument whose dial carries the legend 100 μa will deflect full scale when the current through it is _____ _____ .

11·28 (100 μa) An instrument that deflects full scale for a current of 0.000025 amp has a sensitivity rating of ____ _____ .

11·29 (25 μa) As explained in the introduction to this section (item 2), if the coil resistance of a 5-ma meter were 100 ohms, the sensitivity would be given as 500 mv, 0–5 ma. Thus, a 1-ma instrument having a coil resistance of 25 ohms would be rated as 25 mv, _____ _____ .

11·30 (0–1 ma) A 0–100 microammeter with a coil resistance of 50 ohms is a 5-mv 0–100 microammeter. Also, a 0–100 microammeter with a coil resistance of 500 ohms is a 50-mv _____ _____ microammeter.

11·31 (0–100 μa) A 0–50 microammeter has a coil resistance of 100 ohms. Its sensitivity could be stated as 5 mv, _____ μa.

11·31   (0–50)

The ammeter

The basic meter movement may be converted into an ammeter by connecting a low resistance across the coil terminals. Such a low resistance is called a "shunt." The shunt acts as a bypass for some of the current in the circuit, allowing only a small portion of the total circuit current to pass through the coil. For instance, suppose that the maximum allowable coil current in a given movement is 0.001 amp, and that the instrument is to be inserted in a circuit where the current might reach 1 amp or any value lower than this. We must be prepared, however, for a current as large as 1 amp. It would then be necessary to connect a shunt across the terminals that would "take" 0.999 amp of the total 1.000 amp, thus allowing only 0.001 amp to flow through the coil.

With this arrangement in operation, the meter would read full scale. We know, however, that the total circuit current is 1.000 amp even though only 1/1,000 of this is flowing through the coil. We would then mark the full-scale deflection point 1.000 amp, indicating that this is the *total* circuit current, rather than the current through the coil itself. In other words, we calibrate the instrument in terms of the current of interest to us—the total circuit current which the meter is to read—not in terms of the coil current which is of interest only to the extent that we do not permit the current in the coil to become damagingly high.

Now suppose that the total circuit current drops to 0.5 amp. The shunt will still take 999/1,000 of this total current while the coil takes 1/1,000 of it. Thus, the coil current will be $0.5 \times 1/1,000 = 0.0005$ amp. Note that this current is half of its original magnitude, hence the needle of the meter will drop to half scale which we may now label 0.5 amp. The actual deflection, therefore, is always *proportional* to the total current; once we know what fraction of the total current always flows through the coil, the instrument dial may be marked to read the total current with the assurance that the reading will be correct within the limits of the accuracy of the instrument.

11·32 A shunt is a low resistance connected across the terminals of a meter coil to extend the range of the instrument for current measurements. The shunt bypasses some of the current around the coil, making it possible to measure higher values. In Fig. 11·32, the shunt is symbolized by _____.

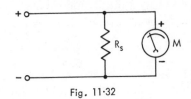

Fig. 11·32

11·33 (R_s) Suppose you have a 50-mv 0–1 milliammeter and wish to extend its range to measure up to 10 ma. First draw a schematic diagram as in Fig. 11·33, showing all the available information. In this diagram, the 10 ma flowing in the lower wire indicates the current from the source entering the meter system. The 10 ma flowing in the upper wire shows the current leaving the system and returning to the _____.

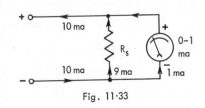

Fig. 11·33

11·34 (source) In Fig. 11·33, the current labeled 9 ma is the current that must flow through the shunt. Similarly, the current labeled 1 ma indicates the maximum current allowed through the _____.

11·35 (meter) Since this is a 50-mv 0–1 ma meter, the resistance of the coil is found from Ohm's law to be ____ _____ .

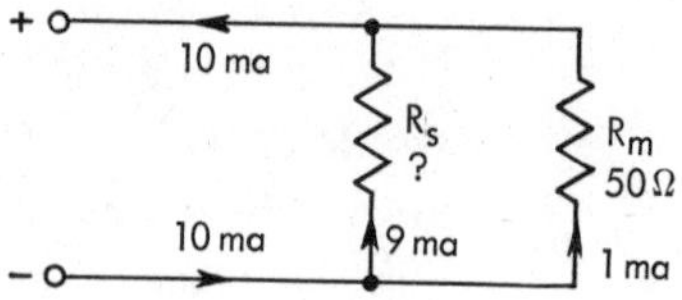

11·36 (50 ohms) An *equivalent* circuit is now drawn in Fig. 11·36. In this diagram, R_m stands for the resistance of the ____ _____ _____ .

Fig. 11·36

11·37 (meter coil) R_s is now easily determined from the ratio law of parallel circuits:

$$\frac{R_s}{R_m} = \frac{I_m}{I_s}$$

In this equation, R_s is the desired shunt resistance, R_m is the resistance of the meter coil, I_s is the shunt current, and I_m is the permissible _____ _____ .

11·38 (meter current) Substituting the known values we can write

$$\frac{R_s}{50} = \frac{1}{9}$$

and cross multiplying, we find that the shunt resistance turns out to be ____ _____ .

11·39 (5.55 ohms) As another example, let us determine the shunt required to extend the range of a 100-mv 0–5 milliammeter to read 50 ma. First you draw the schematic circuit. In this circuit you show the total current from and to the source as 50 ma. The meter current (maximum) is 5 ma. Hence, the shunt current must be ____ _____ .

11·40 (45 ma) The resistance of the coil is now computed from Ohm's law. Since the meter requires 100 mv to cause a full-scale deflection of 5 ma, the resistance of the coil is ____ _____ .

11·41 (20 ohms) The equivalent circuit is now drawn in which you show R_s as the unknown, I_s as 45 ma, I_m as 5 ma, and R_m as ____ _____ .

11·42 (20 ohms) The current ratio equation is now set up. It will look like this:

$$\frac{R_s}{20} = \frac{5}{45}$$

Cross multiplying and solving for R_s gives an answer of

_____ _____ .

11·43 (2.22 ohms) As a further exercise, determine the shunt resistance needed to extend a 0–1 amp movement whose resistance is 0.1 ohm to read 0–10 amp. The answer is ____ ____ .

11·43 (0.011 ohm)

The voltmeter

The basic meter movement may be converted into a voltmeter by connecting a high resistance in series with the coil of the instrument. This high resistance is called a "multiplier." The function of the multiplier is to prevent excessive current from flowing through the meter coil. Since a voltmeter is always connected *across* (in parallel with) the voltage to be measured, a shunt cannot be used because it would short-circuit the source. (Remember that a shunt is a *low* resistance. In the ammeter connection, the total circuit current is limited by the circuit load, whatever it might be, while the ammeter itself is inserted in series with this load. In the case of the voltmeter, however, a series resistance must be included to keep the current low in the coil since the instrument is connected in parallel with the source of voltage.)

11·44 A meter movement may be used to measure voltages by connecting a resistance in series with the coil. Such a series resistor is called a multiplier. In Fig. 11·44, the multiplier is symbolized by _____ .

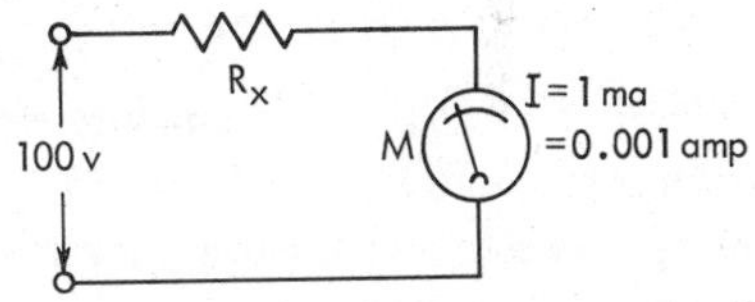

Fig. 11·44

11·45 (R_x) Suppose you have a 50-mv 0–1 ma meter movement that you wish to convert to a 0–100 voltmeter. First determine the meter resistance as for ammeter calculations. The resistance of this meter is ____ _____ .

11·46 (50 ohms) Next draw the equivalent circuit as in Fig. 11·46. Since this is a series circuit, the total current is determined by $I = E/(R_x + R_m)$. Since R_x is the unknown, the equation solved for the unknown turns out to be the quotient E/I minus _____ .

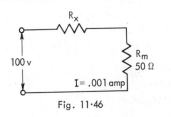

Fig. 11·46

11·47 (R_m) Substituting the known values we have

$$R_x = \frac{100}{0.001} - 50$$

This gives an answer for R_x of _____ ohms.

11·48 (99,950) Thus, all voltmeter multiplier problems may be solved by means of the equation

$$R_x = \frac{E}{I} - R_m$$

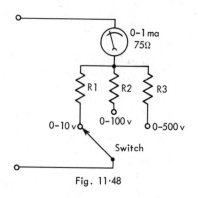

Fig. 11·48

Using this equation, determine $R1$, $R2$, and $R3$ in Fig. 11·48. This is an arrangement used in multitest meters wherein a single meter movement is used with different multipliers for various voltage ranges. For example, with the switch in the 0–10 volt position, $R1$ is the multiplier and

$$R1 = \frac{10}{0.001} - 75 = \text{\_\_\_\_ _____}$$

11·49 (9,925 ohms) Thus, $R2$ is found from

$$R2 = \frac{100}{0.001} - 75 = \text{_____}\ \text{ohms}$$

11·50 (99,925) And finally, $R3$ may be determined by the same method. The value of $R3$ found is _____ ohms.

11·51 (499,925) Multipliers may be connected in a different manner as shown in Fig. 11·51. On the 0–10 volt range, only $R1$ is in series with the meter movement. Hence, $R1$ is found from

$$R1 = \frac{10}{0.001} - 75 = \text{_____}\ \text{ohms}$$

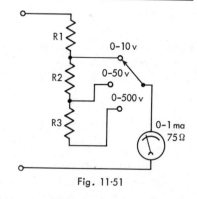

Fig. 11·51

11·52 (9,925) On the 0–50 volt range, resistors $R1$ and $R2$ are both in series with the meter movement. Thus,

$$R2 = \frac{50}{0.001} - (9,925 + 75)$$

$$= \frac{50}{0.001} - 10,000$$

$$= \text{_____}\ \text{ohms}$$

11·53 (40,000) On the 0–500 volt range, all three resistors are in series with the meter movement. Using the same procedure as before, $R3$ is found to be _____ ohms.

11·53 (450,000)

Sensitivity rating of a voltmeter

Voltmeters are often rated for sensitivity in *ohms/volt*. This may be expanded thus: The rating tells how many ohms must be connected in series with the coil to make the meter read full scale when 1 volt is applied to its terminals. Note that the coil resistance is generally so low compared with the multiplier resistance that we may neglect it and speak only of the number of ohms added in the form of the multiplier to produce the desired result.

A very sensitive movement calls for a very high multiplier resistance for full scale at 1 volt applied. Thus, an instrument having a large ohms/volt rating is a very sensitive one. An insensitive movement requires a relatively smaller multiplier, hence will have a smaller ohms/volt rating.

For example, a sensitive 0–20 μa movement needs a multiplier of 50,000 ohms to read full scale at 1 volt applied. That is,

$$R = \frac{E}{I} = \frac{1 \text{ volt}}{20 \times 10^{-6} \text{ amp}} = 0.05 \times 10^6 \text{ ohms} = 50,000 \text{ ohms}$$

11·54 The sensitivity of a voltmeter is expressed in ohms/volt. For example, a 0–1 ma meter movement connected in series with a multiplier of such value as to make the total series resistance 1,000 ohms (total = meter coil + multiplier) will read full scale when _____ volt is applied.

11·55 (1) This meter requires a total of 1,000 ohms in its circuit to produce a full-scale deflection for 1 volt applied. Hence, its sensitivity is said to be 1,000 ohms/_____ .

11·56 (volt) Similarly, a 0–5 ma movement has a sensitivity of $R = E/I = 1/0.005 = 200$ ohms/volt. Also, a 0–100 μa meter movement has a sensitivity of $R = E/I = 1/0.0001$ or _____ ohms/volt.

11·57 (10,000) The sensitivity in ohms/volt of a 0–500 μa meter movement is $R = 1/0.0005 = 2,000$ ohms/volt. Similarly, the sensitivity of a 0–50 μa meter movement is _____

_____ .

11·58 (20,000 ohms/volt) The sensitivity in ohms/volt of a 0–2 ma meter movement is _____.

11·58 (500 ohms/volt)

The ohmmeter

An ohmmeter is an essentially simple instrument used to measure resistance directly. It contains a built-in source of emf (usually a battery) and a basic meter movement in addition to auxiliary resistors used for calibration and zeroing. The fundamental operations involved in the use of a simple ohmmeter are these:

1. The test leads are first shorted together and a built-in potentiometer adjusted until the meter reads full scale. Actually, what is being done here is this: The resistance between the test lead probes is zero because they are touched together. The internal resistances of the instrument are adjusted for full-scale reading, therefore, with *zero resistance* between probes.

2. The probes are then separated and the "unknown" resistance inserted between them. Clearly, the deflection will decrease because of the added resistance in the meter circuit. The new reading may then be marked directly in ohms to correspond with the resistance between the probes. Thereafter, every time the meter deflects this much for a truly unknown resistance, its resistance may be read right off the scale. This is repeated for many different resistances until the scale is completely marked.

Note that an ohmmeter scale reads in the reverse direction as compared with other meters. The lowest resistance (zero) is full scale, while the higher resistances are "down scale."

11·59 An ohmmeter is used to measure resistance directly. It consists of a basic meter movement, a built-in source of emf, and certain required resistors. In the diagram of a simple ohmmeter (Fig. 11·59), E is the voltage source, $R1$ is a variable resistor, and $R2$ is a "safety" resistor which limits the maximum _____ through the meter when A and B are connected.

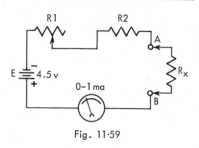

Fig. 11·59

11·60 (current) The basic meter movement in this circuit is a 0–1 ma type. The resistance to be measured is symbolized by _____.

11·61 (R_x) In normal use, A and B are first short-circuited together, and $R1$ is adjusted for full-scale deflection. When this is done, using the values in Fig. 11·59, the total resistance of $R1 + R2$ must be _____ ohms.

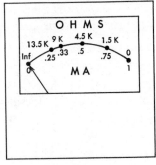

Fig. 11·62

11·62 (4,500) Since the resistance between *A* and *B* is zero, then full-scale deflection of the meter, in terms of ohms, must represent _____ ohms (Fig. 11·62).

11·63 (0) *R*1 is now left undisturbed (4,500 ohms). If a resistor of 4,500 ohms is connected between *A* and *B*, then the total resistance in the circuit would be _____ ohms.

11·64 (9,000) For this condition, the current that would flow through the meter would then be _____ _____ .

11·65 (0.5 ma) If this current flows through a 0–1 ma movement, the deflection of the needle would be _____ scale.

11·66 (half) Thus, at the half-scale point, the meter is marked _____ kilohms.

11·67 (4.5) If R_x is now made 9,000 ohms, the total resistance of the circuit becomes _____ kilohms.

11·68 (13.5) For this resistance, the current in the meter would be _____ ma.

11·69 (0.33) With this current in the meter coil, the needle would deflect to the point that is _____ of the way across the scale.

11·70 (one-third) Hence, this point would be labeled _____ kilohms on the meter scale.

11·71 (9) Using the same procedure, we can find the deflection to expect when R_x = 13.5 kilohms. The answer is a deflection that covers _____ of the scale.

11·72 (one-fourth) Similarly, a resistance of 1.5 kilohms for R_x will produce a deflection over _____ of the full scale.

11·73 (three-fourths) If A and B are left unconnected or completely open, the resistance between these terminals is assumed to be infinite. For this condition, the meter will read

_____ .

11·74 (zero) Examining the meter scale calibrations completed in the above steps, we see that calibrations are _____ in direction from those we find on ammeters and voltmeters.

11·75 (opposite) The milliammeter scale from 0 to 1 in Fig. 11·62 is linear because equal scale steps mean equal current changes. The ohmmeter scale in the same figure is _____ because equal scale steps mean unequal changes in resistance.

11·76 (nonlinear) The ohmmeter circuit just analyzed is called a series type because R_x is connected in series with the rest of the components. For measuring low resistance, a shunt type of ohmmeter is used. In this instrument, the unknown resistor is connected in _____ with the meter (Fig. 11·76).

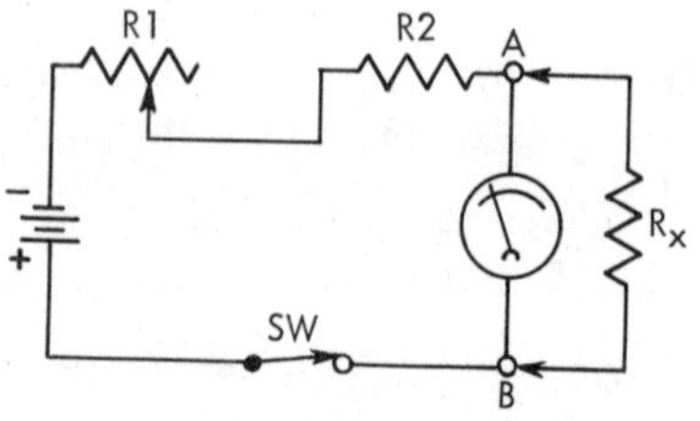

Fig. 11·76

11·77 (parallel or shunt) R1 and R2 are selected (Fig. 11·76) so that the battery used drives the meter to full scale when terminals A and B are open. Hence, when A and B are short-circuited, the meter reading must be _____ .

11·78 (zero) As R_x is made increasingly larger, less current flows through it and more current flows through the _____ .

11·79 (meter) Such a meter is said to be direct-reading, because larger resistances to be measured cause _____ scale readings.

11·80 (larger) If the sum of R1 and R2 is much greater than the resistance of the meter coil (this is normally the case), then changing the meter circuit resistance by adding R_x will have very little effect upon the current from the battery. Such an arrangement constitutes a constant _____ source.

11·81 (current) Since the current from the source is constant, the meter reading will always be the difference between the total (constant) current and the current flowing through _____ .

11·82 (R_x) In a shunt-type ohmmeter, current always flows through the meter whether a resistor is connected across its terminals or not. To prevent the battery from being drained when the instrument is not in use, it must be provided with a

_____ .

11·82   (switch)

A-c meters

This short section is intended only to introduce some of the basic methods used to convert d-c meter movements into instruments that will be capable of measuring a-c circuit values.

11·83   A d'Arsonval meter movement can only measure d-c. To measure a-c, a device which changes a-c to d-c must be inserted in the meter. Such a device, connected in series with the meter movement, allows current to flow in one direction only. As shown in Fig. 11·83, it is called a _____ .

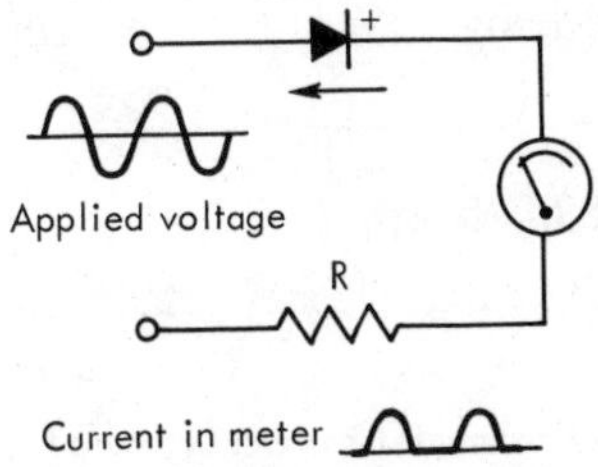

Current in meter

This is called "pulsating d-c"

Fig. 11·83

11·84   (rectifier) In the symbol of a rectifier, the flat platelike portion is usually marked "+." The arrow under the symbol indicates the direction of _____ flow.

11·85   (electron or current) Since the current can flow only one way, the current through the meter must be _____ d-c rather than a-c even though the applied voltage is a-c.

11·86   (pulsating) The rectifier shown in Fig. 11·83 is a copper-oxide type, utilizing certain important properties of crystals to produce unidirectional current flow. Units made of selenium, silicon, and other semiconductors may be used instead of the copper-oxide type, hence these units must also have the ability to _____ a-c.

11·87 (rectify) A thermocouple meter utilizes a different principle. A thermocouple consists of a junction of two dissimilar metals, usually iron and an alloy called _____ (Fig. 11·87).

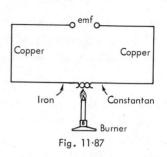

Fig. 11·87

11·88 (constantan) When the junction is heated, an emf appears across the open ends. If a d'Arsonval movement is connected across the open ends (Fig. 11·88) and if the burner is replaced by a piece of resistance wire that becomes hot when current flows through it, the resulting meter system can measure _____ as well as d-c.

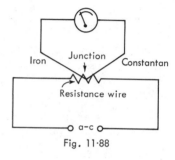

Fig. 11·88

11·89 (a-c) This is so because a-c is just as capable as d-c of producing _____ in a piece of resistance wire.

11·89 (heat)

Effect of meter on accuracy of measurements

A measurement of any kind necessitates the use of some sort of measuring tool. An essential property of any measuring instrument is that *it must operate without changing the thing being measured.* For example, you would not tolerate a yardstick which, when brought in contact with a length to be measured, altered this length so that it was no longer the same as it was before the stick was introduced. Measurements made by any instruments which affect what they measure are of little value, particularly if the effect is a large one.

Electrical meters must be brought into touch with the circuit being measured. When this is done, the instrument *must* have some effect on the circuit. By careful design and proper use, the effect can be reduced to an inconsequence; indeed, it may become so small that it may be completely ignored. Instruments of this high quality are usually costly and time consuming in operation.

For applications which do not warrant the expense or time involved in the purchase and use of very high quality ammeters, voltmeters, ohmmeters, wattmeters, etc., one may turn to instruments that have a greater effect upon the circuit parameter being measured. However, one must be completely aware of the changes introduced thereby. For instance, an ammeter is always connected in series with the circuit being measured and therefore introduces a resistance that was not there previously. A very fine ammeter will have a very low resistance in order that the current not be changed seriously by its insertion. Similarly, a voltmeter is connected in parallel with the emf or voltage drop being measured and will "pull" some current through the source and through other resistances in the circuit. This current will increase voltage drops above what they were previously and so cause the voltmeter to read *lower* than the actual voltage present. Obviously, a good voltmeter must have a very high resistance; this reduces the additional current drawn through the other parts of the circuit to a minimum and hence reduces the error to a minimum.

11·90 An ideal meter should have absolutely no effect upon the circuit being measured. Since real meters have resistance, they do have a definite effect on circuits, hence are not ideal. An ammeter is always connected in _____ with the circuit being analyzed.

11·91 (series) An ideal ammeter would have absolutely zero resistance since only this condition would produce zero effect on a circuit containing a series instrument. Thus, to approach the ideal, a good ammeter must have a very _____ resistance.

11·92 (low) If the resistance of an ammeter is too high, it will cause the current in the circuit to _____ .

11·93 (decrease) The ammeter reading thus obtained would be _____ than it should be for the actual circuit before the meter was connected.

11·94 (smaller or lower) A voltmeter is always connected in _____ with the emf or voltage drop to be measured.

11·95 (parallel) In Fig. 11·95, to measure the voltage drop across R2 we would connect a voltmeter between points _____ and _____ .

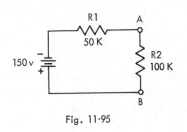

Fig. 11·95

11·96 (A, B) Let us compute the voltage drop across R2 before measuring it. This is found from Ohm's law to be $E = IR$. Since the current flowing through 150 kilohms from a 150-volt source is 0.001 amp, then $E = 0.001 \times 100,000$; and the answer for E across R2 is _____ _____ .

11·97 (100 volts) If the voltmeter connected across $R2$ were ideal, it would then read _____ (Fig. 11·95).

11·98 (100 volts) Using a standard 0–1 ma movement with a multiplier that extends its range to 100 volts full scale, we will be working with an instrument having an ohms-per-volt sensitivity of

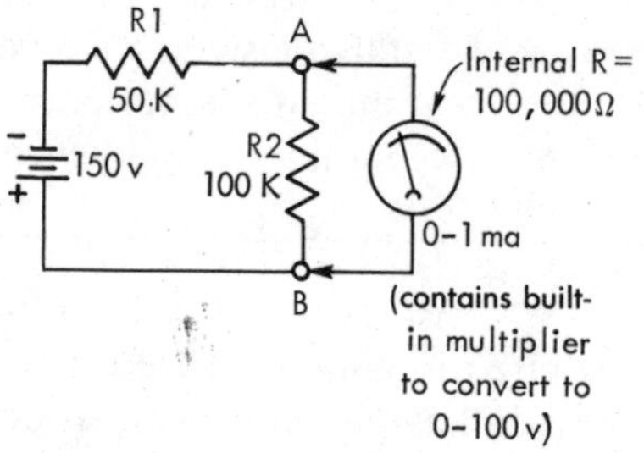

$$R = \frac{E}{I}$$

$$R = \frac{1}{0.001}$$

giving an ohms-per-volt sensitivity of _____ .

Fig. 11·98

11·99 (1,000 ohms/volt) On the 100-volt scale, this instrument would, therefore, have a total internal resistance of _____ (Fig. 11·98).

11·100 (100,000 ohms) It is connected in parallel with $R2$, however; hence, the joint resistance of $R2$ and the meter in parallel is _____ (Fig. 11·98).

11·101 (50,000 ohms) The addition of the voltmeter has reduced the total circuit resistance from its original 150,000 ohms to a new value of _____ .

11·102 (100,000 ohms) The battery is now looking into a circuit containing a total resistance of 100,000 ohms. The battery voltage is 150 volts. The current *now* flowing in the circuit is $I = E/R = 150/100,000 =$ _____ amp.

11·103 (0.0015) Hence, the voltage drop across $R1$ is increased from its original value of 50 volts to a new value of _____ .

11·104 (75 volts) Thus, the voltage left across $R2$ as read by the meter will be only _____ volts in contrast to its unmetered value of 100 volts.

11·105 (75) The meter has disturbed the circuit to the extent that it reads 75 volts instead of 100 volts as it should. An ideal meter—one that would read 100 volts in this circuit—would, therefore, draw absolutely zero current from the circuit. Any instrument that draws *zero* current from a source of voltage must have infinite _____.

11·106 (resistance) A real voltmeter of high accuracy would have a very _____ internal resistance.

11·107 (high) If an instrument having a sensitivity of 20,000 ohms/volt were used instead of the 1,000 ohms/volt type, its accuracy would be substantially _____.

11·108 (higher or better) A vacuum-tube voltmeter has an input resistance of over 15 million ohms. Such an instrument has very _____ effect on the circuit to which it is connected.

11·108 (little)

MEASURABLE BEHAVIORAL OBJECTIVES

Upon completion of a section, you should be able to achieve the objectives listed for it. The frame or frames that cover the related subject matter are indicated immediately following each objective.

The d'Arsonval meter movement (construction)

1 List three types of d'Arsonval meters and their functions in electronics. (11·1, 11·2)
2 Discuss the d'Arsonval meter movement as an ammeter.   (11·3)
3 Discuss the method of mounting the moving elements in a d'Arsonval meter.   (11·9)

The d'Arsonval meter movement (operation)

Define sensitivity of a meter.   (Introduction)
a Discuss current sensitivity.   (11·26)
b Discuss voltage sensitivity.   (11·30)

The ammeter

Discuss the function of the shunt when a d'Arsonval meter is used as an ammeter. (11·32, 11·33)

a Draw an equivalent circuit for an ammeter. (11·36)

b Use Ohm's law to determine the current in the shunt of an ammeter. (11·37)

The voltmeter

Describe the use of a d'Arsonval meter as a voltmeter. (11·44)

a Discuss the function of the "multiplier" resistor. (11·44)

b Draw an equivalent circuit for a voltmeter. (11·46)

c Describe a method that would allow the use of one d'Arsonval meter for different full-scale voltage readings. (11·48)

Sensitivity rating of a voltmeter

1 Define sensitivity of a voltmeter. (11·54)

2 Give numerical examples to show how to determine sensitivity. (11·56)

The ohmmeter

1 Describe the use of a d'Arsonval meter as an ohmmeter. (Introduction)

2 Discuss the need for a built-in source of emf and a "safety" resistor. (11·59)

3 Describe the calibration of an ohmmeter. (11·65, 11·66)

4 Discuss the nonlinearity of the ohmmeter scale. (11·75)

5 Describe the operation of a shunt ohmmeter. (11·76)

A-c meters

1 Describe the use of a d'Arsonval meter as an a-c current meter. (11·83)

2 Discuss the need for a rectifier in an a-c meter. (11·83, 11·85)

3 Describe the construction and use of a thermocouple. (11·87)

Effect of meter on accuracy of measurements

1 Discuss the effect of the shunt resistance on the accuracy of an ammeter reading. (11·91)

2 Discuss the effect of the "multiplier" resistance on the accuracy of a voltmeter reading. (11·98)

part two
alternating current

chapter 12

fundamental concepts of a-c

Direction of current in an a-c circuit

In a direct-current circuit, the current always flows from the negative terminal of the source, through the load, and back to the positive terminal. This is the distinguishing characteristic of d-c; d-c is *unidirectional* with respect to emf and current.

As we have seen in previous introductory discussions, alternating current is characterized by periodic reversals of emf and current. *At any given instant*, current flow still follows the "−" to "+" rule, but as the emf reverses its polarity, so does the current.

12·1 In Fig. 12·1, the electrons leave the "−" terminal of the battery and flow through the lamp going from point _____ to point _____ .

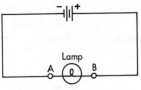

Fig. 12·1

12·2 (*A, B*) In Fig. 12·2, the electrons flow through the lamp going from point _____ to point _____ .

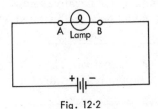

Fig. 12·2

12·3 (*B, A*) In Fig. 12·3, the output emf of the generator sometimes has the polarity indicated as polarity *A*, and other times has the polarity indicated as polarity *B*. When the polarity is that of *A*, the flow of current is indicated by the _____ arrows. (solid/broken)

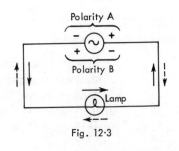

Fig. 12·3

12·4 (solid) When the generator has the polarity labeled polarity B, the current direction is given by the _____ arrows.

12·4 (broken)

12·5 In Fig. 12·5, the current through $R1$ would have the direction illustrated when terminal A of the generator is negative and terminal B positive. Also, the current through $R2$ would have the direction shown when A is positive and B negative. Thus, the current in $R3$ would flow as indicated when terminal A is _____ .

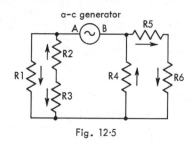

Fig. 12·5

12·6 (negative) The current in $R5$ would flow as shown when terminal B is negative and A positive. Similarly, the current in $R4$ would flow as illustrated when terminal A is _____ .

12·7 (negative) The current in $R6$ would have the indicated direction only if terminal A is _____ .

12·7 (positive)

The meaning of frequency

In the introduction to the d-c section of this program (Chap. 10), we discussed the generation of a sine wave as well as a few of the characteristics of the sine curve. We shall want to review this material briefly at this time. If the reader has forgotten the essence of these discussions, he should look over Frames 10·9 to 10·49 before proceeding.

12·8 A sine wave that completes 60 whole variations in 1 sec is said to contain 60 cycles in 1 sec. The frequency of this a-c is therefore _____ Hz.

12·9 (60) A train of sine waves that contains 20 positive peaks and 20 negative peaks contains _____ cycles.

12·10 (20) A sine wave of a-c voltage that contains 120 reversals of polarity per second has a frequency of _____ Hz.

12·11 (60) In a sine wave of 400-Hz frequency, the number of positive peaks is _____ in 1 sec.

12·12 (400) In a sine wave of 400-Hz frequency, the number of polarity reversals is _____ in 1 sec.

12·13 (800) The power-line frequency in the United States is 60 Hz. In some parts of Canada, the power-line frequency is 50 Hz. In some foreign countries, the power-line voltage reverses its direction 50 times per second, giving a frequency of _____ Hz.

12·14 (25) Alternating currents between about 20 and 20,000 Hz when changed into sound by passing through a loudspeaker or headphones can be heard by the human ear and are therefore called *audio frequencies*. Therefore, when the sound produced by a violin string playing the note C (512 Hz) is reproduced electrically, it is an _____ frequency.

12·15 (audio) An alternating current of 5,000 Hz falls well within the _____ range.

12·16 (audio-frequency) Alternating currents of frequencies higher than 20,000 Hz can be radiated into space as radio waves. Hence, such higher a-c frequencies are called *radio frequencies*. An alternating current of 100,000 Hz is a _____ frequency.

12·17 (radio) Thus, an a-c of 10,000 Hz is an audio frequency; similarly, an a-c of 15,000 Hz is still in the audio-frequency range. An a-c of 35,820 Hz is a _____ _____ .

12·18 (radio frequency) An a-c of 7,800,000 Hz is a _____ _____ .

12·19 (radio frequency) To make the writing of large numbers of cycles more convenient, we define new multiples of the basic frequency unit. One kilohertz (abbrev. kHz) means 1,000 hertz. Thus 10,000 Hz is written as 10 kHz. Similarly, 16,800 Hz is written as _____ kHz.

12·20 (16.8) A frequency of 8,200 Hz is written as 8.2 kHz. Thus, a frequency of 117,000 Hz is written as _____ _____ .

12·21 (117 kHz) A radio frequency of 1,500,000 Hz in kilohertz is expressed as _____ _____ .

12·22 (1,500 kHz) Even the kilohertz is sometimes too small a unit for convenience. In such cases, we use the megahertz (abbrev. MHz). There are 1,000 kHz in 1 MHz. Thus 8 MHz is the equivalent of _____ Hz.

12·23 (8,000,000) In megahertz, the frequency of 1,500 kHz would be written as 1.5 MHz. A frequency of 16,800 kHz would become 16.8 MHz. Thus, a frequency of 187,000 kHz would be written as _____ MHz.

12·24 (187) A frequency of 200,000 Hz is the same as 0.2 MHz. A frequency of 800,000 Hz is the same as _____ MHz.

12·25 (0.8) A frequency of 1,655,000 Hz would be written, in megahertz, as _____ _____ .

12·26 (1.655 MHz) Converting 15,500,000 Hz to kilohertz gives an answer of _____ _____ .

12·27 (15,500 kHz) Converting 15,500,000 Hz to megahertz gives us _____ _____ .

12·28 (15.5 MHz) Converting 15,500 kHz to megahertz gives an answer of _____ _____ .

12·29 (15.5 MHz) The equivalent of 17.225 MHz is _____ kHz.

12·30 (17,225) The equivalent of 17.225 MHz is _____ Hz.

12·30 (17,225,000)

Period, amplitude, and wavelength

It is convenient to describe the sine wave in terms of *period, amplitude,* and *wavelength* for certain purposes. The period of a periodic curve is the time required to complete 1 cycle. The amplitude is the height of the wave measured from the zero axis to the peak, either positive or negative. The wavelength is the distance between corresponding points on two successive waves.

The period of a wave is closely related to the frequency of the wave. If 60 complete cycles are generated in 1 sec, the frequency is 60 Hz. The time required to complete 1 cycle is, therefore, $\frac{1}{60}$ sec. Similarly, the time required to complete 1 cycle of a 30-Hz wave is $\frac{1}{30}$ sec. For the first wave, the period is $\frac{1}{60}$ sec, for the second wave, the period is $\frac{1}{30}$ sec. Clearly, the period of a wave is the reciprocal of its frequency. That is, given the frequency of a wave in hertz, we can immediately state the period as 1/frequency. The period will be given in seconds or fractions of a second, if the frequency is given in hertz.

12·31 Figure 12·31 illustrates 1 cycle of an a-c sine wave. The time required to complete 1 cycle is called the period of the a-c wave. If 1 cycle is completed in $\frac{1}{100}$ of a second, then the period is $\frac{1}{100}$ of a second. Thus, if 1 cycle of an a-c wave is completed in $\frac{1}{60}$ of a second, the period of the wave is _____ .

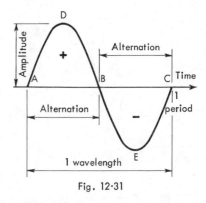

Fig. 12·31

12·32 ($\frac{1}{60}$ sec) If the period of a given a-c wave is $\frac{1}{120}$ sec, then 1 cycle will be completed in _____ sec.

12·33 ($\frac{1}{120}$) In the case of a 120-Hz wave, the frequency is 120 Hz and the period, or time to complete 1 cycle, is $\frac{1}{120}$ sec. Thus, if the frequency of a certain wave is 320 Hz, the period of the wave is 1 over the frequency or _____ sec.

12·34 (⅓₂₀) If the frequency of a given wave is 400 Hz, then the period is 1 over 400 Hz or ¼₀₀ sec. If the frequency is 1,200 Hz, the period must be _____ .

12·35 (¹⁄₁,₂₀₀ sec) A certain wave has a frequency of 45 Hz. Its period, therefore, is _____ .

12·36 (¼₅ sec) From these examples it is clear that the period of a wave is always 1 divided by the frequency. This is called the *reciprocal,* and so we may say that the period is the reciprocal of the frequency. If period is symbolized by t and frequency by f, then we may write the equation:

$$t = \underline{\hspace{2cm}}$$

12·37 (1/f) In Fig. 12·37a and b, 3 cycles are shown being completed in ¹⁄₁₀₀ sec. For each of these waves, the period is, therefore, ⅓₀₀ sec. Since frequency and period are related as their reciprocals, then the frequency of these waves must be $f = 1/t$. That is

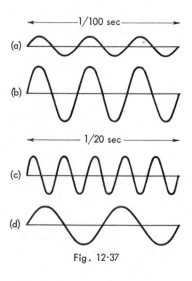

$$f = \frac{1}{\frac{1}{300}} = 300 \text{ Hz}$$

Similarly, in Fig. 12·37c, 5 cycles are completed in ¹⁄₂₀ sec so that the period of each cycle must be ¹⁄₁₀₀ sec and the frequency must be

$$f = \frac{1}{\frac{1}{100}} = 100 \text{ Hz}$$

Thus, in Fig. 12·37d, the period is ¼₀ sec and the frequency is _____ .

Fig. 12·37

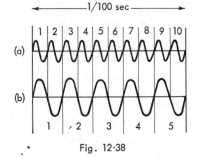

Fig. 12·38

12·38 (40 Hz) Ten cycles are shown in Fig. 12·38a. The period of this wave is _____ .

12·39 (¹⁄₁,₀₀₀ sec) The frequency of the wave in Fig. 12·38a is _____ .

12·40 (1,000 Hz) The frequency of the wave in Fig. 12·38b is _____.

12·41 (500 Hz) The period of the wave in Fig. 12·38b is _____.

12·42 (⅟₅₀₀ sec) The amplitude of a wave is the height of the peak of the wave above the zero horizontal axis. Thus, in Fig. 12·31, the amplitude of the positive peak is measured from point D down to the axis. Similarly, the amplitude of the negative peak is measured from the axis down to point _____.

12·43 (E) In Fig. 12·37, the amplitude of wave a is _____ than the amplitude of wave b.

12·44 (smaller) In Fig. 12·37c and d, the amplitudes of both waves are the _____.

12·45 (same) In Fig. 12·38, the wave with the larger amplitude is wave _____.

12·46 (b) A single cycle of a sine wave contains 2 *alternations,* one positive and one negative, as shown in Fig. 12·31. Thus, the total number of alternations in 12·37a is 6. Also, the number of alternations in 12·37c is _____.

12·47 (10) The total number of alternations in Fig. 12·37d is 4. The total number of alternations in Fig. 12·38a is _____.

12·48 (20) The number of *negative* alternations in Fig. 12·38b is _____.

12·49 (5) A 60-Hz wave contains _____ alternations/sec.

12·50 (120) A wave having a frequency of 400 Hz contains _____ alternations/sec.

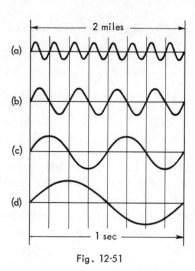

Fig. 12·51

12·51 (800) Some imaginary waves are shown in Fig. 12·51. For each wave, the distance covered is 2 miles, and in each case the time required to cover this distance is 1 sec. Thus, the *speed* or *velocity* of *a* is 2 miles/sec; that of *b* is 2 miles/sec; that of *c* is 2 miles/sec; and finally, the wave in *d* must have a velocity of _____ .

12·52 (2 miles/sec) Since, in Fig. 12·51*a*, there are 8 complete cycles, the *wavelength* (see Fig. 12·31) must be ¼ mile. By similar reasoning, the wavelength of *b* must be ½ mile. Thus, the wavelength of *c* must be _____ mile.

12·53 (1) The wavelength of the wave in Fig. 12·51*d* is

_____ .

12·54 (2 miles) The wave in Fig. 12·51*a* covers the distance in 1 sec, hence its period is ⅛ sec and its frequency is 8 Hz. As determined in Frame 12·52, its wavelength is ¼ mile. When the wavelength is multiplied by the frequency, we obtain the velocity ¼ × 8 = 2 miles/sec. The frequency of the wave in *b* is 4 Hz, and its wavelength is ½ mile. Multiplying wavelength times frequency we obtain ½ × 4 = _____ .

12·55 (2 miles/sec) Similarly, in Fig. 12·51*c* the wavelength is 1 mile, and the frequency is 2 Hz. The product is again 2 miles/sec. Thus, in Fig. 12·51*d*, the wavelength is 2 miles and the frequency is 1 Hz, hence the velocity again turns out to be _____ .

12·56 (2 miles/sec) We can now say that velocity of a wave equals its wavelength times its frequency. If velocity is symbolized by v, frequency by f, and wavelength by λ (Greek lambda), the equation that relates these three terms is

$$v = \text{_____}$$

12·57 $(f \times \lambda)$ The equation can be written in two other important forms: (1) in which f is the unknown and (2) in which λ is the unknown. The first of these is

$$f = \frac{v}{\lambda}$$

The second form of the equation thus reads

$$\lambda = \underline{\hspace{2cm}}$$

12·58 (v/f) We put these equations to use in electronics in many ways. For example, the velocity of a radio wave through space is about 186,000 miles/sec. The wavelength of a 60-Hz a-c wave is found from the third form of the equation. Thus

$$\lambda = \frac{v}{f}$$
$$\lambda = \frac{186,000}{60}$$
$$= 3,100 \text{ miles}$$

Therefore, the wavelength of a 120-Hz a-c wave is _____
_____ .

12·59 (1,550 miles) The wavelength of a wave having a frequency of 10,000 Hz or 10 kHz is 18.6 miles. The wavelength of a 100,000-Hz or 100 kHz wave is _____ _____ .

12·60 (1.86 miles) The wavelength of a wave having a frequency of 1,000 kHz is _____ _____ .

12·61 (0.186 miles) The velocity of radio waves is often given in meters per second. [One meter (abbrev. m) = 39.37 in., or a little more than 3 ft.] The velocity in meters per second is 3×10^8 or 300,000,000 m/sec. Thus, a wave having a frequency of 100 kHz has a wavelength of 3,000 m. The wavelength of a wave with a frequency of 1,000 kHz is, therefore, _____ m.

12·62 (300) A wave having a frequency of 3,000 kHz has a wavelength of _____ m.

12·62 (100)

Information Panel

The second form of the wave equation is especially useful in determining the frequency of an electromagnetic wave, given the wavelength.

Examples

1. What frequency is associated with a wavelength of 100 m?

$$f = \frac{v}{\lambda}$$

$$f = \frac{3 \times 10^8}{10^2}$$

$$= 3 \times 10^6$$

$$= 3,000,000 \text{ Hz}$$

$$= 3,000 \text{ kHz}$$

$$= 3 \text{ MHz}$$

2. What is the frequency of a wave whose wavelength is 10 m?

$$f = \frac{v}{\lambda}$$

$$f = \frac{3 \times 10^8}{10}$$

$$= 3 \times 10^7$$

$$= 30,000,000 \text{ Hz}$$

$$= 30,000 \text{ kHz}$$

$$= 30 \text{ MHz}$$

12·63   The frequency of a 1-m wave is _____ .

12·64   (300,000 kHz or 300 MHz) The frequency of a 300-m wave is _____ .

12·65   (1,000 kHz or 1 MHz) The frequency of a 20-m wave is _____ MHz.

12·65   (15)

Phase relationships

The sine wave with its time axis divided in degrees is illustrated in Fig. 12·66. The term "phase," as referred to any wave, relates to the position of a point on the wave in terms of the markings on the horizontal axis. For example, point *A*, located on the curve itself, is said to be in the 45° phase because a vertical line dropped through *A* passes through the 45° marking on the time axis; by the same reasoning, point *B* on the curve is in the 90° phase.

Two waves superimposed on the same axis are said to be *in phase* when they attain corresponding amplitudes at the same phases. Thus, the waves in Fig. 12·70 are in phase with each other. When corresponding amplitudes occur at different phases, the waves are then out of phase as in Figs. 12·71, 12·75, and 12·77.

The extent to which two waves are out of phase with each other is measured in degrees. To determine the number of degrees of *phase difference* that exists between two waves, it is necessary to select two corresponding points, determine their phases, and then subtract the smaller phase angle from the larger.

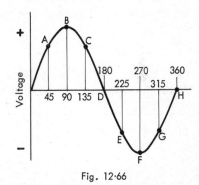

Fig. 12·66

12·66 In Fig. 12·66, point *A* is said to be at the 45° phase; point *B* is at the 90° phase; point *C* is at the _____ phase.

12·67 (135°) In Fig. 12·66, point *D* is at the 180° phase. Thus, point *E* is at the _____ phase.

12·68 (225°) Point *G* in Fig. 12·66 is at the _____ phase.

12·69 (315°) The 360° phase of a sine wave may also be called the _____ degree phase.

12·70 (zero) In Fig. 12·70, waves *A* and *B* are in phase because they reach their peaks and all other corresponding amplitudes at the same instants in time (same phase). Thus, wave *C* is _____ _____ with *A* and *B*.

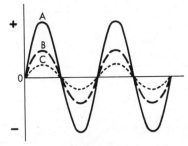

Fig. 12·70

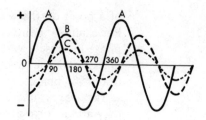

Fig. 12·71

12·71 (in phase) In Fig. 12·71, wave A is out of phase with wave B since A reaches its peak and zero at different phases than wave B. Wave C is _____ _____ _____ with wave A, but _____ _____ with wave B.

12·72 (out of phase, in phase) In Fig. 12·71, wave A at the 0° phase has zero amplitude and is beginning to move in a positive direction. Wave B, on the other hand, reaches its 0° positive-going amplitude at the _____° phase.

12·73 (90) Thus, since there is a phase difference of 90° between wave A and wave B, wave B is said to lag behind wave A by _____°.

12·74 (90) In the same diagram, wave C also lags behind and is out of phase with wave A by 90 _____.

12·75 (degrees) Referring to Fig. 12·75, wave A reaches its positive-going zero amplitude at the 90° phase, while B reaches its positive-going zero amplitude at the _____° phase.

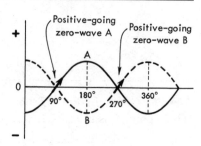

Fig. 12·75

12·76 (270) Hence, in Fig. 12·75, wave B lags behind wave A and is out of phase with wave A by _____°.

12·77 (180) In Fig. 12·77, wave A reaches its positive-going zero amplitude at the _____ degree phase.

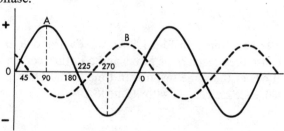

Fig. 12·77

12·78 (zero) In the same figure, wave B reaches its positive-going zero amplitude at the _____ phase.

12·79 (225°) Wave B may then be said to lag behind A by _____°.

12·79 (225)

Maximum, instantaneous, average, and effective values of the a-c sine curve

The *maximum* or *peak* value of an a-c voltage or current is the highest value attained during a single cycle, on either a positive or negative alternation.

The *instantaneous* value of voltage or current is the magnitude of the quantity at any given instant. If you are asked to state the instantaneous value of some voltage wave, you must also be told the *phase* at which this instantaneous voltage is to be read.

The *average* value of a single alternation is 0.636 times the peak value. It is *not 50 per cent of the peak value,* as many students tend to say. We shall not derive this relationship since this derivation is not necessary for the manipulations required in basic electricity. The student should commit to memory, however, the fact that the average voltage or current in a single alternation of *sinusoidal* (sine wave shape) a-c may be found by multiplying the peak value by 0.636.

The *effective* value of a voltage or current in a-c has an entirely different meaning than the average just discussed. To understand the significance of the effective value of a voltage or current, consider this example: a direct current of 1 amp—that is, a steady flow of 1 amp—causes a certain conductor to heat to a certain temperature in a fixed period of time. An alternating current of 1 *amp peak value,* however, causes only 70.7 per cent (0.707) as much heat as the direct current of 1 amp. We say, therefore, that a *peak* current of any magnitude is only 0.707 times as effective in producing heat as a steady current of the same magnitude. The inability of the a-c to produce the same heating effect as d-c of the same magnitude as the peak a-c is due to the fact that the a-c reaches this magnitude for a relatively short time in each cycle. All the rest of the time, the magnitude is less than peak. On the other hand, d-c of a given magnitude is "always up there," so to speak, maintaining the same high value throughout the duty period. Thus, the effective value of any a-c current or voltage = 0.707 × peak value.

12·80 The *maximum* value of an alternating voltage is also called the *peak* value. The peak voltage of an a-c wave is the highest voltage that is reached on either a positive or negative alternation. Thus, point B in Fig. 12·66 may be called a _____ value.

12·81 (peak) Similarly, in the same figure, point F may be called a _____ peak value of the a-c cycle.

12·82 (negative) In the same figure, the positive peak value occurs at the 90° phase. Thus, the negative peak value occurs at the _____ phase.

12·83 (270°) In Fig. 12·71, the first positive peak of wave B occurs at the _____ phase.

12·84 (180°) The *instantaneous* value of voltage or current is the value of voltage or current at one particular instant. For example, in Fig. 12·84, the instantaneous value of the voltage at phase C is 20 volts. The instantaneous voltage at phase A is zero volts. Also, the instantaneous voltage at phase D is _____ volts.

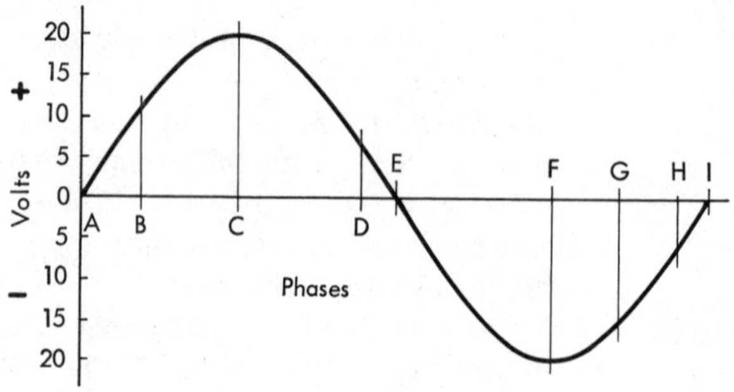

Fig. 12·84

12·85 (5) The instantaneous voltage at phase E is 0 volts. The instantaneous voltage at phase B is _____ volts.

12·86 (10) The instantaneous voltage at phase F is -20 volts. The instantaneous voltage at phase G is _____ _____.

12·87 (-15 volts) The instantaneous voltage at phase H is

_____ _____ .

12·88 (-5 volts) If the base line is divided up into 10 phases, we can describe 10 instantaneous values for these phases. If it were divided into 100 phases, then we could describe 100 instantaneous values as referred to these phases. Thus, if there is an infinite number of phases, there must be an _____ number of instantaneous values.

12·89 (infinite) During a single alternation, the *average* value of all the instantaneous voltages turns out to be 0.636 times the peak value. Thus, if the peak value is 100 volts, the average value is 63.6 volts. If the peak value is 10 volts, the average value is 6.36 volts. Also, if the peak value is 1,000 volts, the average value is ____ _____ .

12·90 (636 volts) If the peak value of a current is 10 amp, the average current is 6.36 amp. Thus, if the peak current is 100 amp, the average current is ____ _____ .

12·91 (63.6 amp) If the peak voltage is 200 volts, the average voltage is ____ _____ .

12·92 (127.2 volts) The average value of a positive alternation is 0.636 × peak; the average value of a negative alternation is −0.636 × peak. The average of these two is zero. Hence, the average value of a voltage or current over an entire cycle is _____ .

12·93 (zero) An a-c with a peak value of 1 amp causes the same heating effect as a d-c of 0.707 amp. An a-c with a peak of 10 amp causes the same heating effect as a d-c of 7.07 amp. Thus, an a-c with a peak of 100 amp causes the same heating effect as a d-c of _____ amp.

12·94 (70.7) An a-c with a peak value of 1,000 amp causes the same heating effect as a d-c with a value of 707 amp. Thus, an a-c of 0.1 amp causes the same heating effect as a d-c of _____ amp.

12·95 (0.0707) An a-c with a peak value of 30 amp has the same heating effect as a d-c with a value of _____ amp.

12·96 (21.21) From the foregoing, it is clear that *effective* a-c values are always equal to peak value times _____ .

12·97 (0.707) To find the *peak* value when the *effective* value is known, we would divide the effective value by 0.707. Thus:

$$\text{eff} = \text{peak} \times 0.707$$

and

$$\text{peak} = \text{eff}/0.707$$

But dividing a number by 0.707 is the same as multiplying the number by the reciprocal of 0.707. The reciprocal of 0.707 is _____ .

12·98 (1.41) The peak value of an effective a-c of 100 volts is $100 \times 1.41 = 141$ volts. Thus, the peak value of an effective a-c of 10 volts is _____ _____ .

12·99 (14.1 volts) The peak value of an effective a-c voltage of 1,000 volts is _____ _____ .

12·100 (1,410 volts) Alternating current and voltage meters are always calibrated to read *effective values* unless otherwise marked. Thus, an a-c voltmeter on a line having a peak value of 100 volts will read 70.7 volts. An a-c ammeter in a circuit carrying 1-amp peak will read _____ _____ .

12·101 (0.707 amp) An a-c ammeter that reads 7.07 amp tells you that the peak current in the circuit is 10 amp. An a-c ammeter that reads 10 amp tells you that the peak current in the circuit is _____ _____ .

12·102 (14.1 amp) An a-c voltmeter that reads 120 volts tells you that the peak voltage of that a-c line is _____ _____ .

12·103 (169.2 volts) The peak voltage of an a-c line in which a meter reads 80 volts is _____ volts.

12·104 (112.8) The peak circuit current in a certain location is 18 amp. A meter in this circuit will read _____ amp.

12·104 (12.73)

Sometimes the average value of an a-c voltage or current is known and we want to find the effective value from this. To find the effective value when the average value is given, multiply the average value by 1.11. This constant is obtained as follows. First we write

$$E_{peak} \times 0.707 = E_{eff}$$

Next we write
$$E_{peak} \times 0.636 = E_{av}$$

Now we divide the top equation by the bottom causing the E_{peak} terms to drop out:

$$\frac{0.707}{0.636} = \frac{E_{eff}}{E_{av}}$$

Transposing E_{av} to the left side, we have

$$E_{eff} = \frac{0.707}{0.636} \times E_{av}$$

Dividing 0.707 by 0.636 yields 1.11, hence

$$E_{eff} = 1.11 \times E_{av}$$

12·105   If a certain average voltage is 100 volts, the corresponding effective voltage is 111 volts. Likewise, if the average voltage is 10 volts, the effective voltage is _____ .

12·106   (11.1 volts) An average voltage of 80 volts is equal to an effective voltage of _____ .

12·106   (88.8 volts)

MEASURABLE BEHAVIORAL OBJECTIVES

Upon completion of a section, you should be able to achieve the objectives listed for it. The frame or frames that cover the related subject matter are indicated immediately following each objective.

Direction of current in an a-c circuit

Differentiate between d-c and a-c currents and emfs.   (Introduction)
a   State the rule for determining the direction of current in any circuit. (12·1)
b   Define instantaneous current and emf.   (12·5)

The meaning of frequency

1   Describe the shape of a sine wave.   (12·8, 12·12)
2   State the range of audio frequencies.   (12·14)
3   State the range of radio frequencies.   (12·16)
4   Convert megahertz to kilohertz to hertz.   (12·27)

Period, amplitude, and wavelength

1 Define the period of an a-c waveform. (12·31)
2 Relate frequency and period for an a-c signal. (12·33)
3 Define what is meant by the amplitude of a sine wave. (12·42, 12·46)
4 Define the wavelength for a sinusoidal wave. (12·51, 12·52)
5 State the velocity of radio waves. (12·58)
6 Relate velocity and frequency to wavelength. (12·58)

Phase relationships

Illustrate two sinusoidal waves in phase and out of phase. (12·70, 12·77)

Maximum, instantaneous, average, and effective values
of the a-c sine curve

1 Define the maximum or peak value of an a-c voltage or current. (12·80)
2 Illustrate a sinusoidal wave and give instantaneous values at several points. (12·84)
3 Define the average value of a sine wave in relation to its peak value. (12·89)
4 Define the effective value of a sine wave in relation to its peak value. (12·93, 12·97)
5 Relate average and effective values of a sine wave. (12·105)

chapter 13

inductance

Self-inductance

The frames in this section provide a short review of *self-inductance* in coils. You will recall that the property of a coil to induce a counter emf across its own terminals as the result of a changing current in its turns is called the self-inductance of the coil. The concepts of self-inductance are needed at this time if we are to proceed successfully to the following topics.

13·1 The property of a coil carrying a changing current to induce a counter emf across its own terminals is called the _____ of the coil.

13·2 (self-inductance) The self-inductance of a coil is measured in _____ .

13·3 (henrys) A coil has a self-inductance of 1 henry if a current flowing through it changes at the rate of 1 amp/sec and thereby induces a potential of _____ _____ across the coil terminals.

13·4 (1 volt) If the number of turns in a coil is increased, the self-inductance of the coil _____ .

13·5 (increases) If a nonmagnetic core is replaced by a good magnetic core in a coil, the self-inductance of the coil _____ .

13·6 (increases) According to Lenz's law, the action of self-inductance opposes changes in the current flowing through a coil since the counter emf bucks the applied emf. Since an alternating current is a changing current, a coil placed in an a-c circuit will _____ the rise and fall of the current.

13·7 (oppose) Opposition to natural growth and decay of an alternating current must result in a _____ in the magnitude of the current flowing through the coil.

13·8 (decrease) Since a coil causes a reduction of the current in an a-c circuit, the coil is behaving just like a _____ behaves in a d-c circuit.

13·8 (resistor)

Inductance in series

Mutual inductance exists between two coils that are placed sufficiently close to one another so that the lines of force from one of the coils cut through the turns of the other when a current flows in one or both coils. As we have seen, mutual inductance is measured in *henrys*.

The term "inductance" implies the development of an induced voltage when conditions are right for such a counter emf to appear. In the case of self-inductance, the back emf appears across the terminals of a coil owing to the changing current in the same coil: in the case of mutual inductance (symbolized by M and measured in henrys), the back emf is induced in a second coil owing to a changing current in the first.

If two coils are connected in series but are placed so far apart that the magnetic interaction between them is negligible, then mutual inductance, or M, is zero. For this situation, the total inductance is merely the sum of the individual inductances, each coil behaving as though it were alone in the circuit. As the coils are moved closer, however, magnetic interaction begins as mutual inductance begins to operate. Now the back emf developed is due not only to the self-inductance of the individual coils, but is due as well to the mutual inductance between them. A simple mathematical relationship exists between individual inductances and the self-inductance between coils as discussed in Frames 13·9 to 13·19.

Suppose we have two coils, $L1$ and $L2$, so placed that the mutual inductance M between them *adds* to the back emf each would produce when isolated. Then, effectively, the inductance of $L1$ due to the presence of $L2$ is really $L1 + M$; because the system is symmetrical, we can say that the inductance of $L2$ due to the presence of $L1$ is really $L2 + M$. Thus, the total inductance is $L1 + M + L2 + M$, or $L1 + L2 + 2M$. When coils connected in series add this way, they are said to be in *series aiding*. If the turns of one of the coils are reversed in direction, the M factor subtracts from the total inductance, the total inductance becoming $L1 + L2 - 2M$. This arrangement is called *series opposing*.

13·9 When two inductors (or coils) are placed close enough together so that the magnetic field of one coil cuts the turns of the other, it is said that _____ inductance exists between the two coils.

13·10 (mutual) When two identical coils (Fig. 13·10) are connected in series and are so far apart that they cannot influence each other, their individual inductances merely add up. If the inductances are $L1$ and $L2$, respectively, then the total inductance of this combination (measured in henrys) would be _____.

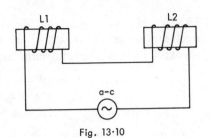

Fig. 13·10

13·11 ($L1 + L2$) If the two coils are brought together as in Fig. 13·11 so that mutual inductance exists between them (symbolize mutual inductance in henrys by M), then the inductance of $L2$ is the sum of $L2$ and M, or $L2 + M$. Since the coils are identical, then the new inductance of $L1$ due to the effect of $L2$ must be _____.

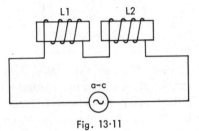

Fig. 13·11

13·12 ($L1 + M$) Since the mutual inductance M adds once to $L1$ and once to $L2$, then the total inductance of the system must be $L1 + L2 +$ _____.

13·13 ($2M$) If one of the coils is now reversed in winding directions as shown in Fig. 13·13, then the mutual inductance of M subtracts from the total inductance of the system *twice*. This means that the total inductance of the system is now $L1 + L2 -$ _____.

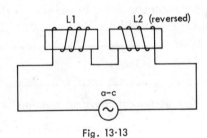

Fig. 13·13

13·14 ($2M$) When $2M$ is added to the sum of the individual inductances, the coils are said to be in series aiding. When the coils are wound so that $2M$ is subtracted from the sum of the inductances, the coils are said to be in _____ opposing.

13·15 (series) The final formula for the series-aiding connection is

$$L_t = L1 + L2 + 2M$$

where L_t is the total inductance of the system in henrys. Thus, the final formula for series opposing is _____.

187

13·16 $(L_t = L1 + L2 - 2M)$ Two 1-henry coils are connected in series aiding so that the mutual inductance between them is 0.1 henry. The total inductance is, therefore,

$$L_t = L1 + L2 + 2M$$
$$L_t = 1 + 1 + 0.2$$
$$= 2.2 \text{ henrys}$$

Similarly, if the inductance of one coil is 3 henrys and the inductance of the other is 2 henrys, with a mutual inductance of 0.4 henry, the total inductance is (in series aiding)

$$L_t = L1 + L2 + 2M$$
$$L_t = \underline{\quad\quad}\underline{\quad\quad\quad}$$

13·17 (5.8 henrys) A 6- and an 8-henry coil are connected in series aiding with a mutual inductance of 0.23 henry. The total inductance is 14.46 henrys. Thus, if the 6-henry coil is replaced by a 12-henry coil with no other changes made, the total inductance would be _____ _____ .

13·18 (20.46 henrys) The total inductance of a series-aiding combination in which $L1 = 20$ millihenrys (abbrev. mh), $L2 = 25$ mh, and $M = 1$ mh is _____ _____ .

13·19 (47 mh) The total inductance of a series-opposing combination consisting of the same values as those given in Frame 13·18 would be _____ _____ .

13·19 (43 mh)

Voltage-current phase relationship

In a purely resistive circuit (a circuit containing only resistance, that is, no inductance or capacitance), the current and voltage are always in phase. When an inductance is present in an a-c circuit, a shift of phase occurs and the current is found to *lag behind the voltage*. If the circuit is *purely inductive,* the current lag is 90°. However, no circuit can ever be purely inductive since resistance is always present regardless of how small it may be. Therefore, in all real circuits containing inductance, the current lags behind the voltage by some angle greater than 0° but less than 90°.

13·20 Figure 13·20 illustrates the voltage and current flowing in a certain a-c circuit containing only pure resistance. Since the voltage and current reach their positive and negative peaks at the same time, these waves are said to be in the _____ phase.

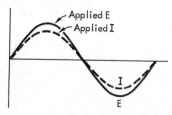

Fig. 13·20

188

13·21 (same) Since an a-c circuit containing resistance only does not have in it any device that causes a phase change between voltage and current, the voltage and current are always

_____ _____ .

13·22 (in phase) Figure 13·22 shows the current flowing through a coil fed by an a-c generator. The current is sine wave in shape. The rate of change of current is *least* at the 0, 180, and 360° phases because there is little change of vertical motion for a considerable distance along the time axis at these points. The rate of change is *greatest* at the 90 and _____° phases because, at these points, the current is either swooping upward or downward very rapidly.

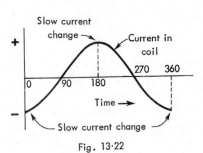

Fig. 13·22

13·23 (270) Since induced counter emf is greatest where the rate of change of current is greatest, then the largest instantaneous counter emfs must be generated at the _____ and _____° phases in Fig. 13·22.

13·24 (90, 270) Refer to Fig. 13·24. The back emf is shown as a dashed line while the current is shown as a _____ line.

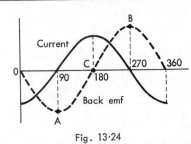

Fig. 13·24

13·25 (solid) As we have seen, maximum back emf is induced at the 90 and 270° phases of the current. Thus, *peak* counter emf appears at the points labeled _____ and _____ in Fig. 13·24.

13·26 (*A, B*) At the 90° phase, the current passes through zero with its greatest rate of change, and it is going from the *negative* into the *positive* region. Therefore, the current at the 90° phase can be said to be _____-going.

13·27 (positive) Thus, at the 90° phase, the induced emf must be *negative* (point *A*) so that it can oppose the positive-going current. By similar reasoning, the induced emf at the 270° phase must be _____ so that it can oppose the negative-going current.

13·28 (positive) The back emf is always opposite in direction to the applied emf according to Lenz's law; thus, the applied emf must be out of phase with the induced emf by _____° as shown in Fig. 13·28.

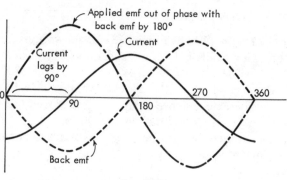

Fig. 13·28

13·29 (180) The applied emf is, therefore, positive-going at the 0° phase having reached zero amplitude at this point. On the other hand, the current does not reach the positive-going zero amplitude until the 90° phase. Hence, the current lags behind the applied voltage by _____°.

13·30 (90) When a circuit contains a pure inductance (theoretically zero resistance), the current always _____ behind the applied voltage by _____°.

13·30 (lags, 90)

Inductive reactance

Because the emf induced in a coil is always in phase opposition to the applied emf, a coil in an a-c circuit acts to reduce the flow of current. Since we reserve the word "resistance" for a heat-dissipative type of load in either d-c or a-c circuits, we shall use a new word to signify opposition in the case of an inductor: *inductive reactance.* The inductive reactance of a coil is the opposition in *ohms* offered by the coil to the current.

The extent to which a coil opposes the current is determined by the inductance L of the coil and the frequency f of the a-c used. The relationship is a direct proportion and may be stated in this way: The inductive reactance X_L of a coil is directly proportional to the inductance of the coil L and the frequency f of the a-c.

Such a proportion may be written

$$X_L \propto fL$$

A proportion, however, is of little value in itself. It becomes much more useful when converted into an equation. To do this, it is necessary to insert a constant of proportionality. In this case, we want X_L to be measurable in ohms; it may be shown mathematically that X_L will be given in ohms when the frequency is in hertz and the inductance in henrys, if the right side of the equation is multiplied by 2π. That is

$$X_L \text{ (ohms)} = 2\pi f L$$

when f is in hertz, and L is in henrys.

Inductive reactance resembles resistance since it is measured in ohms and represents an opposition to current. Thus, inductive reactance may be used in a form of Ohm's law, particularly expressed for a-c circuits as given below. This form of Ohm's law is valid only for a purely inductive circuit.

$$I = \frac{E}{X_L}$$

Note that X_L replaces R. I will be in amperes if E is in volts and X_L is in ohms.

13·31 The opposition offered by an inductor or coil to the flow of a-c is called "inductive reactance" and is symbolized by X_L. Since it behaves like resistance in that it opposes the current, inductive reactance like resistance is measured in _____ .

13·32 (ohms) The amount of opposition, or X_L, offered by an inductor depends, first of all, upon the inductance L of the coil in henrys. If the inductance is made larger, the inductive reactance becomes larger since more back emf is generated. Thus, it turns out that X_L is directly _____ to L.

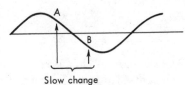

Slow change

13·33 (proportional) The inductive reactance is also larger if the frequency of the a-c is greater. A higher frequency means a _____ rate of change of current as shown in Fig. 13·33.

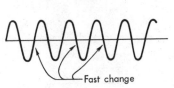

Fast change

Fig. 13·33

13·34 (greater) If the rate of change of current is large, the back emf is _____ .

13·35 (large) A large back emf means a _____ inductive reactance.

13·36 (large) Therefore, inductive reactance is _____ proportional to frequency.

13·37 (directly) If frequency f is in hertz and inductance L is in henrys, then we can make the inductive reactance come out in ohms by inserting the quantity 2π into the equation as a proportionality constant. Thus, the equation may be written as

$$\text{\underline{\hspace{2cm}}} = 2\pi f L$$

13·38 (X_L) To find the inductive reactance X_L of a coil, merely substitute in the above equation. Thus, the inductive reactance of a 10-henry coil at 60 Hz is

$$X_L = 2 \times 3.14 \times 60 \times 10$$
and so $\quad X_L = \text{\underline{\hspace{2cm}}}$ ohms

13·39 (3,768) Similarly, the inductive reactance of a 30-henry coil at 30 Hz is _____ .

13·40 (5,652 ohms) In the circuit of Fig. 13·40, the current flowing is found by first determining X_L (this was done in Frame 13·38) and then substituting in Ohm's law. The inductive reactance was found to be 3,768 ohms. Thus, the current is

$$I = \frac{120}{3,768}$$

$$= \text{\underline{\hspace{2cm}}} \text{ amp}$$

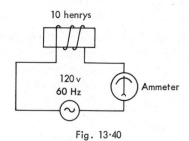

Fig. 13·40

13·41 (0.032) The current flowing through a 30-henry coil when connected to a 120-volt, 30-Hz line is _____ amp.

13·41 (0.021)

MEASURABLE BEHAVIORAL OBJECTIVES

Upon completion of a section, you should be able to achieve the objectives listed for it. The frame or frames that cover the related subject matter are indicated immediately following each objective.

Self-inductance

1 Define self-inductance of a coil. (13·1)
2 Relate counter emf to self-inductance. (13·6)
3 Account for self-inductance by making use of Lenz's law. (13·6)

Inductance in series

Describe the effect of two inductors on each other. (13·9)
   a State the rule for combining series inductors with zero mutual inductance. (13·10)
   b State the rule for combining series inductors with series aiding connection. (13·12)
   c State the rule for combining series inductors with series opposing connection. (13·15)
   d Define the units for inductance and mutual inductance. (13·16)

Voltage-current phase relationship

1 Illustrate the voltage and current at the terminals of a resistor in an a-c circuit. (13·20)
2 Relate the change of current to the induced emf in an inductor. (Introduction)
3 State the phase relationship of voltage and current for a pure inductor. (13·29)

Inductive reactance

Define inductive reactance. (13·31)
   a Give a mathematical equation for inductive reactance. (13·37)
   b Define the units of inductive reactance. (13·38)

chapter 14

capacitance

Basic concepts of capacitance

A capacitor is an electrical device which consists essentially of two conducting plates of metal separated by an insulator or *dielectric*. As we shall show in these frames, a capacitor can store electric energy in the form of a charge. This fundamental action accounts for many of the properties of capacitors used in electric circuits.

14·1   Assume that we have a square metal plate to which a piece of wire is soldered, and that this plate is insulated from its surroundings. If a rubber rod that has been charged by rubbing with fur is now touched to the wire, electrons will spread out to all parts of the plate (Fig. 14·1). Thus the plate takes on a _____ charge.

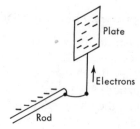

Fig. 14·1

14·2   (negative) If two conducting plates are placed near each other as in Fig. 14·2 and are then touched to a negatively charged rod and a positively charged rod as shown, the plates will become charged—one negative and the other _____ .

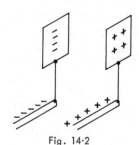

Fig. 14·2

14·3   (positive) Now imagine the rods removed as in Fig. 14·3. The plates will remain charged. The reason is that the opposite charges attract each other, becoming what is known as *bound charges*. They cannot reach each other to intermingle because the air separating them is an insulator or _____ .

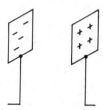

Fig. 14·3

14·4 (dielectric) The plates are now connected to a galvanometer. The galvanometer needle deflects momentarily (Fig. 14·4). This deflection could only have occurred as a result of a momentary _____ in the wires.

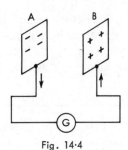

Fig. 14·4

14·5 (current) Thus, energy must have been stored in the system. Two or more conducting plates separated by an insulator make up a *capacitor*. The insulating material is called the "dielectric." In Figs. 14·1 to 14·4, the dielectric is the _____ between the plates.

14·6 (air) In Fig. 14·6, the conducting sections of the capacitor are made of aluminum and the dielectric is made of _____ .

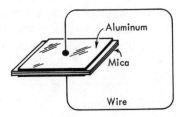

Fig. 14·6

14·7 (mica) In the capacitor of Fig. 14·7, the dielectric is made of _____ .

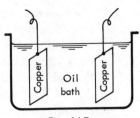

Fig. 14·7

14·8 (oil) Figure 14·8 illustrates the schematic symbols of various types of inductors and capacitors. Figure 14·8a shows a fixed inductor with an air core. Figure 14·8b shows a fixed _____ with an iron core.

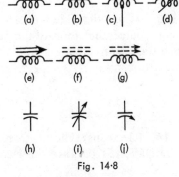

Fig. 14·8

195

14·9 (inductor) Figure 14·8c illustrates an inductor with a fixed tap somewhere along its length. The arrow through the inductor in Fig. 14·8d indicates that the value of the inductance may be changed. This type of inductance is variable rather than

_____ .

14·10 (fixed) The inductor in e is also variable as indicated by the arrow, but in this case it has a(n) _____ core.

14·11 (iron) In drawing f, a fixed inductor is illustrated, but in this case the core is powdered iron, symbolized by the dashed lines. The inductor in g is also a powdered iron core type, but this time its inductance is _____ as shown by the arrows.

14·12 (variable) In drawing h, the standard symbol of a fixed capacitor is given. When an arrow is drawn through the lines as in i, this indicates that the capacitor is variable (plates are movable with respect to each other). Sketch j shows another symbolic method of designating a _____ capacitor.

14·12 (variable)

Charge and discharge of a capacitor

Capacitors perform several very important jobs in a-c circuits. As discussed in these frames, one of these functions is to block the flow of d-c from a load but to permit a-c to act upon the load. The action in a-c circuits is explained by the fact that a capacitor can discharge and charge through a series load at the frequency of the applied a-c. Although electrons do not flow through the dielectric of the capacitor, the load "sees" the periodic charge and discharge as a current having all the characteristics of the original applied a-c.

14·13 When the plates of a capacitor are connected to a voltage source, the atoms of the dielectric become distorted because the negative plate attracts the protons and the positive plate attracts the _____ in the atoms (Fig. 14·13).

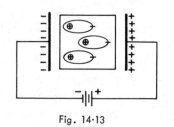

Fig. 14·13

14·14 (electrons) The neutrons in the nucleus of the atoms are not affected because the electric charge on a neutron is

_____ .

14·15 (zero) Even when the source of voltage is removed, the charges remain on the plates and the atoms of the dielectric remain in the distorted condition, provided that the plates are left insulated from each other. In this condition, the capacitor is said to be in a state of _____ (Fig. 14·15).

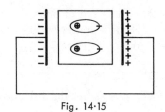
Fig. 14·15

14·16 (charge) When the plates are connected together by means of a conductor (Fig. 14·16), electrons move from the negative plate to the positive plate owing to electrostatic attraction, and the capacitor becomes *discharged*. In this case, the atoms of the _____ are restored to their undistorted form.

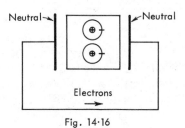
Fig. 14·16

14·17 (dielectric) A capacitor of a standard type can be charged in either direction. In Fig. 14·17a, the negative end of the battery is connected to plate A and positive end to plate B, making A "minus" and B "plus." When the battery is reversed (Fig. 14·17b), plate A becomes the _____ plate and B becomes the _____ plate.

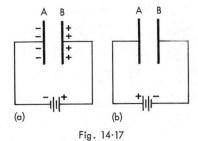
Fig. 14·17

14·18 (plus, minus) A capacitor behaves rather differently when connected across an a-c source (Fig. 14·18). Assume that the generator is instantaneously positive on the left side as in 14·18a. Electrons are attracted out of plate A and flow down to the generator as shown by arrow 1. Simultaneously, the source drives electrons up (arrows 2 and 3) through the center-zero galvanometer into plate B, making the galvanometer deflect toward the _____ side.

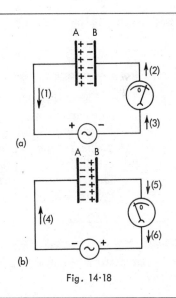
Fig. 14·18

14·19 (right) When the generator polarity reverses, electrons are rapidly driven up to plate A (Fig. 14·18b) as shown by arrow 4, and down from plate B, through the galvanometer (arrows 5 and 6), causing the instrument to show a deflection toward the _____ side.

14·20 (left) All through this time, the current flowing *through* the dielectric material is _____ since this is an insulator.

14·21 (zero) Yet the galvanometer "sees" a(n) _____ current.

14·22 (alternating) Thus, in a capacitor, no current flows through the dielectric, but if the source is a-c, then an alternating current flows in the wires connecting the two plates. If a resistor is connected as shown in Fig. 14·22, then a(n) _____ current would flow through this resistor, too.

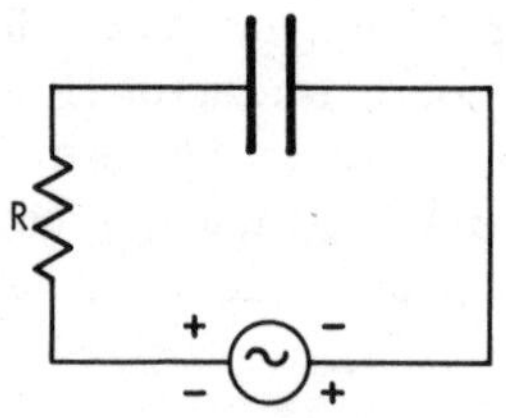

Fig. 14·22

14·23 (alternating) The resistor in Fig. 14·22 may be considered as the *load* in the circuit. We may conclude by saying that a capacitor connected in series with a load and an a-c source permits a(n) _____ current to flow through the load, although absolutely no electrons move from plate to plate through the dielectric.

14·23 (alternating)

Factors that govern capacitance

The ability of a capacitor to store a charge is called "capacitance" (*C*). The capacitance of a capacitor in the process of manufacture is controlled by variations in the following: **1,** the total area of the conducting plates; **2,** the distance separating the plates; and **3,** the nature and properties of the dielectric used. These frames describe several methods used in capacitor fabrication and the ways in which the magnitude of capacitance is controlled.

14·24 The capacity for storing energy is called "capacitance." Large capacitors can store more energy and therefore have a greater _____ .

14·25 (capacitance) As the area of the conducting plates of a capacitor is increased, the ability to store energy increases. Thus, an increase in plate area brings about an increase in the _____ of the capacitor.

14·26 (capacitance) If capacitor A has a 1- by 1-inch plate size, and capacitor B has a 2- by 3-inch plate size, then the greater capacitance is possessed by capacitor _____ .

14·27 (B) As the distance between the plates decreases, the *dielectric* atomic distortion increases; hence, the stored energy increases. Thus, a capacitor with closely spaced plates has _____ capacitance than one with widely spaced plates.

14·28 (more) Capacitor A has a thick dielectric, while capacitor B utilizes a thin dielectric of the same material as A. The plate area is the same in each. The capacitance of capacitor _____ is the greater of the two.

14·29 (B) Some capacitors are adjusted by compressing a mica dielectric by means of a tightening adjusting screw. As the mica dielectric is compressed, the capacitance of the capacitor

_____ .

14·30 (increases) If the plate area is increased and the distance between the plates is decreased, the capacitance of the capacitor is bound to _____ .

14·31 (increase) Some capacitors are made in the form of a multiplate arrangement (Fig. 14·31). Effectively, this is the same thing as increasing the total plate area. Hence, a capacitor with many plates has _____ capacitance than one with a single plate of the same size as one of the others.

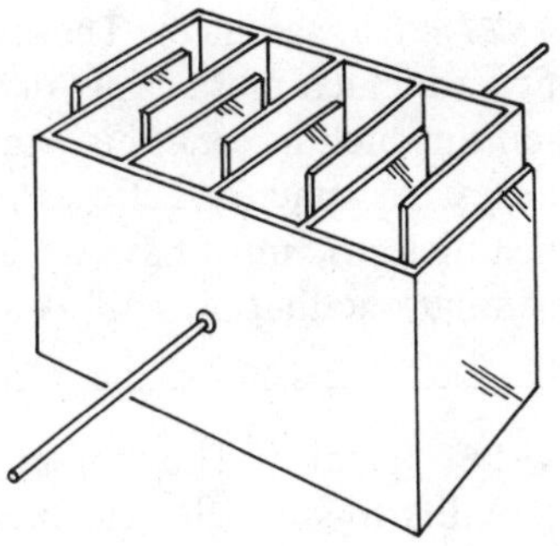

Multiplate Capacitor
Fig. 14·31

14·32 (more) When a multiplate capacitor like that shown in Fig. 14·31 has alternate plates connected together, the total plate area is the sum of the individual plate areas. The total area is best found by counting the dielectric spaces between plates. On this basis, the total area of this capacitor is _____ times the area of a single plate.

14·33 (nine) If one plate from *each side* of the capacitor in Fig. 14·31 is removed, the total area would then be _____ times the area of one plate.

14·34 (seven) If one plate were removed from *one side* but not the other, the total area would then be _____ times the area of one plate.

14·35 (eight) In the rolled capacitor shown in Fig. 14·35, the dielectric material is _____ _____ .

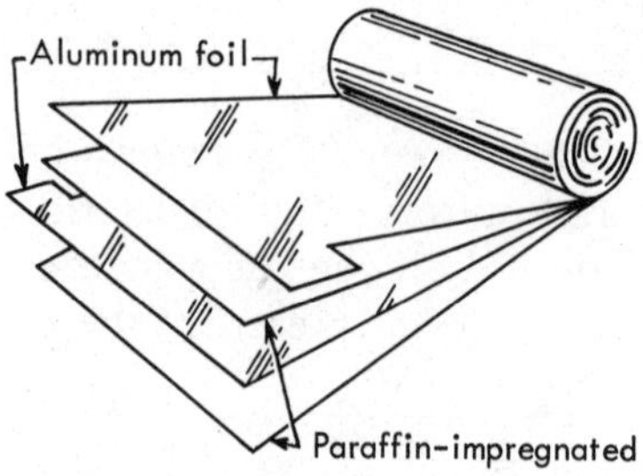

Tubular Paper Capacitor

Fig. 14·35

14·36 (paraffin-impregnated paper) Such a capacitor can be given a large plate area and a very small separation distance between plates, hence this capacitor can be given a very large

_____ .

14·37 (capacitance) The electron orbits in a material like mica are much more easily distorted by electric fields than in a medium such as air. This enables mica to store more electric energy in capacitor action than air. Thus, a capacitor with a mica dielectric must have a _____ capacitance than a similar one that uses air as a dielectric.

14·38 (greater) The characteristic of a dielectric that describes its ability to store electric energy is called the "dielectric constant." Air is used as a reference and is given a dielectric constant of one. Mica can store six times as much energy for given dimensions as air, hence mica has a dielectric constant of

_____ .

14·39 (6) Size for size, the capacitance of a mica dielectric capacitor is six times as great as an equivalent air capacitor. The dielectric constant of polystyrene is 2.5. Hence, size for size, the capacitance of a polystyrene capacitor is _____ times as great as an air capacitor.

14·40 (2.5) Rutile (a form of titanium dioxide) has a dielectric constant of approximately 100. A rutile dielectric capacitor would therefore have a capacitance that is _____ times as great as an equivalent-sized air capacitor.

14·40 (100)

Units of capacitance

The term "capacitance" relates directly to the amount of charge, or charge energy, that can be stored in a capacitor. The unit for the measurement of capacitance is the *farad*. The farad is that capacitance which will store *one coulomb* of charge when the potential applied across the capacitor terminals is *one volt*. The defining equation for capacitance is

$$C \text{ (farads)} = Q \text{ (coulombs)}/E \text{ (volts)}$$

14·41 The unit of capacitance is the *farad*. The farad is defined as that capacitance which will store 1 coulomb of charge when a potential of 1 volt is connected across the capacitor. Thus, a capacitor that stores 2 coulombs at 1 volt has 2 farads of capacitance. A capacitor that stores 10 coulombs at 1 volt of potential has a capacitance of _____ farads.

14·42 (10) A capacitor that stores 4 coulombs at 1 volt has a capacitance of 4 farads. A capacitor that stores 8.3 coulombs at 1 volt has a capacitance of _____ .

14·43 (8.3 farads) A capacitor that stores 6.28 coulombs at 1 volt has a capacitance of _____ .

14·44 (6.28 farads) The charge taken on by a capacitor on this basis is given by $Q = CE$, where Q is the charge, coulombs; C is the capacitance, farads; and E is the voltage, volts. Thus, the charge taken on by a 10-farad capacitor at 3 volts is 30 coulombs. Similarly, the charge taken on by a 0.001-farad capacitor at 100 volts is _____ coulomb.

14·45 (0.1) A 0.5-farad capacitor connected across a 100-volt source will charge up to a value of _____ coulombs.

14·46 (50) The farad is much too large a unit for practical purposes. Thus, we make much use of the microfarad (μf) which equals one one-millionth of a farad. There are 1,000,000 μf in 1 farad; there are 3,500,000 μf in 3.5 farads. Thus, 0.5 farad is the same capacitance as _____ μf.

14·47 (500,000) We are still working with numbers that are too large when applied to practical capacitors. A reasonably large capacitor used in a radio power supply is 10 μf. This is the equivalent of 10^{-5} farad. Similarly, a 1-μf capacitor is the equivalent of _____ farad.

14·48 (10^{-6}) A 0.5-μf capacitor has a given capacitance. This value can also be expressed in farads by multiplying 0.5 by 10^{-6}. That is, the capacitance of a 0.5-μf capacitor expressed in *farads* is _____ farad.

14·49 (0.5×10^{-6}) A radio tuning capacitor has a capacitance of 365×10^{-6} μf. This is a very small number (0.000365). A more convenient unit for such small capacitances is the *picofarad* (abbrev. pf). One microfarad contains 1,000,000 picofarads, expressed in powers of ten, i.e., _____ pf.

14·50 (10^6) The picofarad is a tiny unit, hence there will be one million times as many picofarads in a given capacitance as there are microfarads. That is, to find the number of picofarads in a 0.000365-μf capacitor, we multiply 0.000365 by _____ .

14·51 (1,000,000) But 1 million expressed as a power of 10 is 10^6. Hence, a 365×10^{-6} μf capacitor expressed in picofarads is $365 \times 10^{-6} \times 10^6$. Here, $10^{-6} \times 10^6 = 1$ so that the result of this multiplication is _____ since the exponential terms drop out.

14·52 (365) Thus, a 365×10^{-6} μf capacitor has a capacitance of _____ pf.

14·53 (365) Similarly, a 15×10^{-6} μf capacitor has a value of 15 pf; a 35×10^{-6} μf capacitor has a value of _____ pf.

14·54 (35) To convert the value of a capacitor given in picofarads to a value in microfarads, we reverse the process. That is, we multiply the picofarad value by 10^{-6}. Thus, a 35-pf capacitor has a value of 35×10^{-6} μf; similarly, a 150-pf capacitor has a value of _____ μf.

14·55 (150×10^{-6}) A 10-pf capacitor is the same as one rated $10 \times 10^{-6} = 10^{-5}$ μf. A 100-pf capacitor is the same as one rated $100 \times 10^{-6} =$ _____ μf.

14·56 (10^{-4}) A capacitor is marked 0.0005 μf. This capacitor could also be correctly labeled with _____ pf.

14·57 (500) A capacitor is marked 2,500 pf. This capacitor could also be correctly labeled with _____ μf.

14·57 (0.0025)

Capacitance calculations

We have seen that the capacitance of a capacitor is a function of the plate area, the distance separating the plates, and the dielectric constant of the dielectric. If these quantities can be measured for a given capacitor, its capacitance can be found from the following equation:

$$C = 0.2248 \frac{AK}{d}$$

where A is the total plate area in square inches, K is the dielectric constant, and d is the distance in inches between plates.

14·58 In the equation above in which A is plate area, K is dielectric constant, and d is the distance between plates, the symbol C stands for the _____ of the capacitor in *picofarads*.

14·59 (capacitance) In the equation, C is measured in pico-farads. Thus, if the area of one plate (A in the equation) of a two-plate air capacitor is 1 sq in. and the separation between plates is 0.01 in., the capacitance is $0.2248 \times 1 \times 1$ divided by 0.01, or _____ pf.

14·60 (22.48) If the number of plates is now increased to form a multiplate capacitor with 10 dielectric spaces, and neither the dielectric nor the spacing is changed, the capacitance of the capacitor will be $0.2248 \times 10 \times 1$ divided by 0.01, or _____ pf.

14·61 (224.8) If mica (dielectric constant = 6) is now sub-stituted for air, and if no other changes are made in the multi-plate capacitor, the new capacitance will be $0.2248 \times 10 \times 6$ divided by 0.01 or _____ pf.

14·62 (1,349) If the spacing of the plates of the capacitor in Frame 14·61 is now increased to 0.1 in., and if no other changes are made, the capacitance will be _____ pf.

14·63 (134.9) The capacitance of a capacitor having a total plate area of 50 sq in., a dielectric constant of 4.5, and a spacing of 0.001 in. is _____ pf.

14·64 (50,580) Since none of the values in the data in Frame 14·63 has more than two significant figures, the answer should be rounded back to two significant figures. Thus, the number 50,580 rounded back becomes _____ .

14·65 (51,000) Expressed in microfarads, the capacitance of the capacitor is, therefore, _____ μf.

14·66 (0.051) A capacitor having a total plate area of 300 sq in., a plate spacing of 0.003 in., and a dielectric constant of 100 has a capacitance of 0.2248 × 300 × 100, all divided by 0.003. The answer is _____ μf. (Remember to convert picofarads to microfarads in the final answer.)

14·66 (2.2)

Phase relationships for a capacitor

A capacitor in an a-c circuit causes a phase difference to appear between voltage and current. We found a similar situation to occur in the operation of an inductor in an a-c circuit; you will remember that an inductor causes the current to lag behind the voltage by 90° in a purely inductive circuit.

When an a-c circuit is purely capacitive (no resistance or inductance), the phase change is such as to cause the *current to lead the voltage* by 90°. The frames which follow develop this concept first from d-c, then from a-c, considerations.

14·67 In Fig. 14·67, a capacitor, battery, and switch are shown in an open series circuit. Since the switch is open, at the instant depicted, the voltage applied to the capacitor and the current flowing in the wires leading to the capacitor are both equal to _____ .

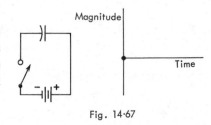

Fig. 14·67

14·68 (zero) *At the instant* of switch closure, the voltage across the capacitor is zero because electrons have not had sufficient time to move into the left plate. Since the capacitor is uncharged, it offers no opposing force, hence the _____ instantaneously reaches its maximum value (Fig. 14·68).

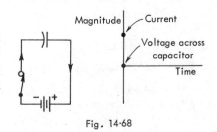

Fig. 14·68

204

14·69 (current) As current flows into the capacitor, its charge gradually builds up until the voltage across it equals the source voltage. Since these voltages are in opposition, the current at this instant becomes _____ .

14·70 (zero) This instant is shown in Fig. 14·70. On the graph in this figure, the broken line therefore indicates the _____ and the solid line indicates the _____ across the capacitor.

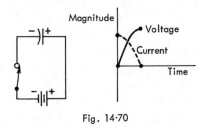

Fig. 14·70

14·71 (current, voltage) Should the applied voltage from the source be a-c, as in Fig. 14·71, the same kind of phase difference is observed over the entire cycle. Since the current is at a negative-going zero point at the 90° phase while the voltage reaches a negative-going zero at the 180° phase, the _____ is leading the _____ by 90°.

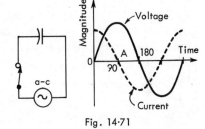

Fig. 14·71

14·72 (current, voltage) Thus, in any theoretically "pure" capacitor circuit containing negligible resistance, the current and voltage are out of phase by _____° .

14·73 (90) Furthermore, in such a circuit, the _____ always leads the _____ by 90°.

14·73 (current, voltage)

Capacitive reactance

A capacitor in a circuit, like an inductor or a resistor, offers some opposition to the current. This opposition is known as *capacitive reactance* and is symbolized by X_c. Capacitive reactance is *inversely* proportional to both capacitance C and to frequency f. That is, if either or both capacitance or frequency are increased, then reactance decreases; if C or f is decreased, then reactance increases. The equation is

$$X_c = \frac{1}{2\pi f C}$$

where X_c = capacitive reactance, ohms
f = frequency, Hz
C = capacitance, farads

It is important to observe that this equation has a reciprocal form when compared with the equation for X_L.

$$X_L = 2\pi f L \qquad X_c = \frac{1}{2\pi f C}$$

The reciprocal nature of these two quantities is very important in certain applications, particularly those met in *filtering* and in *resonance*. These topics will be discussed at a later point.

14·74 Since a capacitor offers increasing opposition to the charging current as its voltage builds up, it limits the flow of current in a-c circuits, just as resistance limits d-c current. This opposition is called "capacitive reactance," and like resistance, is measured in _____ .

14·75 (ohms) Capacitive reactance, symbolized by X_c, decreases as *capacitance* is increased, since the capacitor will accept more charge (coulombs) before its voltage builds up enough to offer serious opposition to the charging current. Hence, X_c is _____ proportional to C.

14·76 (inversely) Thus, a capacitor having a large capacitance will have _____ capacitive reactance than a capacitor with a small capacitance, all other things being equal.

14·77 (less) In addition, a higher frequency results in a smaller X_c. Here again, we are dealing with a relationship in which it is seen that X_c is _____ proportional to frequency f.

14·78 (inversely) At 1,000 Hz, the capacitive reactance is _____ than it is at 60 Hz, for a given capacitor.

14·79 (smaller) From these two inverse proportions, we can now state a simple equation for determining X_c. The factor 2π is inserted to make the capacitive reactance come out in ohms.

$$X_c = \frac{1}{2\pi f C}$$

where f is in hertz, C is in farads, and X_c is in _____ .

14·80 (ohms) Using the equation, we find that the capacitive reactance of an 8-μf capacitor at 60 Hz is

$$X_c = \frac{1}{6.28 \times 60 \times 8 \times 10^{-6}}$$
$$= \text{_____} \text{ ohms}$$

14·81 (332) Similarly, the capacitive reactance of a 0.5-μf capacitor at 5,000 Hz is

$$X_c = \frac{1}{6.28 \times 5{,}000 \times 0.5 \times 10^{-6}}$$

$$= \underline{\hspace{1.5cm}} \text{ ohms}$$

14·82 (64) Using the same equation and procedure, we find that the capacitive reactance of a 0.01-μf capacitor at 1,000 kHz is _____ ohms.

14·83 (16) From the answer obtained in Frame 14·82, it is clear that even a relatively small capacitor can act as a virtually zero path if the _____ is sufficiently high.

14·83 (frequency)

Capacitors in series and parallel

Capacitors may be connected in either parallel or series.

When capacitors are connected in parallel, the net capacitance is found by adding the individual capacitances. Thus,

Parallel: $\qquad C_t = C1 + C2 + C3 + \cdots$

where C_t is the net capacitance.

The net capacitance of capacitors in series is found from a reciprocal equation similar to that encountered when we studied resistors in parallel. Note that this equation applies to C's in *series,* however.

Series: $\qquad \dfrac{1}{C_t} = \dfrac{1}{C1} + \dfrac{1}{C2} + \dfrac{1}{C3} + \cdots$

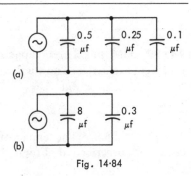

(a)

(b)

Fig. 14·84

14·84 Capacitors are often connected in parallel. In this connection, the total capacitance equals the sum of the individual capacitances. Thus, in Fig. 14·84a, the total capacitance is $C_t = 0.5 + 0.25 + 0.1$ μf $= 0.85$ μf. Similarly, the total capacitance in the circuit of Fig. 14·84b is _____ μf.

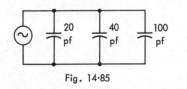

Fig. 14·85

14·85 (8.3) The total capacitance in the circuit of Fig. 14·85 is _____ pf.

14·86 (160) The total capacitance in the circuit of Fig. 14·86 is _____ μf.

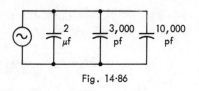

Fig. 14·86

14·87 (2.013) Capacitors are often connected in series. When so connected, the total capacitance is the reciprocal of the sum of the reciprocals of the individual capacitances. Thus, in Fig. 14·87a, the total capacitance is $1/C = 1/4 + 1/4 = 2/4$, so that $C = 4/2 = 2$ μf. Similarly, the total capacitance in the circuit of Fig. 14·87b is _____ .

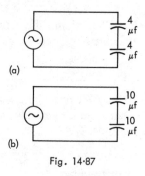

Fig. 14·87

14·88 (5 μf) The total capacitance of the series-capacitor arrangement shown in Fig. 14·88 is found from $1/C = 1/12 + 1/12 + 1/12$, so that C comes out to be _____ μf.

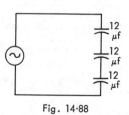

Fig. 14·88

14·89 (4) The total capacitance of the series circuit in Fig. 14·89 is _____ .

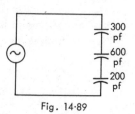

Fig. 14·89

14·90 (100 pf) Three capacitors (0.5, 0.25, and 0.1 μf) are connected in series. The total capacitance of the combination is _____ μf.

14·91 (0.0625) The capacitive reactance of the group of capacitors described in Frame 14·90 when used on a 60-Hz circuit is

$$X_c = \frac{1}{2\pi fC} = \frac{1}{2 \times 3.14 \times 60 \times 0.0625 \times 10^{-6}}$$

$$= \frac{10^6}{2 \times 3.14 \times 60 \times 0.0625}$$

$$= \text{_____ ohms}$$

14·92 (42,400) The current flowing in the capacitor circuit described in Frame 14·90 when the voltage of the 60-Hz source is 120 volts is _____ ma.

14·92 (2.8)

Energy losses in capacitors

Capacitors in a-c circuits suffer from four types of energy losses. In high-quality capacitors, all four kinds of losses are made as small as good manufacturing techniques will permit. These losses are:

1. *Resistance loss.* Loss due to the resistance of the capacitor wires and plates. This loss is usually small and is calculated from I^2R considerations. Resistance loss is measured in watts.

2. *Leakage loss.* Loss due to leakage of current through the dielectric and the consequent development of heat.

3. *Dielectric-absorption loss.* Loss due to the retention of charges by a dielectric which fails to return the charges to the circuit.

4. *Dielectric-hysteresis loss.* Loss due to the additional energy demanded by the dielectric to make it reverse its atomic-distortion pattern as the electric field in an a-c circuit reverses its direction.

14·93 Resistance loss is usually found to be small and is calculated from I^2R considerations. If a capacitor has a resistance of 0.01 ohm at 1 amp, its resistance loss is $I^2R = 1^2 \times 0.01 =$ _____ watt.

14·94 (0.01) A capacitor carrying a current of 10 ma is working on a 60-Hz circuit. The resistance of the capacitor is 0.005 ohm. Its resistance loss is $I^2R = (0.01)^2 \times 0.005 = 5 \times 10^{-7}$ watt. If the resistance were 0.007 ohm, the resistance loss would be _____ _____ .

14·95 (7×10^{-7} watt) A capacitor has a resistance of 0.0087 ohm and carries 150 ma. The resistance loss in this capacitor is _____ watt. (Note: Remember to change milli-amperes to amperes.)

14·96 (1.96×10^{-4}) No dielectric is a perfect insulator, hence some current always leaks through it and develops heat. If a dielectric permits considerable leakage current, its *leakage* resistance is comparatively low. Thus, certain "electrolytic capacitors" have high leakage loss, or low _____ _____ .

14·97 (leakage resistance) Waxed paper dielectrics have lower leakage currents than electrolytic types. Thus, the waxed paper dielectric offers a _____ leakage resistance than the electrolytic dielectric.

14·98 (higher) The leakage resistance of a mica dielectric is much higher than other types, hence the leakage losses in mica dielectric capacitors are normally much _____ than in other types.

14·99 (smaller) A third form of energy loss in a capacitor is known as dielectric-absorption loss. Certain dielectric materials tend to absorb charges and fail to return them to the circuit. Waxed paper absorbs considerable charge, hence waxed paper is said to have a _____ dielectric-absorption loss.

14·100 (high or large) Mica does not absorb charges to the same extent as waxed paper, hence mica capacitors have little _____ loss.

14·101 (dielectric-absorption) Dielectric-hysteresis loss becomes increasingly greater with higher frequencies. Thus, a capacitor with a small hysteresis loss at 60 Hz may have a _____ loss at 10,000 Hz.

14·102 (high) The hysteresis loss of a paper capacitor at 120 Hz is quite small. As the frequency is raised to 5,000 Hz, the hysteresis loss becomes significant. Finally, at 100,000 Hz, the dielectric-hysteresis loss becomes very _____ .

14·103 (large) The energy required to reverse the atomic distortion patterns in a mica dielectric is very small. Thus, mica capacitors have little dielectric loss, even at _____ frequencies.

14·104 (high) An air capacitor (air is the dielectric in this type) has extremely small dielectric loss. Thus, air capacitors are very well suited for use at very high _____ .

14·104 (frequencies)

A capacitor may be rated in terms of the following: **1,** working voltage (abbrev. WV); **2,** surge voltage; or **3,** peak voltage. A voltage rating indicates the maximum voltage at which the capacitor may be used without endangering it. Should the capacitor be used in a circuit in which the voltage applied to it exceeds its voltage rating, the dielectric may puncture. When this occurs, the capacitor may short-circuit and require replacement.

A capacitor may be used in a circuit in which the voltage applied to it is *below its rating without changing its capacitance* or any other operating characteristic. The principal reasons for avoiding the use of high-voltage capacitors in low-voltage circuits are unnecessary bulk, weight, and cost.

14·105 Capacitors are always rated in terms of *operating voltages* as well as capacitance. A capacitor rated at 200 d-c working volts should never be connected across a voltage greater than 200 volts. Similarly, a capacitor rated at 600 working volts should be limited in all cases to no more than _____ volts.

14·106 (600) A capacitor is rated at 500 d-c WV. It is safe to connect this capacitor across a 450-volt d-c line, but it is _____ to connect it across a 1,000-volt line.

14·107 (unsafe) A capacitor having a capacitance of 2 μf at 400 d-c WV has a capacitance of _____ μf when connected across a 200-volt d-c line.

14·108 (2) Capacitors are often rated in terms of *surge voltage*. Surge voltage is the maximum voltage a capacitor can stand for 5 min. A capacitor with a 1,000-volt surge rating can withstand 1,000 volts of d-c for 5 min without harm. A capacitor having a 500-volt surge rating can withstand 500 volts of d-c for _____ _____ without harm.

14·109 (5 min) A capacitor with a surge voltage rating of 1,200 volts is connected across a 1,500-volt source for 5 min. Before this time elapses, it is likely that the capacitor will be

_____ .

14·110 (destroyed) A capacitor has a working voltage rating of 600 volts d-c WV and a surge voltage rating of 1,000 volts d-c. With 1,000 volts applied, the capacitor can operate safely for only 5 min. With 600 volts applied, the capacitor can operate for an _____ length of time.

14·111 (indefinite, unlimited, etc.) Some capacitors are rated in terms of *peak voltage*. Thus, a capacitor marked 500-volts peak can be used indefinitely in an a-c circuit in which the peak voltage does not exceed 500 volts. Similarly, a capacitor rated at 1,000-volts peak can be used in an a-c circuit having a peak voltage of 1,000 for an _____ length of time.

14·112 (indefinite) The peak voltage rating of a capacitor that is to be used on a 120-volt a-c power line cannot be below 169.2 volts. Similarly, the peak voltage rating of a capacitor to be used on a 240-volt a-c line cannot be below _____ volts.

14·113 (338.4) A capacitor that is to be used on a 400-volt a-c line must have a peak voltage rating that is not below _____ volts. (Peak voltage = effective voltage × 1.41.)

14·114 (564) A capacitor has a peak voltage rating of 600 volts. Its surge voltage rating is likely to be _____ than this. (higher/lower)

14·114 (higher)

MEASURABLE BEHAVIORAL OBJECTIVES

Upon completion of a section, you should be able to achieve the objectives listed for it. The frame or frames that cover the related subject matter are indicated immediately following each objective.

Basic concepts of capacitance

1 Name the elements of a mica capacitor. (14·2)
  a Discuss the role of a dielectric material in a capacitor. (14·5)
  b Illustrate schematically a fixed and a variable capacitor. (14·8, 14·9)
2 Discuss the capacitor as an electrical device. (14·3)

Charge and discharge of a capacitor

1 Discuss the behavior of a capacitor when a d-c voltage is applied to it. (14·17)
2 Discuss the behavior of a capacitor when an a-c voltage is connected across it. (14·18)
3 Describe the d-c blocking property of a capacitor. (14·17, 14·23)

Factors that govern capacitance

State three properties of a capacitor that will influence its capacitance. (Introduction)
a Discuss the relationship of a capacitor to its area. (14·24)
b Describe the effect of the distance between plates and of the material used for a capacitor. (14·27, 14·29)
c Describe the construction of several types of capacitors. (14·31, 14·35)

Units of capacitance

State the units of capacitance. (14·41)
a Relate coulombs, volts, and farads. (14·42)
b Relate picofarad to microfarad to farad. (14·46, 14·49)

Capacitance calculations

1 Give a mathematical formula for finding the capacitance of a capacitor from its physical dimensions. (14·58, 14·59)
2 Illustrate the use of the above equation. (14·61)

Phase relationships for a capacitor

1 Describe what will happen when a d-c voltage is applied across a capacitor. (14·67, 14·68)
2 Discuss the charge buildup in a capacitor. (14·69, 14·70)
3 Discuss what will happen when an a-c voltage is applied across a capacitor. (14·71)
4 State the phase relationship of voltage and current for a pure capacitor. (14·73)

Capacitive reactance

Define capacitive reactance. (14·74)
a Give a mathematical equation for capacitive reactance. (14·79)
b Define the units of capacitive reactance. (14·81)

Capacitors in series and parallel

1 State the rule for combining capacitors in parallel. (14·84)
2 State the rule for combining capacitors in series. (14·87)
3 Illustrate the above rules with numerical examples. (14·86, 14·88)

Energy losses in capacitors

1 List four causes of energy loss in capacitors. (14·93, 14·96, 14·100, 14·101)
2 Discuss methods for reducing the above losses. (14·94, 14·104)

Capacitor voltage ratings

1 Discuss the significance of working voltage rating for a capacitor. (14·105, 14·106)
2 Discuss the significance of surge voltage rating for a capacitor. (14·108)
3 Discuss the significance of peak voltage rating for a capacitor. (14·111)

chapter 15

transformers

Mutual inductance in transformer action

A transformer is an electrical device consisting of a primary and secondary winding linked by magnetic flux. The voltage that appears across the *primary* winding is the voltage applied by an external source of emf; the voltage across the secondary is induced by the flux linkage between secondary and primary.

Transformers are normally used on a-c, although they will operate on pulsating d-c, too. The requirement of a periodically changing primary flux must be met, however, otherwise the transformer will not produce a secondary voltage. In addition, unless the rate of change of flux matches the transformer design specifications, the transformer is likely to overheat.

Transformers may be used at power-line frequencies, audio frequencies (20–20,000 Hz), ultrasonic frequencies (20,000–100,000 Hz), and radio frequencies (abbrev. r-f). The design and construction of transformers vary with the frequency at which they are to be used. For example, power transformers and audio transformers are normally built on a rectangular or shell type of silicon steel core. At these relatively low frequencies, good magnetic coupling can be accomplished only by careful geometric design and the utilization of high-quality transformer iron. At the higher frequencies (r-f), a transformer may be designed in the form of two coils wound end to end on an air core, or it may be wound on special types of *ferrite* cores. Ferrite is a high-frequency magnetic material.

15·1 In Fig. 15·1, a fundamental *transformer* is shown to consist of a primary coil and a secondary coil wound on a common iron core. If the switch in the primary circuit is suddenly closed, a _____ field will at once grow throughout the iron core.

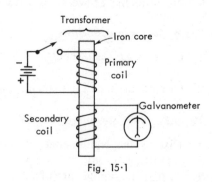

Fig. 15·1

15·2 (magnetic) As the field grows, it will cut through the turns of the secondary coil, thereby inducing an _____ across the terminals of the secondary coil.

15·3 (emf) The galvanometer connected to the secondary winding will show a deflection, indicating that a _____ has appeared in this circuit.

15·4 (current) If the switch is left closed, the galvanometer will drop to zero since an induced emf (hence an induced current) can appear only when the magnetic field is _____ .

15·5 (changing) Should the switch now be opened, the galvanometer will again deflect showing that a current once more was induced in the secondary winding. The direction of this current, however, will be _____ that of the original current when the switch was first closed.

15·6 (opposite) The foregoing steps show that an induced current can flow in a closed secondary circuit when the primary magnetic field is in the process either of expanding or

_____ .

15·7 (collapsing) When a source of alternating emf replaces the battery (Fig. 15·7), a make-break switch is no longer required, since a-c in the primary makes the magnetic field alternately _____ and collapse.

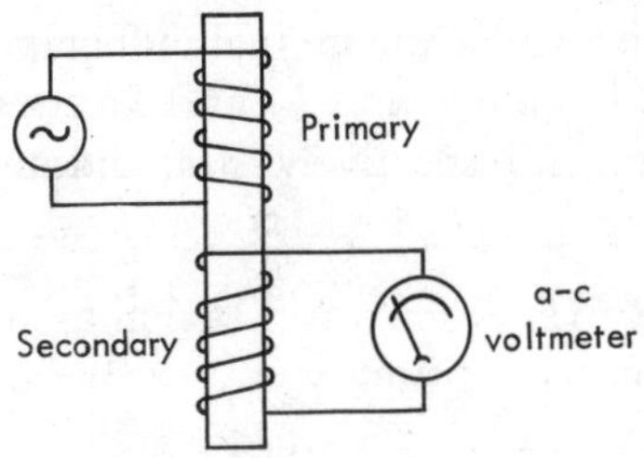

Fig. 15·7

15·8 (expand) In Fig. 15·7, the magnitude of the emf generated in the secondary coil is indicated by the component labeled _____ .

15·9 (a-c voltmeter) Many of the primary lines of force are lost to the system because of the straight shape of the core in Figs. 15·1 and 15·7. By making the core square (Fig. 15·9), almost all the lines of force from the primary cut through the secondary, thereby causing the mutual inductance to be

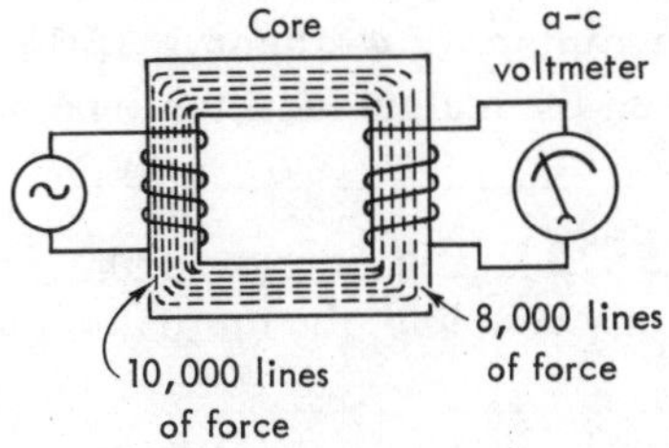

_____ .

Fig. 15·9

15·10 (large) The *coefficient of coupling* between the primary and secondary windings of a transformer is defined as the ratio of the number of lines cutting the secondary to the number of original primary lines. Thus, in Fig. 15·9, 8,000 lines of force out of an initial 10,000 are shown cutting the secondary, hence the coefficient is 8,000/10,000 or _____ .

15·11 (0.8) In the straight-core transformer in Fig. 15·7, the coefficient of coupling might be only 0.5. Thus, if this primary developed 10,000 lines of force, we would know that only _____ lines of force cut through the secondary.

15·12 (5,000) A transformer has a coefficient of coupling of 0.9. In this transformer, 18,000 lines of force cut through the secondary winding. Thus, the primary winding must develop _____ lines of force.

15·13 (20,000) Perfect coupling in which the primary lines were all used with none being lost would lead to a coefficient of coupling of exactly _____ .

15·14 (1.0) The mutual inductance of a transformer is given by the equation:

$$M = k \sqrt{L_P \times L_s}$$

where M is the mutual inductance in henrys, k is the coefficient of coupling, and L_P and L_s are primary and secondary inductances, respectively. Both L_P and L_s are measured in _____ .

15·15 (henrys) Maximum mutual inductance is obtained for given primary and secondary inductances by making k as _____ as possible.

15·16 (large) Since the maximum value that k can attain is unity, then maximum mutual inductance is realized when $k =$ _____ .

15·17 (1) A transformer has a primary of 2.5 henrys and a secondary of 4.2 henrys. If the coefficient of coupling is 0.8, then the mutual inductance between windings is _____ .

15·18 (2.56 henrys) If this were a perfect transformer with unity coupling, the mutual inductance would be _____ .

15·18   (3.2 henrys)

The principle of the conservation of energy demands that the work output from any machine or device must equal the work input. If the efficiency of the machine is 100 per cent (an ideal or perfect machine), then the *useful* work output equals the *total* work output, hence the useful work output equals the work input. Practical machines always have efficiencies of less than 100 per cent. This means that part of the total work output is wasted; thus, the useful work output is less than the work input.

Power is the time rate of doing work or consuming energy. In equation form

$$P = \frac{W}{t}$$

where P = power, W = work, and t = time. If the work or energy W is expressed in *joules* and the time in *seconds,* then the power will be given in joules/second or *watts*. In a *perfect* electrical device the efficiency is 100 per cent, and the power input will equal the useful power output; in a practical transformer, the efficiency is less than 100 per cent, and the useful power output will be less than the power input.

15·19 If the input work to any perfect machine is 150 ft-lb, the output work is 150 ft-lb. If the input work is 382 joules, the output work is 382 joules. Thus, if the output of a perfect machine is 8×10^8 ergs, the input work was _____ .

15·20 (8×10^8 ergs) The output of a perfect machine is 3.7×10^5 dyne-cm. This means that the input work must have been 3.7×10^5 dyne-cm. Since an erg equals 1 dyne-cm, then the input work to this machine must have been _____ ergs.

15·21 (3.7×10^5) One joule = 10^7 ergs. A machine that has an output of 4.5×10^7 ergs, assuming 100 per cent efficiency, must have consumed _____ joules in its input.

15·22 (4.5) If W is in joules, and t is in seconds, then power is in watts. Thus 20 joules of work done in 1 sec represents 20 watts of power. Similarly, 60 joules of work done in 6 sec represents _____ watts of power.

15·23 (10) A certain electric motor can do 1,000 joules of work in 2 sec. Its power consumption is 1,000/2 = 500 watts. A larger electric motor can do the same work in ½ sec, hence its power consumption is 1,000/0.5 = _____ watts.

15·24 (2,000) An electric motor does 7,200 joules of work in 8 sec. Its power consumption is _____ watts.

15·25 (900) Consider a perfect (100 per cent efficient) transformer. Since the working current flows for the same interval in both primary and secondary, and since $W = Pt$ (see equation in introduction to set), then $P_{pri} \times t = P_{sec} \times t$. Since the t's are equal, we may cancel them. When this is done, we see that the primary *power* _____ the secondary *power*.

15·26 (equals) Thus, in a perfect transformer, if the secondary power consumption is 100 watts, the primary input power must be 100 watts. If conditions change so that the secondary power consumption rises to 250 watts, then the primary power input must automatically change to _____.

15·27 (250 watts) In a certain a-c circuit employing a transformer (100 per cent efficiency is assumed), a 1,000-watt floodlight, connected across the secondary, lights to full brilliance. Thus, the power input to the primary must be _____ watts.

15·28 (1,000) See Fig. 15·28. In this transformer, the primary-to-secondary turns ratio is 20:1. The ratio of primary emf to secondary emf is the same as the turns ratio; 100 volts in the primary induces 5 volts in the secondary. If the secondary is now increased to 10 turns (turns ratio now 10:1), the secondary voltage would become _____.

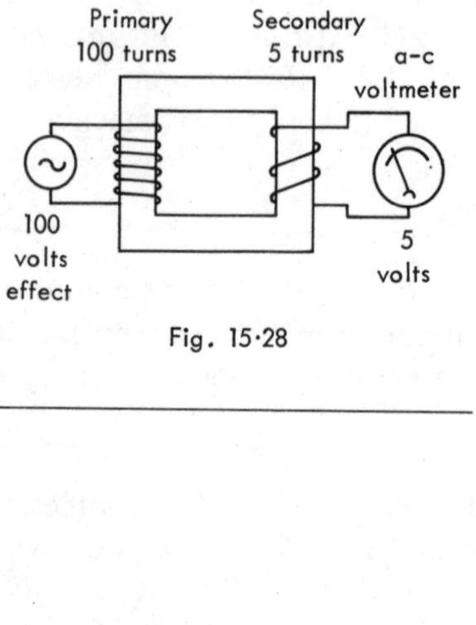

Fig. 15·28

15·29 (10 volts) In the same transformer, if we increase the secondary turns to 20 turns (ratio 5:1), the secondary voltage would become _____ volts.

15·30 (20) In this "step-down" transformer, it is apparent that the primary-to-secondary voltage ratio is the same as the primary-to-secondary turns ratio. Thus, if the primary has 500 turns and the secondary 50 turns (ratio 10:1), a primary voltage of 20 volts would yield a secondary voltage of _____.

15·31 (2 volts) In the transformer shown in Fig. 15·31, the turns ratio, primary-to-secondary, is _____ .

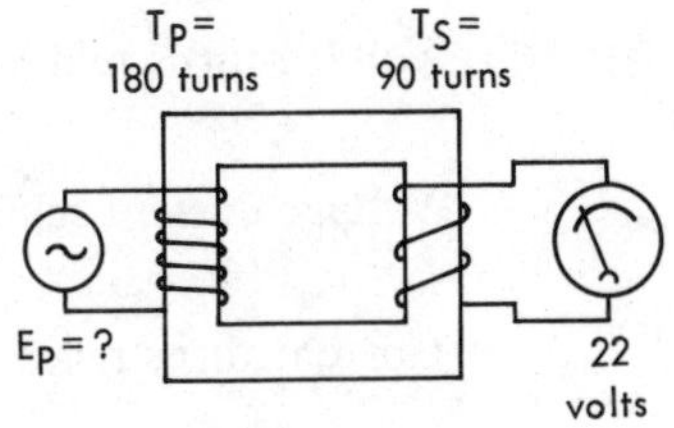

$$T_P = 180 \text{ turns} \qquad T_S = 90 \text{ turns}$$

$$E_p = ? \qquad 22 \text{ volts}$$

Fig. 15·31

15·32 (2:1) Since the secondary voltage of this transformer is 22 volts, the primary voltage must be _____ volts.

15·33 (44) The voltage ratio–turns ratio relationship is best expressed in a simple equation thus:

$$\frac{E_p}{E_s} = \frac{T_p}{T_s}$$

If a given perfect transformer has a primary voltage of 120 volts and a secondary voltage of 30 volts, its turns ratio must be _____ .

15·34 (4:1) The same equation holds for "step-up" transformers in which the secondary voltage is *higher* than the primary voltage. A transformer has a turns ratio of 1:4 (note that this is one primary to four secondary turns). Thus, a voltage of 25 primary volts turns into 100 secondary volts. In the same transformer, 120 volts applied to the primary would yield _____ secondary volts.

15·35 (480) A certain power transformer (assume 100 per cent efficiency) steps up the voltage from 120 primary volts to 120,000 secondary volts. The turns ratio of this transformer, primary to secondary, must be _____ .

15·36 (1:1,000) A toy train transformer that yields 12 secondary volts from a 120-volt a-c source has a turns ratio of

_____ .

15·36 (10:1)

Ideal transformers (calculations)

The behavior of ideal transformers can be calculated from the following set of basic equations (100 per cent efficiency is assumed throughout):

Voltage-turns relationship:
$$\frac{E_p}{E_s} = \frac{T_p}{T_s}$$

Voltage-current relationship:
$$\frac{E_p}{E_s} = \frac{I_s}{I_p}$$

Current-turns relationship:
$$\frac{T_p}{T_s} = \frac{I_s}{I_p}$$

Conservation of energy relationship: $P_{pri} = P_{sec}$ or $E_p I_p = E_s I_s$

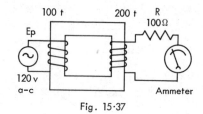

Fig. 15·37

15·37 A perfect transformer having the characteristics shown in Fig. 15·37 is connected to a 120-volt line. The turns ratio of this transformer is _____.

15·38 (1:2) The voltage produced across the secondary winding is, therefore, _____ volts.

15·39 (240) Since R is 100 ohms, then the current indicated by the ammeter in the secondary circuit (according to Ohm's law) is _____ amp.

15·40 (2.4) The power consumed in the secondary winding circuit, according to the power equation $P = EI$, must be _____ watts.

15·41 (576) According to the law of conservation of energy, if this transformer is perfect, the power fed to the primary circuit must be _____ .

15·42 (576 watts) But the voltage across the primary winding is 120 volts. To produce a power input of 576 watts, therefore, the primary current must be $I_{pri} = P_{pri}/E_{pri}$ or _____ amp.

15·43 (4.8) This illustrates the self-regulating action of a transformer wherein the primary current automatically adjusts itself so that the power input equals the power output. If R in Fig. 15·37 were decreased to 50 ohms, then the secondary current would be _____ amp.

15·44 (4.8) This makes the secondary power equal to
_____ watts.

15·45 (1,152) The primary power (100 per cent efficiency) would then have to become _____ watts to satisfy the law of conservation of energy.

15·46 (1,152) This, in turn, would mean that the primary current would have to rise to _____ amp to produce this power input.

15·47 (9.6) The voltage-current relationship in a transformer is thus dependent upon conservation of energy. Since $P_{pri} = P_{sec}$, then $E_p I_p = E_s I_s$. Changing this to a pair of ratios by cross multiplying, we obtain $E_p/E_s =$ _____ (see top of preceding page).

15·48 (I_s/I_p) Summarizing, we might say that if a transformer steps up the voltage by a factor of x, then it steps the current down by a factor of x. If it steps the voltage down by a factor of z, then it steps the current _____ by a factor of z.

15·49 (up) The ratio $E_p/E_s = T_p/T_s$ has been established. Also, the relation $E_p/E_s = I_s/I_p$ has been established. Combining these expressions, we can obtain the connection between turns ratio and *current ratio*. Thus, $T_p/T_s =$ _____.

15·50 (I_s/I_p) Applying the relationships just established, we can find the secondary voltage, secondary current, and primary current in a perfect transformer such as that in Fig. 15·50. First, the turns ratio is 60 to 300 or _____.

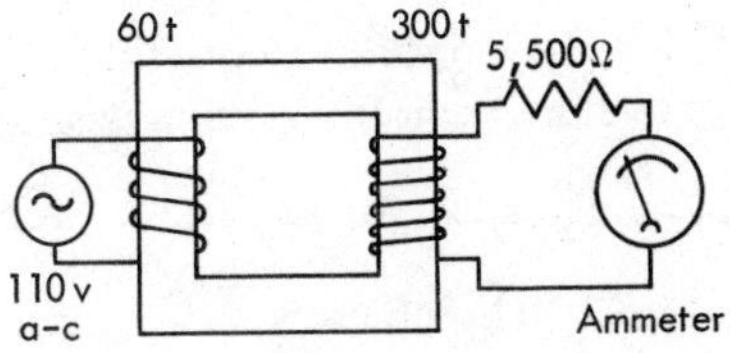

Fig. 15·50

15·51 (1:5) The secondary voltage appearing across the transformer terminals must therefore be _____.

15·52 (550 volts) Since the resistance in series with the secondary winding is 5,500 ohms, the secondary current must therefore be _____ _____.

15·53 (0.1 amp) The secondary power is found by multiplying the secondary current by the secondary voltage. Hence, in this example the secondary power is _____ _____.

15·54 (55 watts) From the law of conservation of energy, we may say that the primary power dissipation is _____ _____ assuming 100 per cent efficiency.

15·55 (55 watts) Thus, the current flowing in the primary must be _____ amp.

15·56 (0.5) Using the turns-current relationship established in Frame 15·49, we can check this reasoning by determining the primary current in a second way. Thus, $T_p/T_s = I_s/I_p$. Now, substituting the turns ratio of T_p/T_s and 0.1 amp for I_s, we find that I_p again turns out to be _____ _____.

15·56 (0.5 amp)

Practical transformer efficiency

The equations given in the introduction to the preceding section may be corrected as follows, for use with practical transformers in which efficiencies are less than 100 per cent:

$$\text{Efficiency, per cent} = \frac{\text{power output}}{\text{power input}} = \frac{E_s I_s}{E_p I_p} \times 100$$

Note: The factor 100 in the above equation is used merely to convert the decimal answer into per cent. It may be omitted when you manipulate this equation if you remember that a given efficiency ratio in decimals should be converted into per cent in the final answer.

15·57 The efficiency of a transformer is defined as the ratio of its *power* output to its *power* input. Since the power output is equal to the power input in a *perfect* transformer, the ratio equals 1. Expressed in per cent, we can say that a perfect transformer has an efficiency of _____ per cent.

15·58 (100) If the power output of a transformer is three-fourths of its power input, the efficiency is 0.75/1 or 75 per cent. If the power output is two-thirds of the power input, the efficiency is 0.66/1 or _____ per cent.

15·59 (66) If the power output of a transformer is one-half of its power input, the efficiency is 0.5/1 or _____ per cent.

15·60 (50) If the power input is 100 watts and the power output is 75 watts, the efficiency is 75/100 or 75 per cent. Similarly, if the power input is 120 watts and the power output is 90 watts, the efficiency is 90/120 or _____ per cent.

15·61 (75) If the power output is 2 watts and the power input is 2.2 watts, the efficiency is _____ per cent.

15·62 (90.9) From the definition of power input, the efficiency of a transformer can be defined as the ratio E_sI_s/E_pI_p. Using this definition, it is easy to solve a transformer problem of the type given in Fig. 15·62. First, determine the turns ratio from the voltage ratio. The turns ratio is _____ .

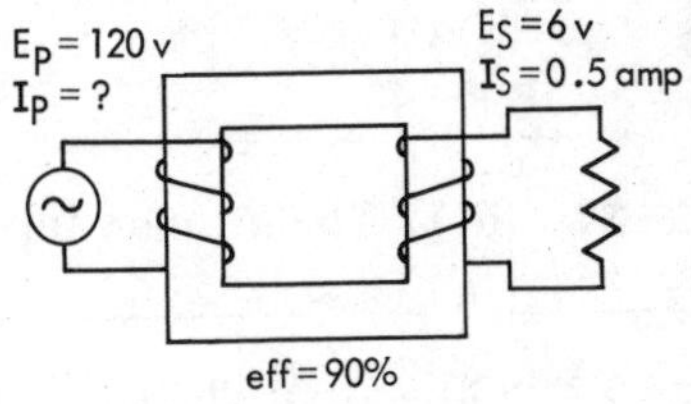

$E_p = 120$ v
$I_p = ?$

$E_S = 6$ v
$I_S = 0.5$ amp

eff = 90%

Fig. 15·62

15·63 (20:1) From the figures given, the power consumed by the load in the secondary circuit is E_sI_s or _____ watts.

15·64 (3) Since the efficiency of the transformer is given as 90 per cent, we can now write the equation $0.90 = E_sI_s/E_pI_p$, and substituting the known secondary power for E_sI_s, we find that $0.90 =$ _____$/E_pI_p$.

15·65 (3) We now have $0.90 = 3/E_pI_p$. We want to determine the value of I_p. Therefore, let us multiply both sides of the equation by E_pI_p to obtain $0.90\ E_pI_p =$ _____ .

15·66 (3) Finally, we can divide both sides of the equation by 0.90. This gives us $E_pI_p =$ _____ .

15·67 (3/0.90) Solving for E_pI_p (this is power in the primary), we obtain $E_pI_p =$ _____ watts.

15·68 (3.3) We know that the primary voltage is 120 volts. Hence, the primary current may now be found by solving $E_pI_p = 3.3$ watts, for I_p. Thus, $I_p = 3.3/120 =$ _____ amp.

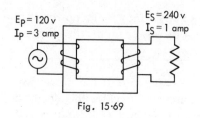

Fig. 15·69

15·69 (0.027) As a practice exercise in transformer efficiency, find the efficiency of the transformer in Fig. 15·69. Do this by using the equation, efficiency = power output/power input. The efficiency thus turns out to be _____ _____ .

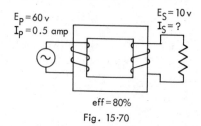

eff = 80%

Fig. 15·70

15·70 (66.6 per cent) As a second practice exercise, note Fig. 15·70. The turns ratio, primary to secondary, of this transformer is _____ .

15·71 (6:1) The primary input power is _____ _____ .

15·72 (30 watts) The secondary output power must be 80 per cent of the input power from the efficiency definition. Hence, the secondary output power is _____ _____ .

15·73 (24 watts) The secondary current must therefore be _____ _____ amp.

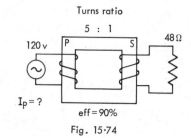

eff = 90%

Fig. 15·74

15·74 (2.4) As a final practice exercise, study Fig. 15·74 and note that the object is to find the primary current rating this transformer would have to have. As a first step, you would want to determine the voltage developed across the _____ .

15·75 (secondary) From the turns ratio and the known primary voltage, the secondary output voltage would be _____ volts.

15·76 (24) This secondary voltage applied across 48 ohms would give rise to a secondary current of _____ amp.

15·77 (0.5) From this we can determine the power being dissipated in the secondary circuit. That is, the power in the secondary circuit is $E_s I_s$ or _____ watts.

15·78 (12) The secondary power is 90 per cent of the primary power or, the primary power = secondary power divided by 0.90. Thus, the primary power must be _____ watts.

15·79 (13.3) Since the primary voltage is known to be 120 volts, then the primary current may be found from the relation, primary power = $E_p I_p$, or I_p = primary power/E_p or _____ amp.

15·79 (0.11)

The autotransformer

An autotransformer (Fig. 15·80) has a single winding that is tapped somewhere along its length to provide three terminals altogether (A,B,C). The winding BC is considered as the primary, while the winding included between C and A is the secondary. Although primary and secondary are connected at terminal B, the principle of operation remains the same as for a two-winding, four-terminal standard type of transformer. That is, the voltage-current-turns ratio equations apply equally well to the autotransformer.

15·80 An *autotransformer* has only one winding. In the illustration (Fig. 15·80) a total of 300 turns has been wound on a core, with a tap brought out at the hundredth turn. A-c may now be applied between terminals B and C. Since this is the input, the coil between B and C may be considered as the _____ winding.

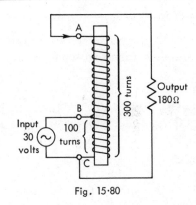

Fig. 15·80

15·81 (primary) The secondary of an autotransformer includes all the turns on the coil. Hence, the secondary of the transformer in Fig. 15·80 has _____ turns.

15·82 (300) The same relationship as used for two-winding transformers applies to autotransformers relative to turns and voltage ratios. Thus, $E_p/E_s = T_p/T_s$. In the transformer of Fig. 15·80, the output voltage must be _____ volts.

15·83 (90) If the secondary resistor is 180 ohms (Fig. 15·80), then the secondary load current is _____ amp.

15·84 (0.5) The secondary load power dissipation on this basis must therefore be _____ watts.

15·85 (45) Assuming 90 per cent efficiency, the primary power input must be _____ watts.

15·86 (50) Hence, the primary current flowing in the coil *BC* must be _____ amp.

15·87 (1.66) Since coil section *BC* carries both the primary and secondary load currents, the wire used for this coil must be designed to carry _____ amp continuously.

15·88 (2.16) The coil section *AB*, however, carries only the _____ current.

15·89 (secondary) Thus coil section *AB* may be wound with wire that need carry only _____ amp continuously.

15·90 (0.5) This accounts for the fact that almost all step-up autotransformers are wound with _____ different sizes of wire.

15·91 (two) However, since the primary doubles as a section of the secondary, the principal advantage of an autotransformer over a normal two-winding type is that it uses less _____ .

15·92 (wire) If tap *A* is made movable, the autotransformer becomes a variable transformer. As the tap is moved downward toward *B*, the secondary voltage _____ .

15·93 (decreases) When the movable tap finally coincides with point *B*, the output voltage of the autotransformer becomes _____ volts.

15·94 (30) If the tap were moved between *B* and *C*, the secondary winding would then have fewer turns than the primary. (Note that the primary is always coil *BC*.) Thus, the transformer would become a _____ type.

15·95 (step-down) If the tap were exactly midway between
B and C, the output voltage would then be _____ _____.

15·95   (15 volts)

MEASURABLE BEHAVIORAL OBJECTIVES

Upon completion of a section, you should be able to achieve the objectives
listed for it. The frame or frames that cover the related subject matter are
indicated immediately following each objective.

Mutual inductance in transformer action

Discuss the operation of a transformer.   (15·1, 15·2)
a Relate the steady and changing magnetic field to transformer action.
(15·4, 15·5)
b Distinguish between the primary and the secondary of a transformer.
(15·1)
c Define the coefficient of coupling.   (15·10)
d Give an equation relating the coefficient of coupling inductances of
primary and secondary, and the mutual inductance of a transformer.
(15·14)

Power and efficiency

1 Define efficiency for any machine.   (Introduction)
a Discuss the efficiency of a transformer.   (15·25)
b Relate power and work.   (15·25)
2 State the voltage ratio—turns ratio relationship in an equation form.
(15·33)
3 Define step-up and step-down transformers.   (15·30, 15·34)

Ideal transformers

Define an ideal transformer.   (15·41)
a State the voltage-current-turns ratio relationship for an ideal transformer.   (15·49)
b Illustrate the above ratios by the use of numerical examples.
(15·50)

Practical transformers

1 Define efficiency in per cent.   (15·57)
2 Illustrate the use of the above equation with examples.   (15·58, 15·74)

The autotransformer

1 Describe the physical construction of an autotransformer. (15·80)
2 Compare a transformer to an autotransformer. (15·81)
3 State the voltage-turns ratio relationship for an autotransformer. (15·82)
4 Discuss the direction and magnitude of currents in the primary and secondary of an autotransformer. (15·86, 15·87)
5 Discuss the advantages and disadvantages of an autotransformer. (15·90, 15·92)

chapter 16

power in a-c circuits

Power in a simple a-c circuit

A-c circuits employ resistors, capacitors, and/or inductors as "opposition" devices. Of the three, the only component that actually dissipates power is the resistor. When current flows through a resistor, some of the power is transformed into heat which is radiated away and lost to the circuit forever. This loss should be thought of as power *dissipation*. Inductors and capacitors, however, return to the circuit whatever energy they store. Thinking in terms of perfect or ideal inductors or capacitors, energy may be stored in either an inductor or capacitor during one portion of the a-c cycle, but it is returned to the circuit during some other portion. Since the energy is not lost to the circuit as in the action of a resistor, inductors and capacitors (ideal) are *nondissipative* elements.

The power dissipated in a resistor in an a-c circuit may be found from any one of three basic equations:

$$P = \frac{E_{eff}^2}{R} \qquad P = E_{eff} I_{eff} \qquad P = I_{eff}^2 R$$

where the subscript "eff" means effective value.

16·1 The simplest a-c series circuit consists of a pure resistance connected to the source of emf. In such a circuit, the effective current equals the effective voltage divided by the

_____ .

16·2 (resistance) The power developed or dissipated may be found from one of three relationships: **1,** $P = E_{eff} \times I_{eff}$; **2,** $P = E_{eff}^2/R$; and **3,** $P =$ _____ .

16·3 ($I_{eff}^2 \times R$) All the power delivered to a purely resistive load is converted into a different form of energy. This form of energy is _____ .

16·4 (heat) Suppose an inductor is used to replace the resistor. If it is a perfect inductor (zero resistance), the only opposition it offers to the flow of current is in the form of its inductive _____ .

16·5 (reactance) Energy is required to build up the magnetic field of the inductor. All this energy is returned to the circuit in the form of induced current when the field collapses as the a-c passes through zero. Hence, the net power dissipated by a pure inductor is _____ .

16·6 (zero) Another way to look at this effect is this: the resistance R of a pure inductor is zero. Since power may be expressed as $P = I^2R$, we can see that power dissipation must be _____ if R is zero.

16·7 (zero) The current in a pure inductor always lags behind the impressed emf by _____° .

16·8 (90) The current flowing in a purely inductive circuit in which the inductive reactance is X_L and the voltage is E may be found from the equation $I =$ _____ .

16·9 (E/X_L) Inductive reactance is found by substituting in a simple equation the value of the frequency and the inductance. This equation is $X_L =$ _____ .

16·10 ($2\pi fL$) Another simple a-c circuit comprises a perfect capacitor (zero resistance of leads and plates) connected directly to the source of emf. The opposition offered by the capacitor to the flow of current in such a circuit is given by its capacitive _____ .

16·11 (reactance) Energy is required to store up an electrostatic charge in such a capacitor. All this energy is returned to the circuit, however, when the capacitor discharges as the a-c goes through zero. Hence, the net power dissipated by a pure capacitor in an a-c circuit is _____ .

16·12 (zero) The current in a pure capacitor always _leads_ the voltage by _____ electrical degrees.

16·13 (90) The current flowing in a purely capacitive circuit in which the capacitive reactance is X_c and the voltage is E may be found from the equation $I =$ _____ .

16·14 (E/X_c) Capacitive reactance is found by substituting the values of frequency and capacitance in a simple equation. This equation is _____ .

16·15 [$X_c = 1/(2\pi f C)$] No inductor can be constructed with zero resistance, although R may be made very small in large-wire coils. Thus, in any practical inductor, the power dissipation is never quite _____ .

16·16 (zero) No capacitor can be constructed with zero loss. There is always some resistance and some leakage. Thus, in a practical capacitive a-c circuit, the power dissipation is always somewhat greater than _____ .

16·16 (zero)

MEASURABLE BEHAVIORAL OBJECTIVES

Upon completion of a section, you should be able to achieve the objectives listed for it. The frame or frames that cover the related subject matter are indicated immediately following each objective.

Power in a simple a-c circuit

Give three equations for determining the power in an a-c circuit. (16·2)

a Account for the power dissipated in a resistor. (16·3)

b Describe the amount of power that will be dissipated in a pure inductor or capacitor. (16·5, 16·13)

c Discuss the energy flow in and out of a pure inductor. (16·4)

chapter 17

a-c resistive circuits

Phasors in an a-c resistive circuit

Phasors are very useful in analyzing a-c circuits. A phasor diagram is nothing more than a system of arrows which show, by their respective lengths, the magnitudes of the quantities they represent. In addition, the angle made by a phasor with a reference line shows the lag or lead, in electrical degrees, between this phasor and the preselected reference line. These frames introduce the use of phasors in a simple a-c circuit.

17·1 Since a resistor does not store energy like a capacitor or inductor, and since it does not cause a current lag or lead, a-c resistive circuits are handled as though they were d-c circuits. Thus in the circuit in Fig. 17·1 the current flowing (from Ohm's law) is _____ _____ .

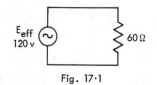

Fig. 17·1

17·2 (2 amp) In a circuit such as that of Fig. 17·2a, the applied voltage E, the voltage drop across the resistor R1 (E1), and the current I are all in the same _____ as shown in Fig. 17·2b.

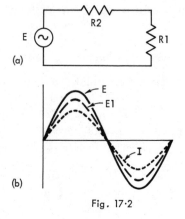

Fig. 17·2

17·3 (phase) This phase relationship is more clearly shown and better handled when drawn in phasor form. Since E, E1, and I are all in phase, they may be shown as polar phasors as in Fig. 17·3. As indicated, they are drawn so that their angles with the horizontal axis in the first quadrant are _____ degrees.

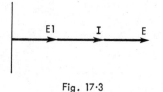

Fig. 17·3

17·4 (zero) Since $E1$ is the result of a voltage drop across $R1$, we may replace $E1$ in the phasor picture with the symbol _____ as shown in Fig. 17·4.

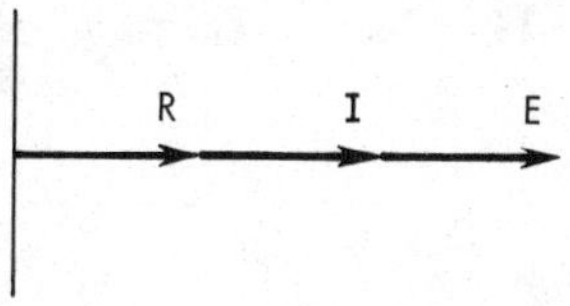

R   I   E

Fig. 17·4

17·5 (R) Thus, the phasor picture of a purely resistive circuit indicates that applied voltage E, resultant current I, and circuit resistance R are all in the same _____ .

17·6 (phase) We shall designate all phasor rotations in the standard polar convention. That is, as shown in Fig. 17·6, the quadrant designated I is the first quadrant, the quadrant designated IV is the fourth quadrant, the quadrant designated A is the _____ quadrant.

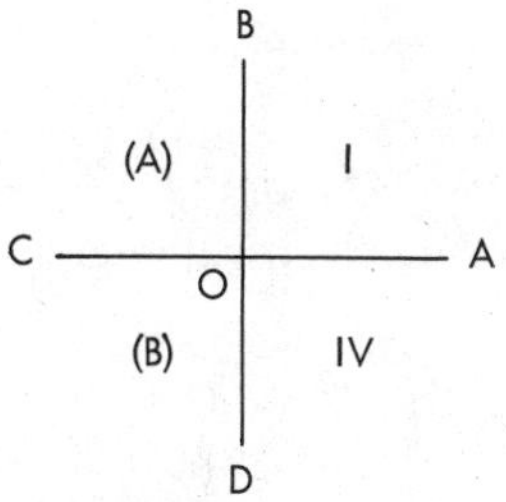

Fig. 17·6

17·7 (second) Similarly, in Fig. 17·6, the quadrant designated B is the _____ quadrant.

17·8 (third) According to convention, all phasors are considered to start on the axis labeled _____ in Fig. 17·6.

17·9 (OA) Hence, this axis is designated as _____ degrees.

17·10 (zero) From this axis, phasors may rotate in a counterclockwise direction from I, to II, to III, to IV. Hence, axis OC is 180°, and OD is _____°.

17·11 (270) In Fig. 17·11, phasor **OA** lies along the 0° axis. Phasor **OB** has proceeded to 90° and is, therefore, *ahead* of **OA**. Hence, in terms of lag or lead, phasor **OB** _____ phasor **OA**.

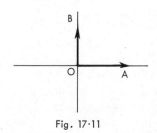

Fig. 17·11

17·12 (leads) The angle of lead in Fig. 17·11 is _____ electrical degrees.

17·13 (90) In Fig. 17·13, phasor **OF** leads phasor **OE** by _____ electrical degrees.

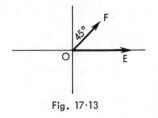

Fig. 17·13

17·14 (45) In Fig. 17·14, phasor **OH** _____ phasor **OG** by 30 electrical degrees.

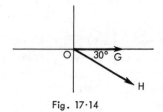

Fig. 17·14

17·15 (lags) Magnitudes are indicated in phasor diagrams by the length of the phasor drawn to some convenient scale. For example, in Fig. 17·11, phasor **OA** is seen to have a larger magnitude than phasor **OB**. In Fig. 17·13, it is evident that the quantity with the larger magnitude is indicated by phasor_____ .

17·16 (**OE**) Similarly, in Fig. 17·14, the quantity having the smaller magnitude is shown as phasor _____ .

17·17 (**OG**) In Fig. 17·17, the phasor in quadrant IV is phasor _____ .

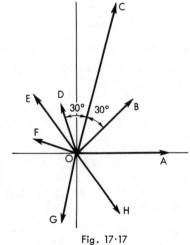

Fig. 17·17

17·18 **(OH)** In Fig. 17·17, the quantity having the largest magnitude is designated by phasor _____ .

17·19 **(OC)** In Fig. 17·17, the quantity that leads **OB** by about 90° is shown by the phasor _____ .

17·20 **(OE)** In Fig. 17·17, the phasor which is out of phase by 180° with phasor **OE** is _____ .

17·20 **(OH)**

MEASURABLE BEHAVIORAL OBJECTIVES

Upon completion of a section, you should be able to achieve the objectives listed for it. The frame or frames that cover the related subject matter are indicated immediately following each objective.

Phasors in an a-c resistive circuit

1 Indicate that all currents and voltages in resistive a-c circuit are in phase. (17·1 to 17·5)
   a Compute the effective value of all currents and voltages in a resistive a-c circuit. (17·1)
   b Recognize that the phase angle between the various currents and voltages is zero. (17·2, 17·3, 17·5)
   c Represent the voltages and currents in a resistive circuit by phasors lying along the positive horizontal axis with lengths proportional to the magnitude of the signal. (17·3, 17·4)
2 Describe the use of phasors to represent arbitrary sinusoidal signals in an a-c circuit. (17·6 to 17·20)
   a Describe the axes and four quadrants in which the phasor may lie. (17·6 to 17·8, 17·17)
   b Indicate the direction for measuring zero phase angle and the direction of rotation for which the phase angle increases. (17·8 to 17·10)
   c Identify the length of the phasor as representative of the magnitude of the signal. (17·15, 17·16, 17·18)
   d Determine the lag or lead of one phasor with respect to another. (17·11 to 17·14, 17·19, 17·20)

chapter 18

RL circuits

Voltage and current relationships in phasor diagrams

These frames discuss the methods by which phasors may be used to pictorialize phase relationships and the means by which such phasors may be used in electrical calculations.

18·1 In Fig. 18·1, a series circuit comprising a resistor and an inductor in series with an a-c source is shown. In this *RL* circuit, the current in the resistor is _____ to the current in the inductor because in a series circuit of *any* type the current is everywhere the same.

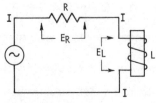

Fig. 18·1

18·2 (equal) The voltage drop across the resistor is designated as E_R. The voltage drop across the _____ is shown as E_L.

18·3 (inductor) As shown previously, there is no phase difference between the current *I*, the voltage across the resistor E_R, and the resistance *R*. Hence all three of these quantities are shown to lie along the _____ degree axis in Fig. 18·3.

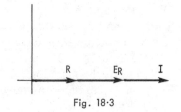

Fig. 18·3

18·4 (zero) The current through the inductor *lags* behind the voltage across the inductor by 90°, as explained previously. Hence, the voltage across the inductor *leads* in this position. This phasor is labeled _____ in Fig. 18·4.

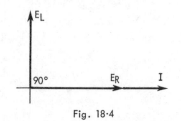

Fig. 18·4

18·5 (E_L) When two resistors are in series, there is no phase shift in the voltages, hence they are diagrammed as phasors as in Fig. 18·5. Since these phasors are in the same phase, the sum of the voltage drops ($E1$ and $E2$) may be taken arithmetically so that the total voltage drop (Fig. 18·5) equals _____ volts.

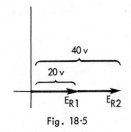
Fig. 18·5

18·6 (60) But, if two voltage drops are out of phase by 90°, the total voltage drop cannot be determined arithmetically since the peaks are being reached at different instants in time. Thus, we dispense with arithmetic addition and use _____ addition.

18·7 (phasor) In phasor addition, we first construct a geometric figure around the two original phasors. This geometric figure for a 90° phase difference is a rectangle as shown in Fig. 18·7. If the phase difference were anything but 90°, the polygon would then have to be a _____ .

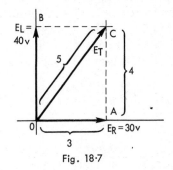
Fig. 18·7

18·8 (parallelogram) We then draw the diagonal of the polygon with one terminus at the origin of the quadrants and the other terminus at the remote end of the polygon. This diagonal in Fig. 18·7 is labeled _____ .

18·9 (OC) Using suitable scales, or basic trigonometry, the resultant phasor **OC** may be specified in magnitude. In Fig. 18·7, E_R is 30 volts and E_L is 40 volts so that the right triangle **OAC** must be a $3:4:5$ type. Hence, the total voltage E_T must be _____ volts.

18·10 (50) This drawing usually is simplified as in Fig. 18·10 in which a right triangle is drawn having E_R as the horizontal leg, E_L as the vertical leg, and the total voltage drop or phasor sum of E_L and E_R shown as the _____ of the right triangle.

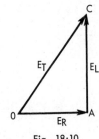
Fig. 18·10

18·10 (hypotenuse)

This is a brief review of the Pythagorean theorem. You will recall that this theorem states that in a right triangle, the square of the hypotenuse equals the sum of the squares of the sides.

It is often very useful to be able to recognize two special triangles: the $3:4:5$ type, and the $5:12:13$ type. Both of these, as well as the general approach to the solution of right triangles, appear in these frames. This fundamental geometry is very important in setting up and solving electrical problems involving phasors.

18·11 In any right triangle, the square of the hypotenuse equals the sum of the squares of the sides. Thus in Fig. 18·11a, the square of the hypotenuse equals $3^2 + 4^2$ or $9 + 16$, or 25. Similarly, in Fig. 18·11b, the square of the hypotenuse is $6^2 + 2^2$, or $36 + 4$, or 40. Also, in Fig. 18·11c, the square of the hypotenuse is $1^2 + 8^2$, or _____ .

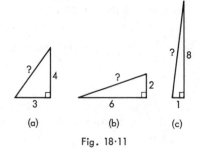

(a)　　　　(b)　　　　(c)

Fig. 18·11

18·12 (65) In Fig. 18·12a, the square of the hypotenuse is $16 + 25 = 41$. In Fig. 18·12b, the square of the hypotenuse is $36 + 36 = 72$. Thus, in Fig. 18·12c, the square of the hypotenuse is _____ .

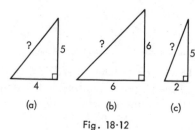

(a)　　　　(b)　　　　(c)

Fig. 18·12

18·13 (29) In Fig. 18·13, the square of the hypotenuse is _____ .

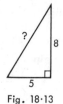

Fig. 18·13

18·14 (89) In Fig. 18·14, the square of the hypotenuse is _____ .

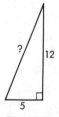

Fig. 18·14

18·15 (169) The actual value of the hypotenuse is found by taking the square root of the sum of the squares of the sides of a right triangle. Thus, in Fig. 18·11a, the hypotenuse is $\sqrt{25}$ or 5. In Fig. 18·11b, the hypotenuse is $\sqrt{40}$ or 6.3. Thus in Fig. 18·11c, the hypotenuse is $\sqrt{65}$ or _____ .

18·16 (8.1) In Fig. 18·12a, the hypotenuse is $\sqrt{41}$ or 6.4. Similarly, in Fig. 18·12b, the hypotenuse is $\sqrt{72}$ or _____ .

18·17 (8.5) In Fig. 18·12c, the hypotenuse is $\sqrt{29}$ or _____ .

18·18 (5.4) In Fig. 18·13, the hypotenuse is $\sqrt{89}$ or _____ .

18·19 (9.4) In Fig. 18·14, the hypotenuse is $\sqrt{169}$ or _____ .

18·20 (13) It may be noted from the preceding examples that there are two important triangles in which the sides are in a ratio such that the hypotenuse comes out a whole number. The first of these is in Fig. 18·11a in which the ratio is 3:4:5, with the hypotenuse equal to 5. The second is shown in Fig. 18·14 in which the ratio is 5:12:13, with the hypotenuse _____ .

18·21 (13) Thus, any right triangle whose sides are in the ratio 3:4 has a hypotenuse of 5 in the same ratio. Thus, a triangle whose sides are 6 and 8 has a hypotenuse of 10. Similarly, a triangle with sides of 9 and 12 has a hypotenuse of 15. Also, a triangle having sides of 12 and 16 has a hypotenuse of _____ .

18·22 (20) A triangle whose sides measure 18 and 24 has a hypotenuse of 30. Also, a triangle whose sides measure 15 and 20 has a hypotenuse of _____ .

18·23 (25) A triangle whose sides measure 30 and 40 units, respectively, has a hypotenuse that measures _____ units.

18·24 (50) A right triangle with sides equal to 5 and 12, respectively, is also a special case in which the hypotenuse measures 13. Thus, a triangle with sides of 50 and 120 has a hypotenuse of _____ .

18·25 (130) A right triangle having sides that measure 10 and 24 in., respectively, must have a hypotenuse _____ in. in length.

18·25   (26)

Geometric addition of voltages

In a circuit such as that of Fig. 18·26, we may picture the resistance R as consisting of *all* circuit resistances combined, including the resistance that may be present in the conductor. Thus, the inductive reactance of the inductor X_L resides entirely within the coil. This enables us to approach the circuit problem by working with a pure resistance R and a pure inductance L. In such a circuit, the voltage across the resistor lags behind the voltage across the inductor by 90°, enabling us to set up these voltages vectorially as in Fig. 18·10. Once this is done, we can construct a right triangle and apply the Pythagorean theorem.

18·26   The laws of right triangles can be put to use in adding phasors. For example, in Fig. 18·26, a series circuit containing a resistor and an inductor is shown. In this circuit, the voltage drop across the resistor is given as 30 volts, and the voltage drop across the inductor is given as _____ _____ .

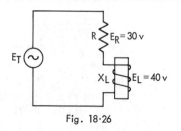

Fig. 18·26

18·27   (40 volts) In Fig. 18·27, the voltage drops are shown in phasor form. If **AB** is the voltage across the resistor E_R and **AC** is the total voltage of the circuit E_t, then **BC** must be the voltage drop across the _____ .

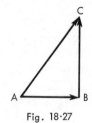

Fig. 18·27

18·28   (inductor) In Fig. 18·28, the voltages have been inserted on the phasors representing E_R and E_L. Using the special 3:4:5 technique, find that the total voltage E_t must be _____ volts.

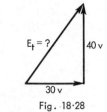

Fig. 18·28

18·29   (50) Figure 18·29 shows another set of phasors in which E_R and E_L are known. The total voltage from the source (using the special rule for 5:12:13 triangles) is _____ _____ .

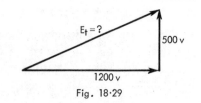

Fig. 18·29

240

18·30 (1,300 volts) If a special triangle is not formed, we may find the total voltage from the square root of the sum of the squares of the sides. In equation form, as applied to Fig. 18·30, this may be written

$$E_t = \sqrt{E_R^2 + \underline{\qquad}}$$

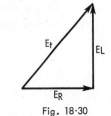

Fig. 18·30

18·31 (E_L^2) The total voltage applied to the RL circuit whose component voltage drops are shown in Fig. 18·31 is _____ _____ .

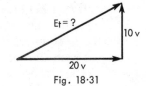

Fig. 18·31

18·32 (22.4 volts) The total voltage applied to the RL circuit in which $E_R = 8$ volts and $E_L = 11$ volts is _____ _____ .

18·33 (13.6 volts) Sometimes we want to know one of the component voltage drops when the source voltage and the other voltage drop are known. To do this, we first square both sides of the equation given in Frame 18·30 and obtain

$$E_t^2 = E_R^2 + \underline{\qquad}$$

18·34 (E_L^2) We then transpose terms to bring the unknown to the left side alone. If we want to find the drop across the inductor, the equation becomes

$$E_L^2 = E_t^2 - \underline{\qquad}$$

18·35 (E_R^2) We then take the square root of both sides to obtain the equation

$$E_L = \underline{\qquad}$$

18·36 ($\sqrt{E_t^2 - E_R^2}$) For example, suppose a voltage of 120 volts is applied to a series RL circuit in which the drop across the resistor is 80 volts. The drop across the inductor is found by substituting in this equation and turns out to be _____ volts.

18·37 (89.8) It is always a good idea to check ratios in case a special triangle is involved. For example, suppose $E_t = 78$ volts and $E_R = 72$ volts. Dividing by 6, we find these in the ratio of $13 : 12$. Hence, the missing vector is $5 \times \underline{\qquad} = \underline{\qquad}$.

18·38 (6, 30) Or another example: E_t is given as 150 volts and E_R is given as 90 volts. These are in the ratio of $3:5$ suggesting a $3:4:5$ triangle. Testing it out, we find that E_L must be

_____.

18·38   (120 volts)

The meaning of impedance

If we label the phasor representations of the resistive and inductive voltage drops as R and X_L, respectively, as in Fig. 18·48, and then identify the hypotenuse of the right triangle thus *formed* as Z, it is evident from the geometry that $Z = \sqrt{R^2 + X_L^2}$. Just what does Z signify?

The process of synthesizing a right triangle from R and X_L is a process of *phasor addition*. The hypotenuse is the *resultant* of the addition; that is, the hypotenuse represents the *phasor sum* of the two components that form the shorter legs of the triangle. Thus, in Fig. 18·48, Z is the phasor sum of R and X_L and represents the *net effective opposition* offered by the series circuit consisting of these two components. The magnitude and direction of Z describe the *total effect* of X_L and R.

The quantity Z is called the "impedance" of the circuit; it is the total number of ohms that an a-c generator looks into while driving a current through the circuit. Once the resistive and reactive components have been combined vectorially by drawing and solving the right triangle, the current may be computed from Ohm's law, using Z as the net opposition factor. Thus, we may write three forms of Ohm's law specifically for a-c circuits in which the impedance Z is known:

$$(a)\ I = \frac{E}{Z} \qquad (b)\ E = IZ \qquad (c)\ Z = \frac{E}{I}$$

These forms are identical with those obtained for d-c except for the substitution of Z, the impedance, for R.

18·39   The total opposition offered to the flow of a-c in an RL circuit is called "impedance" Z. Impedance is given by the equation

$$Z = \sqrt{R^2 + X_L^2}$$

where R is resistance, and X_L is inductive reactance. If the resistance is 3 ohms, and $X_L = 4$ ohms, the impedance of the circuit is _____ ohms.

18·40   (5) The form of the impedance equation suggests the same right-triangle relationship as previously discussed. We can prove it as follows: first we recall the equation that relates E_t, E_R, and E_L in Fig. 18·40 as _____.

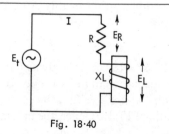

Fig. 18·40

18·41 ($E_t = \sqrt{E_R{}^2 + E_L{}^2}$) Since this is a series circuit, the current in R is _____ _____ the current in X_L.

18·42 (equal to) A voltage drop is the product of a current and an *opposition factor*. Hence, the drop across R equals IR; also, the drop across X_L equals IX_L. Thus, the drop across the total impedance Z must be _____ [see Eq. (*b*) in introduction].

18·43 (*IZ*) Substituting these products for the voltage drops in the equation in Frame 18·40, we may write

$$IZ = \sqrt{I^2R^2 + \underline{\hspace{2cm}}}$$

18·44 ($I^2X_L{}^2$) Squaring both sides of the equation to permit reducing to simpler terms, we have

$$I^2Z^2 = \underline{\hspace{2cm}}$$

18·45 ($I^2R^2 + I^2X_L{}^2$) Dividing through both sides of the equation by I^2, we obtain the result

$$Z^2 = \underline{\hspace{2cm}}$$

18·46 ($R^2 + X_L{}^2$) Taking the square root of each side of the equation, we finally obtain

$$Z = \underline{\hspace{2cm}}$$

18·47 ($\sqrt{R^2 + X^2}$) Noting that this is the same form as the original voltage equation for *RL* circuits, we may then construct a phasor triangle showing R as the horizontal leg (R is the same phase as E_R), X_L as the vertical leg, and _____ as the hypotenuse.

18·48 (*Z*) Such a triangle (Fig. 18·48) is called an "impedance triangle" for *RL* circuits. Thus, if the inductive reactance of a series *RL* circuit is 12 ohms and the resistance is 9 ohms, then the impedance must be _____ ohms.

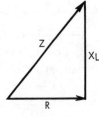

Fig. 18·48

18·48 (15)

For those who require a review of the definitions of the trigonometric functions most used in electricity, we present a brief discussion of the meanings and methods of handling the sine, cosine, and tangent functions. Although the complementary functions (secant, cosecant, and cotangent) may be dispensed with in basic electricity, the reader may want to review these by himself. After he has reestablished his grasp on the sine, cosine, and tangent functions, the use of the complementary functions may be quickly obtained from any standard textbook on trigonometry.

18·49   Trigonometric functions are based on a triangle such as that shown in Fig. 18·49. This is called a right triangle because it contains two acute angles and one _____ angle.

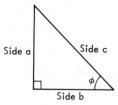

Fig. 18·49

18·50   (right) Side a and side b are called the legs of the triangle. The side opposite the right angle is called the _____ of the right triangle.

18·51   (hypotenuse) The hypotenuse of the triangle in Fig. 18·49 is identified by the letter _____ .

18·52   (c) The sine of any angle in a right triangle is fundamentally defined as the ratio of the side opposite the angle to the hypotenuse of the triangle (Fig. 18·52). That is,

$$\sin \phi = \frac{\text{opposite leg}}{?} \quad \text{or} \quad \frac{\text{side } a}{\text{side } c}$$

For angles between zero and 90 degrees

$$\sin \phi = \frac{opp}{hyp} = \frac{a}{c} \qquad \csc \phi = \frac{hyp}{opp} = \frac{c}{a}$$

$$\cos \phi = \frac{adj}{hyp} = \frac{b}{c} \qquad \sec \phi = \frac{hyp}{adj} = \frac{c}{b}$$

$$\tan \phi = \frac{opp}{adj} = \frac{a}{b} \qquad \cot \phi = \frac{adj}{opp} = \frac{b}{a}$$

Fig. 18·52

18·53   (hypotenuse) For example, in a certain triangle, side $a = 3$ in. and the hypotenuse is 5 in. The sine of the angle ϕ (abbrev. sin ϕ) as in Fig. 18·49 is therefore 3/5 or 0.6. If side $a = 4$ in. and side $c = 5$ in., the sine of the angle (sin ϕ) = _____ .

18·54   (4/5 or 0.8) If the side opposite angle $\phi = 2$ in. and the hypotenuse = 3 in., then sin ϕ = _____ .

18·55 (2/3 or 0.666) Sin $\phi = 0.5$ if side $a = 6$ and side $c = 12$. Also, sin $\phi = 0.5$ if side $a = 7$ and side $c = 14$. Similarly, sin $\phi = 0.5$ if side $a = 8$ and side $c = $ _____ .

18·56 (16) In the triangle of Fig. 18·49, sin ϕ may be found by setting up the ratio of side _____ to side _____ .

18·57 (a,c) In the triangle of Fig. 18·57, the sine of 30° is seen to be opp/hyp = $a/c = 1/2 = $ _____ (decimal form).

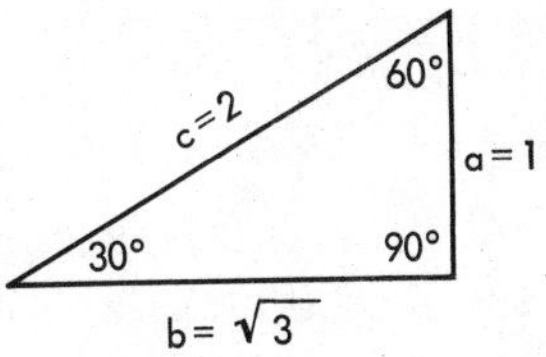

Fig. 18·57

18·58 (0.5) Similarly, the sine of 60° is seen to be opp/hyp = $b/c = $ _____ (in numerical form, leave radical).

18·59 ($\sqrt{3}/2$) In the triangle of Fig. 18·59, the two acute angles are equal, each being _____ ° .

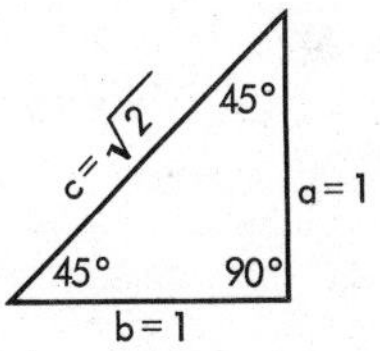

Fig. 18·59

18·60 (45) The sine of either 45° angle is seen to be opp/hyp = 1/_____ .

18·61 ($\sqrt{2}$) Returning to Fig. 18·49, we define the cosine of ϕ (abbrev. cos ϕ) as the ratio of the side adjacent to ϕ to the hypotenuse. That is, as shown in Fig. 18·49, cos ϕ = adj/hyp = $b/$_____ .

18·62 (c) For example, in a given triangle $b = 3$ and $c = 8$. Included between these sides is angle θ. For this triangle, cos $\theta = $ _____ .

18·63 (3/8) In another triangle, cos $\alpha = $ _____ if side $c = 10$ and side $b = 5$.

18·64 (5/10 or 1/2 or 0.5) Thus in any right triangle like that of Fig. 18·49, the cosine of ϕ may be found from the ratio of side _____ to side _____ .

18·65 (b, c) In Fig. 18·57, cos 30° is seen to be the ratio of b to c, or _____ to 2.

18·66 $(\sqrt{3})$ In Fig. 18·59, cos 45° is seen to be the ratio of b to c, or _____ .

18·67 $(1/\sqrt{2})$ In Fig. 18·57, the cosine of 60° is seen to be adj/hyp = a/c = _____ .

18·68 (1/2 or 0.5) Returning to Fig. 18·49, we define the tangent of ϕ (abbrev. tan ϕ) as the ratio of the side opposite ϕ to the side adjacent to ϕ. That is, as given in Fig. 18·52, tan ϕ = opp/adj = $a/$_____ .

18·69 (b) In the triangle of Fig. 18·57, the tangent of 30° (tan 30°) = a/b = 1/_____ .

18·70 $(\sqrt{3})$ Also, in the triangle of Fig. 18·59, tan 45° = _____ .

18·71 (1/1 or just 1) The tangent of any acute angle in a right triangle is, therefore, found by setting up the ratio of the side opposite the angle to the side _____ to the angle.

18·72 (adjacent) In Fig. 18·57, tan 60° = opp/adj = $\sqrt{3}/$_____ .

18·72 (1)

Information Panel

Certain special triangles often encountered have trigonometric functions that are easily reproduced and remembered, making it unnecessary to have recourse to trigonometric tables. The first of these is the 30-60-90 triangle in Fig. 18·57; the second is the 45-45-90 triangle in Fig. 18·59.

In a 30-60-90 triangle, the side opposite the 30° angle is always exactly one-half the hypotenuse. Thus, if we assign a value of 1 to this short side, then the hypotenuse must have a value of 2. Using the Pythagorean theorem, we then find that the remaining leg of the triangle must have the value of $\sqrt{3}$. Thus in a 30-60-90 triangle, the ratio of the sides is *always* 1 to $\sqrt{3}$ to 2, or short leg to long leg to hypotenuse, respectively.

Now refer to the 45-45-90 triangle in Fig. 18·59. This is an isosceles triangle, the two sides opposite the 45° angles being equal to each other. If we assign a value of 1 to side a, then we must assign a value of 1 to side b. Using the Pythagorean theorem, we then find the value of side c to be $\sqrt{2}$. Thus, in a 45-45-90 triangle, the ratio of the sides is *always* 1 to 1 to $\sqrt{2}$, or side to side to hypotenuse, respectively.

18·73 For the special 30-60-90 triangle, then, we should always remember that $\sin 30° = 1/2$, $\cos 30° = \sqrt{3}/2$, and $\tan 30° = $ _____ .

18·74 $(1/\sqrt{3})$ For the special 30-60-90 triangle, we should also remember that $\sin 60° = $ _____ , $\cos 60° = 1/2$, and $\tan 60° = \sqrt{3}/1 = \sqrt{3}$.

18·75 $(\sqrt{3}/2)$ For the special 45-45-90 triangle, we should remember that $\sin 45° = $ _____ , $\cos 45° = $ _____ , and $\tan 45° = $ _____ .

18·76 $(1/\sqrt{2}, 1/\sqrt{2}, 1)$ The value of the trigonometric functions of an angle of 0° is found by visualizing angle ϕ in Fig. 18·49 shrinking more and more, approaching zero as it does so. If ϕ is made smaller and smaller, side a also becomes

_____ .

18·77 (smaller) Finally, when $\phi = 0$, side a has shrunk to zero. Since $\sin \phi = a/c$, then $\sin \phi = 0/c$. However, zero divided by any number is zero, hence $\sin 0° = $ _____ .

18·78 (0) Enter 0 in the proper box in Fig. 18·78. Now let us see what happens to the cosine as ϕ approaches zero. Keeping the right angle unchanged, as ϕ approaches 0 side c becomes shorter and shorter. When $\phi = 0$, side c then becomes exactly the same length as side _____ .

Special Functions

functions	0°	90°
sin		
cos		
tan		

Fig. 18·78

18·79 (b) Thus, when $\phi = 0$, side $b = $ side c. The cosine is defined as b/c, however. Since any number divided by itself is 1, then the cosine of 0° must be equal to _____ .

18·80 (1) Enter 1 in the 0° cosine box in Fig. 18·78. Now for the tangent of 0°. Since tan $\phi = a/b$, and since a becomes zero when $\phi = 0$, then the tangent of 0° is $0/b$. As in the case of sin 0°, then, tan 0° = _____. Enter this in the proper box in Fig. 18·78.

18·81 (0) We can follow a similar procedure to find the functions of 90°. Using Fig. 18·49, visualize what happens when ϕ approaches 90° with side c rotating to the right. As this occurs, side b gets shorter (remember the right angle must be maintained) and side _____ gets longer as side c remains unchanged.

18·82 (a) Finally, when $\phi = 90°$, side b has shrunk to 0 and side a has become the same length as side _____.

18·83 (c) Thus, when $\phi = 90°$, side $b = 0$ and side $a =$ side c. The sine of $\phi = a/c$. But $a = c$ when $\phi =$ _____°.

18·84 (90) Thus, sin 90° is a ratio of two equal numbers. Any number divided by itself is 1. Hence, sin 90° = _____. Enter this in the 90° sine box in Fig. 18·78.

18·85 (1) The cosine of $\phi = b/c$. When $\phi = 90°$, side $b = 0$. Thus cos 90° = $0/c$. However, zero divided by any number is zero, hence cos 90° = _____. Enter this in the 90° cosine box in Fig 18·78.

18·86 (0) The tangent of $\phi = a/b$. When $\phi = 90°$, side $b = 0$. Thus, tan 90° = $a/0$. However, any number divided by zero may be said to be *infinite;* that is, the quotient $a/0 = \infty$. Hence, tan 90° = _____. Enter this symbol in the 90° tangent box in Fig. 18·78.

18·87 (∞) Refer to Fig. 18·87. This drawing shows the four quadrants as used in trigonometry. In the first quadrant (I), both abscissa and ordinate axes are "+." In the second quadrant, the ordinate axis remains "+" but the abscissa axis becomes _____.

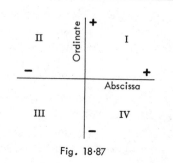

Fig. 18·87

18·88   (−) In the third quadrant (III), both ordinate and
_____ axes are "−."

18·89   (abscissa) In the fourth quadrant (IV), the abscissa is
again positive. In this quadrant, the ordinate axis is _____.

18·90   (negative) Refer to Fig. 18·90. In the triangle shown,
sin φ as always is opp/hyp, but in this case the opposite side is
the ordinate and the hypotenuse is the *distance* from origin to
the end of the ordinate. Thus, we can define sin φ as
ord/_____ when working in quadrants rather than
simple triangles.

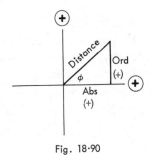

Fig. 18·90

18·91   (distance) In all quadrants, then, sin φ is always defined as ordinate/distance. In the first quadrant, the ordinate
has a positive sign. In *all* quadrants, the distance is *always*
taken as a positive quantity. Hence, in quadrant I, ordinate/
distance is a "+" divided by a "+" = "+" quantity. In
quadrant I, therefore, the sine of any angle is a _____
quantity.

18·92   (+) In quadrant I, the angle may have
any value between 0 and 90°. Thus, when φ has a
value from 0 to 90°, its sine is a _____ quantity.
Enter a "+" sign in box 1 of Fig. 18·92.

	Quadrants			
	I 0–90°	II 90°–180°	III 180°–270°	IV 270°–360°
sin	1	2	3	4
cos	5	6	7	8
tan	9	10	11	12

Fig. 18·92

18·93   (+) In quadrant II, sin φ = ordinate/distance once
again (Fig. 18·93). Again, the ordinate is positive and the distance is positive, hence the quotient ordinate/distance is
_____ and the sine is _____. Enter a
_____ sign in box 2 of Fig. 18·92.

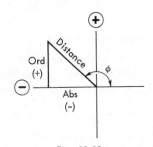

Fig. 18·93

18·94 (positive, positive, +) In quadrant III, Fig. 18·94, the ordinate is "−". Since the distance is positive, then ordinate/distance = −/+. A "−" quantity divided by a "+" quantity gives a "−" quotient, hence sin φ in the third quadrant is _____ . Enter a _____ sign in box 3 of Fig. 18·92.

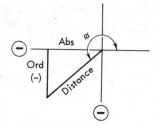

Fig. 18·94

18·95 (negative, −) Thus, any angle larger than 90° but smaller than 180° lies in quadrant II and has a positive sine. Any angle larger than 180° and smaller than 270° lies in quadrant III and has a _____ sine.

18·96 (negative) Finally, in the fourth quadrant (Fig. 18·96) the ordinate is again "−," hence the sine of any angle larger than 270° and smaller than 360° lies in quadrant IV and has a _____ sine. Enter a _____ sign in box 4, Fig. 18·92.

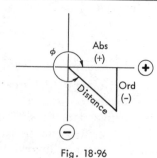

Fig. 18·96

18·97 (negative, −) Looking over the first row of the table in Fig. 18·92, we find that sin φ for quadrants I, II, III, and IV have the signs "+," "+," "−," _____, respectively.

18·98 (−) Now let us repeat the process for cos φ. In Fig. 18·90, cos φ = adj/hyp = abscissa/distance = +/+. Thus, in quadrant I, cos φ is a _____ quantity. Enter a "+" sign in box 5 of Fig. 18·92.

18·99 (positive) In the second quadrant, cos φ is "−" because the distance is "+" but the abscissa is _____ . Enter a "−" sign in box 6 of Fig. 18·92.

18·100 (negative) In quadrant III, cos φ is negative because the abscissa is still negative and the distance is still positive. In quadrant IV, however, the abscissa becomes _____ and therefore the cosine becomes _____ .

18·101 (positive, +) Thus, enter a "−" sign in box 7 and a _____ sign in box 8 of Fig. 18·92.

250

18·102 (+) Reading across the cosine row for quadrants I, II, III, and IV, we find the cosines to be "+," _____, "−," and "+," respectively.

18·103 (−) Now we repeat the same process for the tangent. In the first quadrant tan ϕ is opp/adj = ordinate/abscissa = +/+. Thus in quadrant I, tan ϕ is a _____ quantity.

18·104 (+) Enter "+" in box 9 of Fig. 18·92. In quadrant II, the ordinate is "+" but the abscissa is "−," hence the quotient is "−." Therefore, enter a _____ sign in box 10 of Fig. 18·92.

18·105 (−) In quadrant III, both ordinate and abscissa are "−." A "−" divided by a "−" yields a "+" quotient. Thus, enter a _____ sign in box 11.

18·106 (+) Finally, the tangent becomes a _____ quantity in quadrant IV so that we enter a _____ sign in box 12, Fig. 18·92.

18·107 (negative, −) Reading across the tangent row in Fig. 18·92 for quadrants I, II, III, and IV, we find the signs _____, _____, _____, _____, respectively.

18·108 (+, −, +, −) As shown in Figs. 18·90, 18·93, 18·94, and 18·96, the angle ϕ whose trigonometric functions have been described above is always measured from the abscissa axis to the position of the _____ line. This _____ line is the hypotenuse of each triangle constructed in the respective quadrants.

18·108 (distance, distance)

Phase angles in *RL* circuits

With the completion of the frames in the previous section (Review of Trigonometric Functions), the reader should have the definitions and meanings of the sine, cosine, and tangent clearly in mind, as well as their sign changes as they go from one quadrant to the next.

One additional notational convention should be mentioned here. When we write sin θ = 0.5466, this means that *the sine of the angle theta is 0.5466;* or when we write tan α = 4.855, we read this as the tangent of the angle alpha is 4.855. This should be familiar at this point.

Suppose we want to write "the angle whose cosine is 0.5000 is 60°." There are two ways in common use to do this. They are

$$\arccos 0.5000 = 60°$$
or
$$\cos^{-1} 0.5000 = 60°$$

Thus, if you see $\phi = \arccos - 0.3442$, you would read it as "ϕ is the angle whose cosine is -0.3442." Or if you see $\theta = \tan^{-1} 1.3765$, you would read it as "$\theta$ is the angle whose tangent is 1.3765."

18·109 Ohm's law may be applied to the solution of series RL a-c circuits as well as d-c circuits. The current flowing in such a circuit equals the total voltage divided by the *impedance*. Thus, in equation form, we might write $I =$ _____ .

18·110 (E/Z) The voltage drop across any component of a series a-c RL circuit equals the current in the circuit times the opposition (resistance or reactance) of the component. Thus, the voltage drop across the resistor is IR and the voltage drop across the inductor is _____ .

18·111 (IX_L) If a circuit contains only resistance, the angle of current lead or lag is zero degrees since no phase shift of current occurs in resistive circuits. If the circuit is purely inductive, there is a lagging phase angle (current lagging voltage) of _____ .

18·112 (90°) If a circuit contains both resistance and inductance, the phase angle is still lagging and has a value somewhere between zero degrees and _____ °.

18·113 (90) Since the current in the circuit is always in phase with the voltage across the pure resistance, we can add the current direction as an arrow that extends the phasor representing _____ as shown in Fig. 18·113.

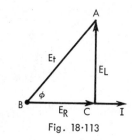

Fig. 18·113

18·114 (E_R) The phase angle, defined as the angle between the current and the total applied circuit voltage, is therefore the angle identified in Fig. 18·113 by the Greek letter _____ (pronounced "fee").

18·115 (ϕ) Since, in any given circuit, the impedance triangle is geometrically *similar* to the voltage triangle, the phase angle is identified in this triangle (Fig. 18·115) as the angle included between R and _____ .

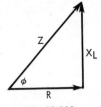

Fig. 18·115

18·116 (Z) The phase angle can be identified by any trigonometric function. For example, $\sin \phi = X_L/Z$. Or, $\cos \phi = R/Z$. Or, finally $\tan \phi =$ _____ .

18·117 (X_L/R) Normally, we will use this definition of ϕ: ϕ is the angle whose tangent is X_L/R. Written in standard trigonometric form, we can state it as $\phi = \arctan X_L/R$, or in another standard form, _____ .

18·117   ($\phi = \tan^{-1} X_L/R$)

Sample *RL* circuit calculation

These frames present a typical problem involving the calculation of all the circuit characteristics.

18·118 A series RL circuit contains a resistor and inductor across a voltage source as shown in Fig. 18·118. We shall determine all the characteristics of the circuit. First, we must find the reactance of the coil from $X_L = 2\pi fL$. Substituting 60 Hz for f and 0.8 henry for L, we find $X_L =$ _____ ohms. (State in round numbers.)

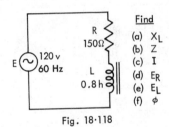

Find
(a) X_L
(b) Z
(c) I
(d) E_R
(e) E_L
(f) ϕ

Fig. 18·118

18·119 (300) The impedance Z is then determined from the formula given previously in Frame 18·46. Substituting $R = 150$ ohms and $X_L = 300$ ohms, the impedance turns out to be _____ .

18·120 (335 ohms) The current in the circuit is determined by using Ohm's law for a-c. That is, $I = E/Z$. Thus, the current in this case turns out to be _____ .

18·121 (0.357 amp) The voltage drop across the resistor E_R is next in line for solution. This is found by substituting in the equation, $E_R = IR$. Thus, the voltage drop across R is _____ _____ .

18·122 (53.5 volts) The voltage drop across the inductor E_L is determined by substituting in the equation, $E_L = IX_L$. When this is done, the voltage drop across the inductor is found to be _____ _____ .

18·123 (108 volts) The phase angle is most easily found from the ratio of X_L/R. That is

$$\phi = \tan^{-1} X_L/R$$

First let us obtain the value of this ratio. Since $X_L = 300$ ohms and $R = 150$ ohms, then this ratio is $300/150 =$ _____ .

18·124 (2) Thus, ϕ is the angle whose _____ is equal to 2.

18·125 (tangent) We must now refer to a table of trigonometric functions, looking along the tangent column to determine what angle has a tangent of 2. We find that an angle of _____ has a tangent of 2.0057.

18·126 (63°30′) This is close enough for our purposes. That is, we might say that the angle whose tangent = 2 is the same (approximately) as the angle whose tangent is 2.0057. Thus, the phase angle is a lagging one and has the value very close to _____ .

18·126   (63°30′)

Power in a-c circuits

The calculation of true power dissipation in a complex a-c circuit depends upon the following idealized conditions:

1. A pure inductance does not dissipate any power whatever. The energy is stored in it in the form of a magnetic field while current is flowing and is returned to the circuit in the form of a current when the source emf drops to zero.

2. Power is dissipated only in resistance, where the electric energy is converted directly into heat.

18·127   Consider a *pure* inductor (zero ohmic resistance). When current flows through it during the a-c cycle, its magnetic field stores the energy fed to it; when the cycle passes through zero, the collapsing field induces an emf that returns *all* the energy to the circuit. Thus, a pure inductor dissipates _____ power.

18·128   (zero) Since the inductor in a series RL circuit dissipates zero power, to find the power consumed we need consider only the _____ in the circuit.

18·129   (resistance) Thus, in a series RL circuit, the power may be determined from the product of the square of the current and the value of the resistance. In the circuit of Fig. 18·118, the power consumed by the circuit, assuming L to be a pure inductance, is I^2R or _____ watts.

18·130   (19.1) The value thus obtained is called the "true power" (abbrev. TP) since it represents *all* the power dissipated in the form of heat. Thus, in a series circuit containing $X_L = 12$ ohms, $R = 8$ ohms, and $I = 10$ amp, the true power is _____ .

18·131   (800 watts) Similarly, in a circuit consisting of an inductive reactance of 1,000 ohms, a resistance of 100 ohms, and a current of 0.03 amp, the true power is _____ .

18·132   (0.09 watt) If the square of the current is multiplied by the total impedance Z of an RL circuit, we obtain a figure called the "apparent power" (abbrev. AP). This figure includes the stored power in the inductor and is *not* the actual dissipated power. In the circuit of Fig. 18·118, the apparent power = AP = $I^2Z = $ _____ watts.

18·133   (43) The *power factor* (abbrev. PF) of an RL circuit is basically defined as the ratio of the true power to the apparent power and tells what fraction of the total apparent power is being utilized in energy conversion. Thus, power factor = PF = TP/AP. In the circuit of Fig. 18·118, the power factor is _____ .

18·134   (0.45) Similarly, in a circuit which dissipates 30 watts in its resistive component and in which an apparent power of 45 watts appears, the power factor is _____ .

18·135 (0.67) Or, considering a circuit in which the true power is 50 watts and the total power, including that of the reactive component, is 55 watts, we can say that PF = _____.

18·136 (0.92) From the foregoing, it can be seen that as the true power begins to approach more closely to the apparent power, the power factor approaches _____.

18·137 (1.0) Hence, in a purely resistive circuit where the true power and apparent power are the same, the power factor must be equal to _____.

18·138 (1.0) On the other hand, when the circuit is purely inductive (resistance = 0), the power factor must be _____.

18·139 (zero) We can obtain a simpler equation for power factor by using these facts: since true power = I^2R and apparent power I^2Z, these alternate values may be substituted in the equation PF = TP/AP. When this is done, the I^2 factor cancels out leaving the equation, PF = _____.

18·140 (R/Z) The accuracy of this equation can be tested by finding the PF for the circuit of Fig. 18·118, where R was 150 ohms and Z was 335 ohms. Substituting in PF = R/Z, we obtain for power factor the value of _____ (compare with Frame 18·133).

18·141 (0.45) Now, referring to the impedance triangle, it is seen that the ratio R/Z is the trigonometric function normally defined as the _____ of the phase angle.

18·142 (cosine) Thus, another definition of power factor R/Z can be written in trigonometric form. That is power factor may be defined as PF = _____.

18·143 (cos ϕ) Checking the validity of this expression, we first recall that the phase angle ϕ in the circuit of Fig. 18·118 was found to be 63°30′. When we look up the cosine of 63°30′, we find it to be _____ (check with Frame 18·140).

18·144 (0.45) Summarizing: the ratio of true to apparent power in a series *RL* circuit is called the _____ _____ .

18·145 (power factor) The power factor can be found by setting up the resistance and impedance of the circuit in the ratio _____ .

18·146 (*R/Z*) The power factor can be found trigonometrically from the expression PF = _____ _____ .

18·147 (cos φ) In a purely resistive circuit, the power factor is _____ .

18·148 (1.0) In a purely inductive circuit, the power factor is _____ .

18·149 (zero) In any real *RL* circuit containing both resistance and reactance, the power factor must lie between _____ _____ _____ .

18·149   (zero and 1.0)

MEASURABLE BEHAVIORAL OBJECTIVES

Upon completion of a section, you should be able to achieve the objectives listed for it. The frame or frames that cover the related subject matter are indicated immediately following each objective.

Voltage and current relationships in phasor diagrams

1   Indicate the voltage-current relationships for inductors and resistors. (18·1 to 18·4)
   a   Recognize that the voltage across a resistor is in phase with the current through it. (18·3)
   b   Recognize that the voltage across an inductor leads the current through it by 90°. (18·4)
2   Add phasor quantities. (18·5 to 18·10)
   a   Realize that phasor quantities cannot generally be added by simple addition. (18·5, 18·6)
   b   Describe the sum of two phasors as the diagonal of a polygon whose sides are the phasors to be added. (18·7 to 18·10)
   c   Identify the polygon as a rectangle when two perpendicular phasors are to be added. (18·7, 18·9, 18·10)

Solution of simple triangles

1 Compute the third side of a right triangle given the other two sides. (18·11 to 18·19)

    a Identify the relationships among the sides of a right triangle as the Pythagorean theorem: (18·11, 18·12)

$$a^2 + b^2 = c^2$$

    where a and b are the lengths of the legs and c is the length of the hypotenuse.

    b Solve for the length of the hypotenuse given the lengths of the legs. (18·13 to 18·19)

2 Recognize certain common right triangles. (18·20 to 18·25)

    a Identify the 3:4:5 triangle. (18·21 to 18·23)

    b Identify the 5:12:13 triangle. (18·24, 18·25)

Geometric addition of voltages

1 Compute the voltages in a series RL circuit using the Pythagorean theorem. (18·26 to 18·30)

    a Recognize that the voltage across the resistor in a series RL circuit lags the voltage across the inductor by 90°. (18·26, 18·27)

    b Identify the sum of the two voltages as the hypotenuse of a right triangle whose legs are the resistor and inductor voltages. (18·27 to 18·30)

2 Calculate any voltage in a series RL circuit given the other two. (18·31 to 18·38)

    a Calculate the total voltage given the resistor and inductor voltages. (18·31 to 18·33)

    b Compute the inductor voltage given the total voltage and the resistor voltage. (18·33 to 18·38)

The meaning of impedance

1 Describe the impedance as the opposition to the flow of current. (18·39 to 18·43)

    a Indicate that the impedance in an a-c circuit is analogous to the resistance in a d-c circuit. (18·42)

    b Identify the three forms of Ohm's law for a-c circuits as being identical to Ohm's law for d-c circuits except that the impedance is substituted for the resistance. (Introduction)

    c Define Z as the symbol for impedance. (18·39, 18·42)

2 Define the impedance in terms of the resistance and the inductive reactance. (18·40 to 18·48)

    a Define X_L as the inductive reactance. (18·42, 18·43)

    b Identify the inductor voltage in terms of the inductor current as $E_L = X_L I$. (18·42)

    c Compute the total voltage in a series RL circuit in terms of the resistor and inductor voltages. (18·40, 18·43)

    d Solve for the impedance as the ratio of total voltage to current resulting in $\sqrt{Z = R^2 + X_L{}^2}$. (18·44 to 18·48)

Review of trigonometric functions

1 Define the various trigonometric functions in terms of a right triangle. (18·49 to 18·72)
   a sine of angle = opposite side/hypotenuse   (18·52 to 18·60)
   b cosine of angle = adjacent side/hypotenuse   (18·61 to 18·67)
   c tangent of angle = opposite side/adjacent side   (18·68 to 18·72)
2 Recognize certain special triangles. (18·73 to 18·75)
   a The sides of a 30-60-90 triangle are in the ratio 1 to $\sqrt{3}$ to 2. (18·72, 18·74)
   b The sides of a 45-45-90 triangle are in the ratio 1 to 1 to $\sqrt{2}$.   (18·75)
   c For all triangles the smallest side is opposite the smallest angle and the largest side is opposite the largest angle.
3 Identify the trigonometric functions of 0° and 90°. (18·76 to 18·86)
   a $\sin 0° = 0$.   (18·76 to 18·78)
   b $\sin 90° = 1$.   (18·81 to 18·84)
   c $\cos 0° = 1$.   (18·78 to 18·80)
   d $\cos 90° = 0$.   (18·85)
   e $\tan 0° = 0$.   (18·80)
   f $\tan 90° = \infty$.   (18·86)
4 The trigonometric functions for angles not between 0 and 90° are defined with respect to a set of axes. (18·87 to 18·90, 18·93 to 18·96, 18·108)
   a The vertical coordinate of a point is the ordinate. It is positive upward and negative downward. (18·87 to 18·89)
   b The horizontal coordinate is the abscissa. It is positive to the right and negative to the left. (18·87 to 18·89)
   c The distance from the origin to the point is the hypotenuse of the right triangle whose legs are the abscissa and ordinate. The hypotenuse is always positive. (18·90)
   d The angle is measured as the counterclockwise rotation from the horizontal right axis to the hypotenuse. (18·90, 18·93 to 18·96, 18·108)
5 The trigonometric functions are defined in terms of the abscissa, ordinate, and hypotenuse. (18·90, 18·91, 18·98, 18·103)
   a sine of angle = ordinate/hypotenuse   (18·90, 18·91)
   b cosine of angle = abscissa/hypotenuse   (18·98)
   c tangent of angle = ordinate/abscissa   (18·103)
6 Identify the algebraic signs of the trigonometric functions according to the quadrant. (18·90 to 18·107)
   a Angles between 0 and 90° are in the first quadrant for which the sine, cosine, and tangent are positive. (18·92, 18·98, 18·103)
   b Angles between 90 and 180° are in the second quadrant for which the sine is positive and the cosine and tangent are negative. (18·93, 18·95, 18·99, 18·104)
   c Angles between 180 and 270° are in the third quadrant for which the tangent is positive and the sine and cosine are negative. (18·94, 18·95, 18·100, 18·105)
   d Angles between 270 and 360° are in the fourth quadrant for which the cosine is positive and the sine and tangent are negative. (18·96, 18·100, 18·106)

Phase angles in RL circuits

1 In a series RL circuit, the total voltage leads the current by an angle between 0 and 90°. (18·109 to 18·114)
   a The resistor voltage is in phase with the current. (18·111, 18·113)
   b The inductor voltage leads the current by 90°. (18·111)
   c The total voltage is the phasor sum of the resistor voltage and the inductor voltage. (18·113, 18·114)

2 The impedance can be represented by an impedance triangle. (18·113 to 18·115)
   a The current through the series resistor and inductor is the same. (18·113)
   b The resistance may be represented by a phasor equal to the resistor voltage. (18·115)
   c The inductive reactance may be represented by a phasor equal to the inductor voltage. (18·115)
   d The impedance is then represented by a phasor equal to the total voltage. (18·115)

3 The phase angle of an impedance is defined as the angle between the current through the impedance and the voltage across it. (18·113 to 18·117)
   a The current through a series RL circuit is in phase with the resistor voltage and therefore with the resistance phasor. (18·113)
   b The voltage across the impedance is represented by a phasor equal to the impedance phasor. (18·113 to 18·115)
   c The phase angle then is the angle between the resistance and impedance phasors. (18·115)
   d The impedance phasor is the hypotenuse of a right triangle whose legs are the resistance and inductive reactance phasors. (18·115)
   e Phase angle $= \arctan X_L/R = \arcsin X_L/Z = \arccos R/Z$. (18·116, 18·117)

Sample RL circuit calculation

Perform a complete analysis of a series RL circuit. (18·118 to 18·126)
   a Find the inductive reactance. (18·118)
   b Find the impedance. (18·119)
   c Find the current. (18·120)
   d Find the resistor voltage. (18·121)
   e Find the inductor voltage. (18·122)
   f Find the phase angle. (18·123 to 18·126)

Power in a-c circuits

1 Define the true power as I^2R. (18·127 to 18·131)
2 Recognize that an inductor stores and returns energy to a circuit. (18·127)
3 Recognize that only the resistance dissipates energy. (18·128, 18·129)
4 Define the apparent power as I^2Z. (18·132)
5 Indicate that the apparent power includes the power stored by the inductor as well as the power dissipated by the resistor. (18·132)

6 Define the power factor as the ratio of real power to apparent power. (18·133 to 18·149)

    a Recognize that the power factor lies between 0 and 1. (18·136 to 18·138, 18·149)

    b Indicate that the power factor for a purely resistive circuit is 1. (18·137, 18·147)

    c Indicate that the power factor for a purely inductive circuit is 0. (18·138, 18·148)

    d Derive the definition of power factor as the ratio of resistance to impedance. (18·139 to 18·141, 18·145)

chapter 19

RC circuits

An *RC* circuit calculation

Calculations in circuits containing only resistance and capacitance are handled in much the same way as in circuits that have resistance and inductance. The difference is, of course, that the phase angle in a capacitive circuit is a leading rather than a lagging one; that is, the current leads the voltage in a capacitive circuit while it lags the voltage in an inductive circuit. The use of phasor pictorialization, as in Fig. 19·6, is very helpful in visualizing the action taking place.

19·1   When a capacitor and resistor are connected in series with an a-c source, a current flows through the circuit. Although the current does not pass through the dielectric of the capacitor, the effect is that of current passage due to the charge and _____ of the capacitor (Fig. 19·1).

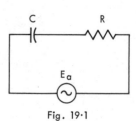

Fig. 19·1

19·2   (discharge) The current flowing in and out of the capacitor plates may be described as the current through the capacitor. As we have seen, the voltage lags behind the capacitor current. Or, said in another way, the current _____ the voltage.

19·3   (leads) The angle of current lead in a purely capacitive circuit (one containing no resistance) is _____°.

19·4   (90) As resistance is added in series with the capacitor, the angle of lead decreases. That is, when a resistor is connected in series with a capacitor and an a-c source, the current leads the voltage by some angle less than _____°.

19·5 (90) Figure 19·5 shows a purely capacitive situation. The current is shown leading the voltage by 90°. As in *RL* circuits, the angle between current and voltage is called the _____ angle.

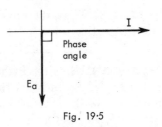

Fig. 19·5

19·6 (phase) In Fig. 19·6, the phase angle is less than 90°. This means that the circuit represented by this phasor diagram must contain some _____ as well as the capacitance.

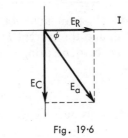

Fig. 19·6

19·7 (resistance) In Fig. 19·6, the phase angle is shown by the symbol _____, just as it was in inductive circuits.

19·8 (ϕ) As proved in Frames 18·39 to 18·48, a right triangle can be formed from the resistance R and the capacitive reactance X_c to give a hypotenuse, which is also called the impedance Z, for *RC* circuits (Fig. 19·8). In this phasor triangle, angle _____ is the phase angle.

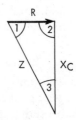

Fig. 19·8

19·9 (1) As in *RL* circuits, Z can be found by solving the right triangle. For example, in Fig. 19·9, the impedance is the hypotenuse of a 3:4:5 triangle, hence the value of the impedance must be _____ ohms.

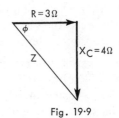

Fig. 19·9

19·10 (5) As in *RL* circuits, the cosine of the phase angle is the side adjacent to ϕ over the hypotenuse. Thus, in Fig. 19·9, the cosine of the phase angle is _____.

19·11 (3/5) From a trigonometric table we find that the angle whose cosine is 3/5 or 0.6 is _____°.

19·12 (53) Thus, the phase angle in Fig. 19·9 is approximately _____ .

19·13 (53°) Using the Pythagorean theorem for any kind of right triangle, we find that the hypotenuse Z is equal to the square root of the sum of the squares of R and X_c. Stated in equation form, as for RL circuits, we may write that $Z = \sqrt{R^2 + \underline{\hspace{1cm}}}$.

19·14 ($X_c{}^2$) In the problem posed by Fig. 19·14, we are asked to find the current I. First we must find the impedance. This may be done using the Pythagorean equation just stated. That is

$$Z = \sqrt{9^2 + 12^2}$$

Thus, Z turns out to be _____ ohms.

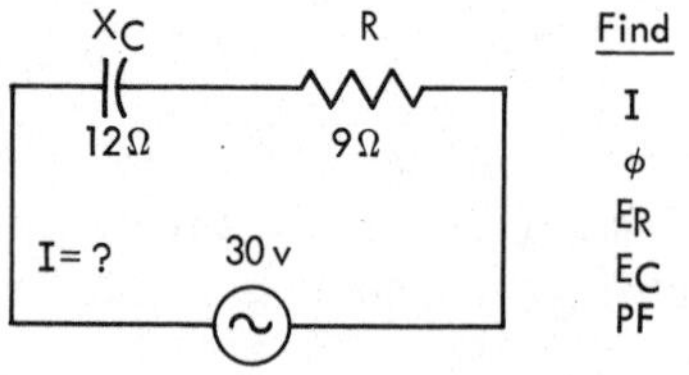

Fig. 19·14

19·15 (15) The current is found from the a-c form of Ohm's law as in RL circuits. That is, $I = E/Z$. Thus, for this case, $I = 30/15$. Thus I is _____ amp.

19·16 (2) Since this circuit is capacitive, the phase angle must be a leading one. Since ϕ is the angle whose cosine is R/Z, we can say that the phase angle is $\cos^{-1} 9/15$ or $\cos^{-1} 0.6$. Thus, $\phi = \underline{\hspace{1cm}}°$.

19·17 (53) To find the voltage drop across the capacitor in Fig. 19·14, we again apply the familiar form of Ohm's law: $E = IX_c$. Substituting the known values, we have $E_c = 2 \times 12$. Thus, the voltage drop across the capacitor is _____ volts.

19·18 (24) In a similar manner, we find that the voltage drop across the resistor is $E_R = IR$. Thus $E_R = 2 \times 9$. Hence, the voltage drop across the resistor is _____ _____ .

19·19 (18 volts) As in RL circuits, the power factor is defined as the cosine of ϕ, or R/Z. Thus, in this problem the power factor is $\cos \phi = 9/15$. Hence, the power factor in decimal notation is _____ .

19·20 (0.6) As in RL circuits, the power dissipated in the circuit is found from $P = I^2R$. Thus, in this problem, the power dissipated is $P = 2^2 \times 9$. Hence, the power dissipated is _____ watts.

19·20 (36)

A typical RC problem

Like an inductor, a capacitor does not dissipate power (ideally). Whatever energy is stored in the capacitor during the charging interval is released to the circuit when the voltage across the capacitor drops during the a-c cycle. For this reason, circuit calculations involving capacitors resemble those involving inductors very closely.

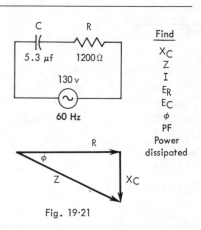

Fig. 19·21

19·21   Referring to the problem in Fig. 19·21, we first find X_c from the relationship $X_c = 1/(2\pi fC)$. Remembering that C is given in microfarads in the problem, we first convert C to farads, then substitute. We obtain $X_c =$ _____ ohms. (Round off to a single digit followed by 2 zeros.)

19·22   (500) The impedance Z of the circuit is then found from the relation

$$Z = \sqrt{R^2 + X_c^2}$$

Substituting 1,200 ohms for R and 500 ohms for X_c, we find the impedance of the circuit to be _____ ohms.

19·23   (1,300) The current in the circuit I is next determined from Ohm's law: $I = E/Z$. Thus, substituting 130 volts for E and 1,300 ohms for Z, we obtain a value for the current equal to _____ amp.

19·24   (0.1) The voltage drop across the resistor E_R is obtained from $E_R = IR$. Thus, substituting 0.1 amp for I and 1,200 ohms for R, we find the value of E_R to be _____ volts.

19·25   (120) Similarly, the voltage drop across the capacitor E_c is $E_c = IX_c$. Thus, substituting 0.1 amp for I and 500 ohms for X_c, the value of E_c turns out to be _____ volts.

19·26   (50) The phase angle is a leading one. To find its value, let us use $\phi = \tan^{-1} X_c/R$. As previously determined, $X_c = 500$ ohms and $R = 1,200$ ohms. Thus, the ratio $X_c/R =$ _____ (to four decimal places).

19·27 (0.4167) A simple trigonometric table shows that the angle whose tangent is 0.4173 is 22°40′. This is close enough for our purposes, and we may therefore say that the phase angle ϕ for this circuit has a value of _____ .

19·28 (22°40′) Power factor is defined as PF = R/Z. We are given $R = 1,200$ ohms, and we have determined that $Z = 1,300$ ohms. The ratio R/Z is therefore $1,200/1,300 =$ _____ . (to three decimal places).

19·29 (0.923) The power dissipated in the circuit is determined from $P = I^2R$. Thus, the power dissipated in the circuit of Fig. 19·21 is _____ watts.

19·29 (12)

MEASURABLE BEHAVIORAL OBJECTIVES

Upon completion of a section, you should be able to achieve the objectives listed for it. The frame or frames that cover the related subject matter are indicated immediately following each objective.

An *RC* circuit calculation

1 Recognize that the charge and discharge of a capacitor in series with an a-c source have the effect of a current flowing through the capacitor. (19·1, 19·2)
2 Realize that the current leads the voltage in a series *RC* circuit. (19·2 to 19·6)
   a State that the voltage across a capacitor lags behind the current through it by 90°. (19·2, 19·3, 19·5)
   b Increasing the series resistance causes the phase angle to decrease. (19·4, 19·6)
3 Determine the impedance diagram of a series *RC* circuit. (19·8, 19·9)
   a Realize that the resistance is depicted by a phasor directed to the right. (19·8)
   b Realize that the capacitive reactance is represented by a phasor directed downward. (19·8)
   c Identify the impedance phasor as the diagonal of the rectangle whose sides are the resistance phasor and capacitive reactance phasor. (19·8, 19·9)
4 Compute the impedance and phase angle. (19·7, 19·9 to 19·13)
   a State that $Z = \sqrt{R^2 + X_c^2}$. (19·9, 19·13)
   b Realize that the phase angle is the angle between the current and voltage. (19·7)

c Recognize that the angle between the resistance and impedance is the phase angle. (19·8)

d Recognize that the cosine of the phase angle is equal to R/Z. (19·10 to 19·12)

5 Compute the current, phase angle power factor, and power dissipated in a series RC circuit. (19·14 to 19·20)

a Determine the impedance as $Z = \sqrt{R^2 + X_c^2}$. (19·14)

b Compute the current as $I = E/Z$. (19·15)

c Determine the phase angle as $\phi = \cos^{-1} R/Z$. (19·16)

d Find the resistor voltage as $ER = IR$. (19·18)

e Find the capacitor voltage as $E_c = IX_c$. (19·17)

f Find the power dissipated as $P = I^2R$. (19·20)

g Find the power factor as $\cos \phi = R/Z$. (19·19)

A typical RC problem

Solve for the current and voltage in a series RC circuit, as well as for the capacitive reactance, impedance, phase angle, power factor, and power dissipated. (19·21 to 19·29)

chapter 20

RCL circuits

The final step in fundamental a-c circuits is the combining of resistance, inductance, and capacitance in a single series circuit. The voltage drops across these components—three in number—are combined vectorially to determine impedance and phase angle. Of great interest in this regard is the fact that inductive reactance and capacitive reactance when represented by phasors are 180° apart. These phasors may then be combined into a single resultant called simply "reactance" by subtracting one from the other. The reactance (difference between X_L and X_c) is finally combined with the resistance in an impedance triangle.

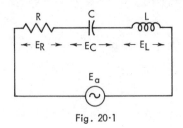

Fig. 20·1

20·1 When all three components are combined in a series circuit (R, C, and L), there are three voltage drops. These are E_R, E_c, and _____ as in Fig. 20·1.

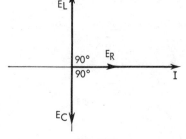

Fig. 20·2

20·2 (E_L) Refer to Fig. 20·2. Note that E_R is drawn on the same axis as I. This means that there is no phase difference between I and E_R since a voltage drop in a resistor is always in phase with the current through the resistor. Thus, the phase angle between I and E_R is a _____ degree angle.

20·3 (zero) The phase angle of 90° between I and E_L shows that the voltage drop across the inductor _____ the current through the inductor by 90°.

20·4 (leads) The phase angle of 90° between I and E_c shows that the voltage drop across the capacitor _____ _____ the current through the capacitor by 90°.

20·5 (lags behind) In terms of resistance and reactances, these phasors may be inserted on the axes in Fig. 20·5. Thus, the resistance phasor used to replace E_R may be shown on the axis labeled **OC** in Fig. 20·5. Similarly, the inductive reactance phasor would be inserted on _____ in this figure.

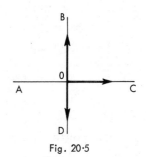

Fig. 20·5

20·6 (**OB**) The capacitive reactance phasor X_c could be shown on the axis labeled _____ in this figure.

20·7 (**OD**) The two reactances X_L and X_c lie on the same straight line. The phase angle between X_L and X_c is, therefore, _____°.

20·8 (180) Since X_L is the positive end of the Y axis, its sign may be considered positive. Also, since X_c lies on the negative side of the Y axis, its sign is taken as _____.

20·9 (negative) Two phasors out of phase by 180° may be added algebraically rather than vectorially. Since X_L is "+" and X_c is "−," the total *reactance* obtained by algebraic addition is $X_L -$ _____.

20·10 (X_c) If, after this addition, the reactance turns out to be a positive quantity, it means that X_L must have been _____ than X_c.

20·11 (larger) In this case, we obtain a drawing such as that of Fig. 20·11 in which X, the net reactance, is positive. As shown by the completed impedance parallelogram, the circuit is inductive because the resistance is shown _____ the impedance.

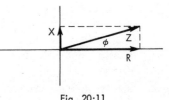

Fig. 20·11

20·12 (lagging) Should the capacitive reactance be larger than the inductive reactance, the net reactance would be negative as in Fig. 20·12. Thus φ would be a leading phase angle and the circuit would be considered _____ in nature.

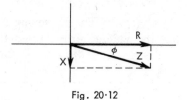

Fig. 20·12

20·13 (capacitive) Summarizing, if X_L exceeds X_c, the circuit is considered _____ in nature and the phase angle φ is a _____ phase angle.

20·14 (inductive, lagging) Summarizing, if X_c exceeds X_L, the circuit is considered _____ in nature and the phase angle φ is a _____ phase angle.

20·14 (capacitive, leading)

MEASURABLE BEHAVIORAL OBJECTIVES

Upon completion of a section, you should be able to achieve the objectives listed for it. The frame or frames that cover the related subject matter are indicated immediately following each objective.

Phase relationships in an *RCL* circuit

1 Draw the phasor representation of the current and voltages in a series *RCL* circuit. (20·1 to 20·4)
  a Recognize that the resistor voltage is in phase with the current. (20·2)
  b Recognize that the inductive voltage leads the current by 90°. (20·3)
  c Recognize that the capacitive voltage lags the current by 90°. (20·4)
2 Determine the impedance diagram of a series *RCL* circuit. (20·5, 20·6)
  a Recognize that the impedances are proportional to the voltages. (20·5)
  b Draw the resistance phasor to the right. (20·5)
  c Realize that the inductive reactance phasor points up. (20·5)
  d Draw the capacitive reactance phasor downward. (20·6)
3 Find the impedance phasor. (20·7 to 20·14)
  a Recognize that the capacitive and inductive reactance phasors are out of phase by 180°. (20·7)
  b Realize that the combined reactance is the algebraic sum of the inductive and capacitive reactances. Thus $X = X_L - X_c$. (20·8 to 20·10)
  c Determine the impedance phasor as the vector sum of the resistance phasor and combined reactance phasor. (20·11, 20·12)
  d Identify an impedance as inductive or capacitive. (20·13, 20·14)

chapter 21
resonance

Introduction to resonance

We have seen that in a circuit containing resistance, inductance, and capacitance, the inductive reactance X_L and capacitive reactance X_c are 180° out of phase with each other. From the phasor point of view, these quantities are in phase opposition, the net reactance being the algebraic sum (actually the difference since X_L is always positive and X_c is always negative). It is therefore possible to choose values of L and C such that, at a specific frequency, the two reactances are equal in magnitude. Being in phase opposition, they will cancel each other under these conditions. When this occurs, the only opposition remaining in the circuit is the resistance; that is, if X_L and X_c are equal and opposite, the reactance becomes zero and the impedance becomes equal to the residual resistance in the circuit. This condition is called "resonance" and leads to important differences in circuit behavior.

21·1 If the inductance and capacitance in an *RCL* circuit are chosen properly, it is possible to make X_L equal to X_c. Under these conditions, the algebraic sum of X_L and X_c must be equal to _____ .

21·2 (zero) In Fig. 21·2, X_L and X_c are shown equal to each other. Under these conditions, the net reactance which is the algebraic sum of the two reactive components is _____ .

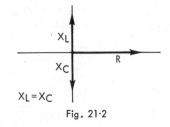

Fig. 21·2

21·3 (zero) With the net reactance equal to zero in a circuit containing equal values of inductive and capacitive reactance, the only opposition left in the circuit is that of the _____ as in Fig. 21·3.

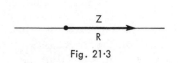

Fig. 21·3

21·4 (resistance) Thus, in a circuit containing equal values of X_L and X_c, the impedance becomes the same figure as the _____ of the circuit.

21·5 (resistance) Such a circuit—that is, one in which $X_L = X_c$—is called a "resonant circuit." In a resonant circuit, the total impedance consists only of the _____ in the circuit.

21·6 (resistance) If X_L is *not* equal to X_c, the net reactance of the circuit is not zero. In this case, the impedance must be found by adding the reactances algebraically and then adding the net reactance thus determined to the resistance by means of _____ addition.

21·7 (phasor) For example, in the circuit of Fig. 21·7, the net reactance is $X = X_L - X_c$. Thus the net reactance is _____ ohms.

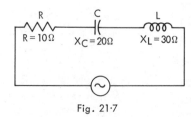

Fig. 21·7

21·8 (10) The net reactance must now be added vectorially to the resistance. That is

$$Z = \sqrt{R^2 + X^2}$$

In this circuit, therefore, the impedance is _____ ohms.

21·9 (14.1) If, however, the reactances are both 20 ohms as in Fig. 21·9, then the net reactance is zero, and the impedance becomes equal to the resistance. Thus, in this circuit the impedance is equal to _____ ohms.

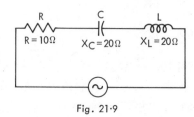

Fig. 21·9

21·10 (10) When the reactances are equal, the circuit is then in a _____ condition.

21·11 (resonant) Since the reactances in a resonant circuit cancel out, the impedance takes on the lowest possible value since it becomes equal to the _____ of the circuit.

21·12 (resistance) Thus, in an *RCL* circuit, the impedance is at a minimum when the circuit is in the condition of

_____ .

21·12 (resonance)

The resonant frequency of an *RCL* circuit

There is only one frequency of the a-c supplied to an *RCL* circuit for which inductive and capacitive reactances are exactly equal. This frequency is called the "resonant frequency." The ability to determine the resonant frequency of a given coil-and-capacitor combination is a definite asset to the technician. Fortunately, we can develop a relatively simple equation which will give us the resonant frequency if L and C are known.

21·13 The inductive reactance X_L of a coil was shown to be the product of 2π times the frequency times the inductance, or $2\pi fL$. In this equation, X_L is in ohms if f is in hertz and L is in

_____ .

21·14 (henrys) This equation also shows that X_L is "frequency sensitive." That is, if the frequency of the a-c voltage applied to the coil is increased, the inductive reactance must

_____ .

21·15 (increase) The capacitive reactance of a capacitor was shown to be determinable from the equation, $X_c = 1/(2\pi fC)$. In this equation, X_c comes out in ohms if the frequency is in hertz and the capacitance is in _____ .

21·16 (farads) X_c is also frequency sensitive, but in a sense opposite to that of inductive reactance. That is, if the frequency of the a-c source supplying voltage to the capacitor rises, the capacitive reactance _____ in proportion.

21·17 (decreases) Consider a circuit in which X_L is considerably larger than X_c, for the frequency that happens to be available from the a-c source at the time. Since X_L and X_c are *not* equal in this circuit, then the circuit cannot be in a_____ condition.

21·18 (resonant) Now suppose that the frequency of the a-c source is slowly *reduced*. This will cause X_L to decrease in proportion, while X_c _____ in the same proportion.

21·19 (increases) Since X_L was initially larger than X_c, the two reactances will begin to approach each other in magnitude. Thus, if the frequency is chosen just right, it is possible to make X_L and X_c come out _____ to each other.

21·20 (equal) When the frequency is correctly selected to make $X_L = X_c$, the circuit will then be in _____.

21·21 (resonance) To find the correct resonant frequency for any coil and capacitor combination, we need an equation. We can derive this equation by saying first that, at resonance, X_L must be _____ to X_c.

21·22 (equal) Since $X_L = 2\pi fL$ and $X_c = 1/(2\pi fC)$, we may substitute these identities in place of X_L and X_c to obtain an equation that reads $2\pi fL = 1/$_____.

21·23 ($2\pi fC$) Thus far we have (for resonance) the equation, $2\pi fL = 1/(2\pi fC)$. Multiplying both sides of the equation by $2\pi fC$, we obtain $4\pi^2 f^2 LC =$ _____.

21·24 (1) To obtain f^2 alone on the left side of the equation, we can divide both sides through by $4\pi^2 LC$. When this is done, we obtain the result: _____.

21·25 [$f^2 = 1/(4\pi^2 LC)$] To obtain f alone, we must take the square root of both sides of the equation. When this is done, we have the result: $f =$ _____.

21·26 [$1/(2\pi \sqrt{LC})$] Thus, if the inductance L and the capacitance C of any LC combination are known, the _____ frequency can be found by substituting in this equation.

21·27 (resonant) The resonant frequency f will come out in hertz if L is in henrys and C is in _____.

21·28 (farads) As an example, let us find the resonant frequency of a circuit containing an inductance of 20 henrys and a capacitance of 5 μf. Before substituting in the equation, we must first convert microfarads into _____.

274

21·29 (farads) Five microfarads is the same as _____ × 10^{-6} farad.

21·30 (5) The value of 2π is 2 × 3.14 or _____.

21·31 (6.28) Thus, in its final form with all values substituted, we can write the equation as follows: $f =$ _____.

21·32 [$1/(6.28 \sqrt{20 \times 5 \times 10^{-6}})$] Multiplying out the numbers under the radical, taking the square root, and then multiplying by 6.28, we obtain as the simplified value for the denominator _____.

21·33 (62.8×10^{-3}, or 6.28×10^{-2}) Let us write the entire fraction thus far:

$$f = \frac{1}{62.8 \times 10^{-3}}$$

But the quantity 10^{-3} may be moved to the numerator, thereby changing it to 10^3. Rewriting the fraction with 10^3 in the numerator instead of 10^{-3} in the denominator, we have $f =$ _____.

21·34 ($10^3/62.8$) Dividing through, we obtain the value of the resonant frequency. This turns out to be _____ Hz.

21·35 (15.9) Thus, if a coil of 20 henrys and a capacitor of 5 μf are connected in series with an a-c source whose frequency is 15.9 Hz, the circuit will be in the _____ condition.

21·36 (resonant) In this condition, the inductive and capacitive reactances will be _____.

21·37 (equal) Also, in this condition the circuit impedance will be at its _____ value.

21·38 (minimum) As a matter of fact, in this condition, the circuit impedance will have the same value as the residual _____ in the circuit.

21·39 (resistance) Since the impedance of a resonant circuit is at a minimum, the current through such a circuit must be at _____ for any given voltage applied to it.

21·40 (maximum) Furthermore, since the reactive components cancel each other at resonance, the only component left is resistive. Hence, the phase angle between current and voltage in a resonant circuit must be _____ .

21·41 (zero) Finally, since Z equals R in a resonant circuit, and since power factor $PF = R/Z$, then the power factor of a resonant circuit must be equal to _____ .

21·42 (one) Reviewing, a resonant circuit has the following characteristics: **a.** The two reactive components are _____ in reactance. **b.** The impedance of the circuit equals the _____ of the circuit. **c.** The current is at _____ for a given voltage. **d.** The phase angle between voltage and current is _____ . **e.** The power factor is _____ .

21·42 (**a.** equal, **b.** resistance, **c.** maximum, **d.** zero, **e.** one)

Calculation of a series resonant circuit

The phenomenon of resonance introduces new and important aspects in the performance of a-c circuits. Among these is the appearance of a new capability: the development of a *voltage gain*. The ability of a resonant circuit to display voltage gain gives rise to the concept of the Q of the circuit to be discussed next.

21·43 Consider the series resonant circuit shown in Fig. 21·43. We know that this is a resonant circuit because X_c is shown to be equal to _____ , since both are 200 ohms.

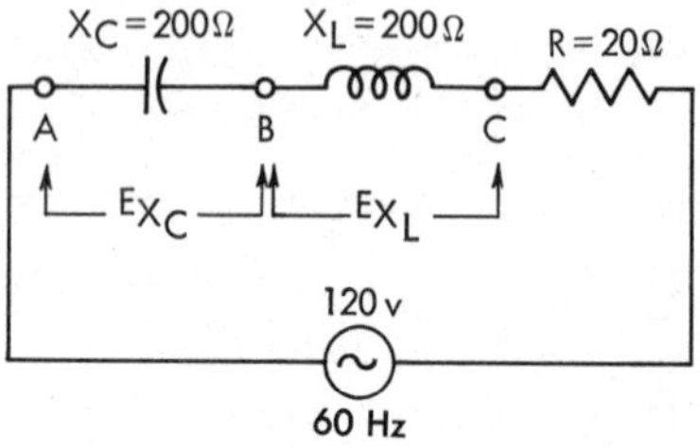

Fig. 21·43

21·44 (X_L) Let us compute the current in this circuit. Since it is resonant, the total impedance Z must be equal in value to the _____ of the circuit.

21·45 (resistance) Hence, the current in the circuit as determined from Ohm's law is $I = E/Z$, or for the resonant case, $I = E/R$. Thus, the current is 120 volts divided by 20 ohms or _____ .

21·46 (6 amp) The inductive reactance is, however, 200 ohms. This does not change just because the circuit is resonant. The current flowing through the coil in this series circuit is the same as the current anywhere else in the circuit, hence the current through the coil is _____ .

21·47 (6 amp) The voltage drop produced by 6 amp of current flowing through 200 ohms of inductive reactance is $E = IX_L$. Thus, the voltage drop across the coil is _____ .

21·48 (1,200 volts) The applied voltage is only 120 volts, yet a voltage drop of 1,200 volts appears across the coil. This is called a "voltage gain" and is found by taking the ratio of the drop across the coil to the applied voltage. That is, the voltage gain = E_{X_L}/E_a = _____ .

21·49 (10) In a series circuit, the current is everywhere the same. Hence, in the circuit of Fig. 21·43, the current through the capacitor is also _____ .

21·50 (6 amp) The capacitive reactance, however, is still 200 ohms. With a current of 6 amp flowing through it, the voltage drop must be equal to IX_c. Thus, the voltage drop across the capacitor is _____ volts.

21·51 (1,200) Here again, we see that the resonant circuit can produce a voltage gain of _____ when the drop across the capacitor is compared with the applied voltage.

21·52 (10) The phase angle between the voltage across the capacitor and the voltage across the inductor is 180°, however. This means that these two voltages cancel each other. Thus, if a voltmeter is connected from A to C in Fig. 21·43, the meter would read _____ .

21·53 (zero) But, taken individually, the voltage drops across the reactive components are quite real. That is, both E_{X_L} and E_{X_C} are individually equal to _____ volts.

21·54 (1,200) The voltage drop E_{X_L} is obtained from the product IX_L; the voltage drop across the resistor is obtained from the product IR. Thus, $E_R = 6$ amp $\times$ 20 ohms = _____ volts.

21·55 (120) Voltage gain, defined as the ratio of inductive voltage drop to resistive voltage drop, may, therefore, also be defined as IX_L/IR. Since the same current I flows in both components, this ratio can be reduced to _____ by canceling I's.

21·56 (X_L/R) This simplified ratio, which also represents the voltage gain of this resonant circuit, is known as the Q of the circuit. Thus, the Q of this circuit is $X_L/R = 200/20 = $ _____.

21·57 (10) The Q of a resonant circuit gives the voltage gain of the circuit. Thus, if R in Fig. 21·43 is increased to 40 ohms instead of 20 ohms, the Q would become $200/40 = $ _____.

21·58 (5) It is evident, then, that the Q of a circuit must decrease when the resistance of the circuit _____.

21·59 (increases) As an exercise, consider the circuit of Fig. 21·59. This is a resonant circuit as shown by the fact that the two reactances are _____.

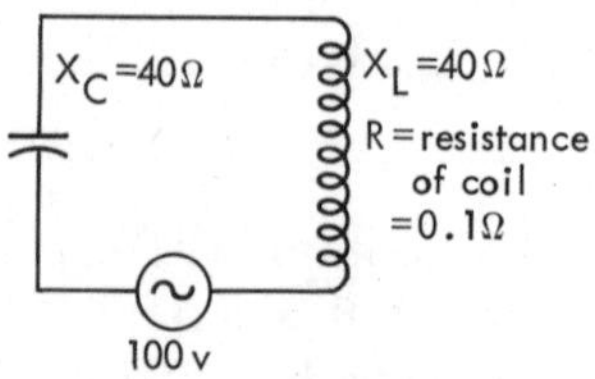

Fig. 21·59

21·60 (equal) The only resistance present is the inevitable resistance of the coil and the wire leads. The resistance is 0.1 ohm total. At resonance, the impedance equals the resistance, and the current is found from E/R. Thus, the current in this circuit is _____.

21·61 (1,000 amp) The voltage drop across the inductor is equal to IX_L. Hence the voltage drop across the inductor is _____ volts.

21·62 (40,000) The voltage drop across the capacitor is equal to IX_c. Hence the voltage drop across the capacitor is _____ volts.

21·63 (40,000) The voltage gain of this circuit is found from the ratio of the voltage across the inductor and the voltage applied. Thus, the voltage gain is $40,000/100 = $ _____.

21·64 (400) The Q of this circuit is the ratio of X_L to R. Thus, this circuit has a Q of _____ .

21·64 (400)

The resonance curve

A graph of current versus frequency in an *RCL* circuit shows that the current peaks at the resonant frequency (Fig. 21·65). At frequencies above and below resonance, the current drops to lower values. The resonance curve, when properly interpreted, permits the establishment of the concept of the *passband* of a resonant system. This concept is widely used in calculations of tuning systems for radio and television receivers as well as in radar and navigational systems.

21·65 If the current through a resonant circuit such as that of Fig. 21·43 is measured at various frequencies, and if the current is plotted in a graph such as that of Fig. 21·65, we obtain the *resonance curve* of the circuit. This curve shows that the current rises to its _____ value at the resonant frequency.

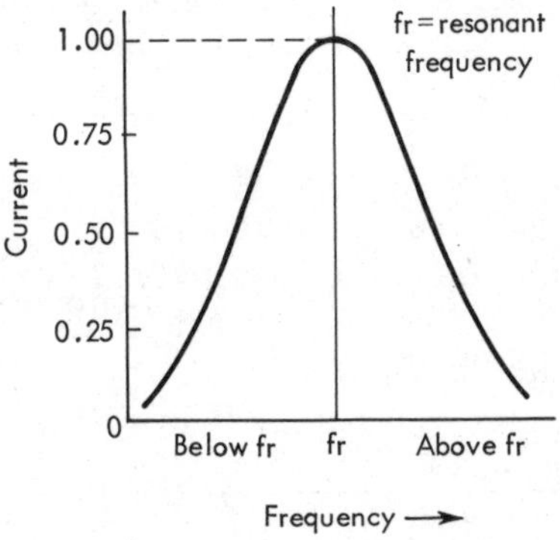

Fig. 21·65

21·66 (maximum) At any frequency lower than the resonant frequency, the current in the circuit is less than it is at the resonant frequency; at frequencies higher than resonance, the current is _____ than it is at resonance.

21·67 (less) In Fig. 21·65, the maximum value of the current is given the arbitrary value of _____ .

21·68 (one) This does not mean that the current in this circuit is, of necessity, 1 amp. It merely indicates that we will use 1 to represent the _____ value of the current in our discussion that follows.

21·69 (maximum) The power dissipated in this circuit at the resonant frequency is given by the familiar equation involving $P, I,$ and R. That is, power dissipated: $P =$ _____ .

21·70 (I^2R) If an audio-frequency alternating current were flowing through earphones, it would produce an audible sound. The sound would be loudest when the power being fed to the headphones is greatest. Since the power is greatest when the current is greatest, the sound would be loudest when the maximum _____ flowed in the headphones.

21·71 (current) We see from Fig. 21·65 that maximum current flows in this circuit when the current in the circuit has a frequency *equal to the resonant frequency* of the *LC* circuit. Hence, the sound in the headphones would be loudest when the frequency of the headphone current equals the _____ frequency of the *LC* circuit.

21·72 (resonant) The current decreases on each side of resonance. Thus, the power in the headphones must also _____ on each side of resonance.

21·73 (decrease) When the power dissipated in the earphones drops to about half its resonant value, the loudness of the sound is considered to have dropped to its limit of usefulness. Since the original power is designated by P, we designate the "half-power point" by P_1. By definition, the half-power point P_1 is half of P. In simple equation form, $P_1 = $ _____ .

21·74 ($P/2$) We wish to find the current I_1 flowing at the half-power point when the power is P_1. The general formula for power is $P = I^2R$. Substituting P_1 in place of P and I_1 in place of I, the power at the half-power point is given by the expression, $P_1 = $ _____ .

21·75 (I_1^2R) The power at the half-power is half of the power at resonance. The power at resonance is I^2R; the power at the half-power point is I_1^2R. Thus, we can write $P_1 = P/2$, or $I_1^2R = I^2R/$_____ .

21·76 (2) In examining this equation, $I_1^2R = I^2R/2$, we note that the same R appears on both sides. Hence, we can divide through by R and obtain $I_1^2 = I^2/$_____ .

21·77 (2) We now have the equation $I_1^2 = I^2/2$. To simplify it, we will take the square root of both sides. The square root of $I_1^2 = I_1$; the square root of $I^2 = I$; the square root of 2 is $\sqrt{2}$. Thus, we have $I_1 = I/$_____ .

21·78 ($\sqrt{2}$) The square root of 2 is 1.414. Thus, the number 1.414 can be substituted for $\sqrt{2}$ in the above equation, yielding the new form: _____ .

21·79 ($I_1 = I/1.414$) As a final step, we can divide the numerator (really $1 \times I$) by 1.414 to obtain the reciprocal form of the equation. Thus, since $1/1.414 = 0.707$, the equation can be written as _____ .

21·80 ($I_1 = 0.707I$) In this equation, I_1 is the current at the half-power point where the reproduced sound has just reached its limit of usefulness, and I is the current at the _____ frequency.

21·81 (resonant) Thus, this equation tells us that the loudness dropoff becomes serious when the current in the circuit falls from its original value of I to a low value that is _____ .

21·82 ($0.707I$) A current value of $0.707I$ appears at two different off-resonance frequencies (Fig. 21·82). One of these is called f_1, and the other is called _____ .

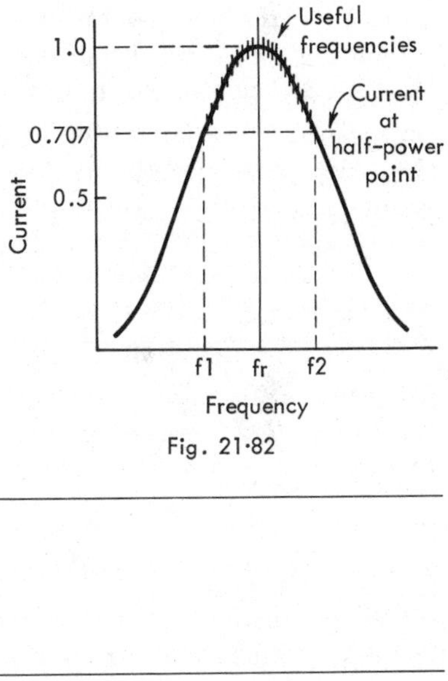

Fig. 21·82

21·83 (f_2) In Fig. 21·82 all the frequencies between the upper and lower limits set for f_1 and f_2 are labeled the _____ _____ .

21·84 (useful frequencies) These frequencies are considered "useful" because they produce currents that can, when passed through headphones, produce a _____ that is not very seriously weaker than the _____ produced by the maximum current.

21·85 (sound, sound) For this reason, the range of "useful" frequencies can be termed the *bandwidth* of the resonant circuit. In the illustration, the bandwidth ranges over all frequencies between f_1 and _____ .

21·86 (f_2) Thus, f_1 and f_2 mark the limits of the *passband* of this circuit. Hence, f_1 and f_2 are the frequencies at which the circuit current falls to 0.707 times its value at the _____ frequency.

21·86   (resonant)

The meaning of selectivity

Resonant circuits are used in both radio transmitting and radio receiving circuits. In the case of a receiver, the resonant circuit affords a means for selecting one particular received radio frequency over others. Assuming two radio-frequency signals, one of 1,000 kHz and the other of 1,200 kHz, let us imagine both of these being fed to a resonant circuit simultaneously. If the circuit has been adjusted to be resonant to 1,200 kHz, then it is *not* resonant to 1,000 kHz. The 1,200-kHz signal will then produce a relatively large current in the resonant circuit, while the current due to the 1,000-kHz signal will be substantially smaller, even negligible.

If a resonant circuit is to be capable of thus separating and distinguishing between two closely adjacent frequencies, its resonant curve must be sharp and steep-sided. Otherwise, its passband will be so large that both the wanted and unwanted signals will be received together. A circuit having a sharp resonant curve will, therefore, be highly selective, i.e., capable of selecting one and rejecting the other of two closely adjacent frequencies. In contrast, a circuit with a broad resonant curve (passband too wide) will have poor selectivity leading to interference between signals that lie close to each other in the spectrum.

21·87   Consider the resonance curve in Fig. 21·87. The resonant frequency of the circuit which produced this curve is _____ Hz.

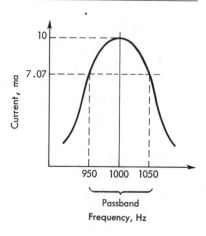

Fig. 21·87

21·88   (1,000) The current value at the resonant frequency is _____ .

21·89 (10 ma) The half-power current is _____ .

21·90 (7.07 ma) The lower-frequency limit of the passband obtained by projecting the intersection of the half-power current and the curve downward to the horizontal axis is

_____ .

21·91 (950 Hz) The upper-frequency limit of the passband obtained by projecting the further intersection of the half-power current and the curve downward to the horizontal axis is

_____ .

21·92 (1,050 Hz) The bandwidth of this circuit is defined as $f_2 - f_1$. As stated above, f_2 is 1,050 Hz and f_1 is _____ Hz.

21·93 (950) Hence, the bandwidth of this circuit is _____ Hz.

21·94 (100) In contrast with the curve of Fig. 21·87, we have the resonance curve of Fig. 21·94. In this steeper-sided curve, the bandwidth stretches between narrower limits. In this curve f_1 is _____ Hz.

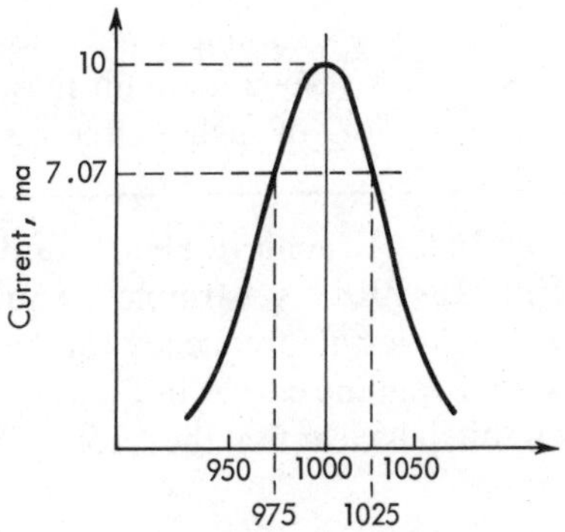

Fig. 21·94

21·95 (975) In Fig. 21·94, the upper limit of the passband is given by the frequency f_2. This frequency is _____ Hz.

21·96 (1,025) Hence, the bandwidth, or range of useful frequencies in the circuit responsible for this curve, is _____ .

21·97 (50 Hz) The curve of Fig. 21·87 has a bandwidth of 100 Hz. According to our half-power standard, any frequency within this range will cause the circuit to pass a sizable current. For this reason, we call the range over which the bandwidth extends the "passband." The passband in Fig. 21·87 is from 950 to _____ Hz.

21·98 (1,050) Since the circuit whose curve is given in Fig. 21·87 will respond to any frequency from 950 to 1,050 Hz, we say that it has *broad selectivity;* i.e., it does not discriminate seriously against any frequency in its _____ .

21·99 (passband) In comparison to this, we can say that the circuit responsible for Fig. 21·94 has *better selectivity* since it passes fewer frequencies in its passband and *rejects* a _____ number of frequencies.

21·100 (greater) Thus, a circuit having a narrower passband, hence a smaller bandwidth, is said to have better _____ than one with a wider passband or bandwidth.

21·100 (selectivity)

The effect of circuit Q on selectivity

An improved understanding of the factors affecting the selectivity of a resonant circuit may be achieved by studying the relationship between the Q of such a circuit and the resonant curve obtained.

21·101 To achieve a better understanding of selectivity, study Fig. 21·101a. A variable frequency a-c generator feeds the *RCL* circuit; its frequency can be varied from, say, 500 to 1,500 kHz. From the curves in Fig. 21·101b and c which apply to this circuit, it is clear that the resonant frequency is _____ kHz.

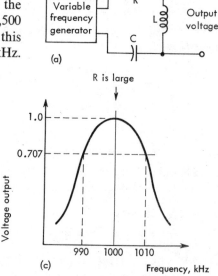

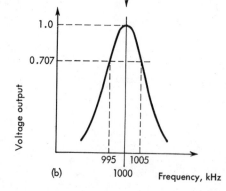

Fig. 21·101

284

21·102 (1,000) If the series resistance is made small, we find experimentally that the resonance curve it produces is that given in Fig. 21·101b. When the size of R is _____, we obtain the curve of Fig. 21·101c.

21·103 (large) Consider first the narrower resonance curve of Fig. 21·101b. As the generator frequency is brought up from 500 kHz to higher frequencies, the half power is reached at _____ kHz.

21·104 (995) The current flowing in the circuit now is 0.707 times the current that flows when the circuit is _____.

21·105 (resonant) This, by the standards previously adopted, constitutes a reasonably large current. Since the voltage drop across L is proportional to the current ($E_L = IX_L$, remember), then a reasonably large voltage will develop across L. In the circuit drawing, this voltage is labeled _____ voltage.

21·106 (output) As the frequency is raised still further, maximum current will flow at 1,000 kHz. Thus, the maximum drop across L—or the maximum output voltage—develops at a frequency of _____ kHz.

21·107 (1,000) Continuing to raise the frequency further, the output voltage drops to 0.707 of its maximum value once again at _____ kHz.

21·108 (1,005) Hence, the bandwidth of this circuit is _____ kc.

21·109 (10) Also, the passband of this circuit extends from _____ to _____ kHz.

21·110 (995, 1,005) Since the passband begins at 995 kHz, this circuit will reject, or fail to respond to, all frequencies _____ 995 kHz.

21·111 (below) Also, since the passband ends at 1,005 kHz, this circuit will reject, or refuse to respond to, all frequencies _____ 1,005 kHz.

21·112 (above) Such a circuit may be said to have 10 kHz selectivity. Now compare this with the curve of Fig. 21·101c for a large series resistance. The bandwidth of the circuit now is _____ kHz.

21·113 (20) The passband now extends from _____ to _____ kHz.

21·114 (990, 1,010) Thus, this circuit will begin to reject frequencies only when they drop below _____ kHz or rise above _____ kHz.

21·115 (990, 1,010) Its response is much broader than it was when R was small. This is said to be poorer *selectivity* because the circuit no longer rejects frequencies close to its _____ frequency.

21·116 (resonant) Thus, it is seen that the selectivity of a resonant circuit depends to a great extent on the size of the series _____ .

21·117 (resistance) If the series resistance is _____ , the selectivity is narrow or *sharp*.

21·118 (small) If the resistance is _____ , the selectivity is wide or *broad*.

21·119 (large) The Q of a resonant circuit is equivalent to the Q of the coil alone, since most resonant circuits use capacitors that do not affect the Q significantly. The Q of a coil is given by the relationship, $Q =$ _____ .

21·120 (X_L/R) The resistance of the coil R appears in the denominator of the fraction. Thus, if R becomes larger while X_L remains constant, the Q of the coil must _____ .

21·121 (decrease) As we have seen, a high resistance in a resonant circuit results in broad selectivity, while a low resistance results in _____ selectivity.

21·122 (sharp) Since Q is dependent upon resistance, and since the series resistance determines the sharpness of selectivity, we can say that the sharpness of selectivity depends upon the _____ of the coil.

21·123 (Q) A high-Q circuit contains a coil with very little series resistance compared with its inductive reactance. Thus, a high-Q resonant circuit must have _____ selectivity.

21·124 (sharp) A low-Q circuit contains a coil with relatively large series resistance compared with its inductive reactance. Thus, a low-Q circuit must have _____ selectivity.

21·124 (broad)

A summary of series resonance

Frames 21·125 to 21·133 summarize the concepts developed previously in the study of series resonance. Careful attention to each idea is essential to continued progress; this summary emphasizes the highlights.

21·125 In summarizing the ideas of series resonance, we might first say that a circuit containing a coil and capacitor is considered in resonance at a given frequency when the inductive _____ of the coil equals the capacitive reactance of the capacitor.

21·126 (reactance) The resonant frequency of this circuit can be determined if L and C are known. The equation used to find resonant frequency is _____ .

21·127 [$f = 1/(2\pi\sqrt{LC})$] When a circuit is in series resonance, its _____ is at its minimum value and is equal only to the resistance of the circuit.

21·128 (impedance) When a circuit is in series resonance, the _____ flowing through it is at its maximum.

21·129 (current) The power factor of a series resonant circuit always equals _____ .

21·130 (one) At the half-power frequency, the current in a series resonant circuit is _____ times the maximum value of the current.

21·131 (0.707) The bandwidth of a series resonant circuit is the arithmetic difference between the two _____ frequencies.

21·132 (half-power) The passband of a series resonant circuit is the band of frequencies included between the upper half-power frequency and the _____ half-power frequency.

21·133 (lower) The selectivity of a series resonant circuit is governed almost entirely by the _____ of the coil.

21·133 (Q)

Parallel resonance

A resonant condition may also be obtained by connecting a coil and capacitor in parallel rather than in series (see Fig. 21·134). The basic principles remain unchanged when these components are connected in parallel, but the effect of the parallel circuit upon the external circuit is considerably different from the series connection.

21·134 A resonant condition can also be obtained when a coil and capacitor are connected in parallel. In Fig. 21·134, the coil and its own internal resistance are in series, but the series group is in _____ with the capacitor.

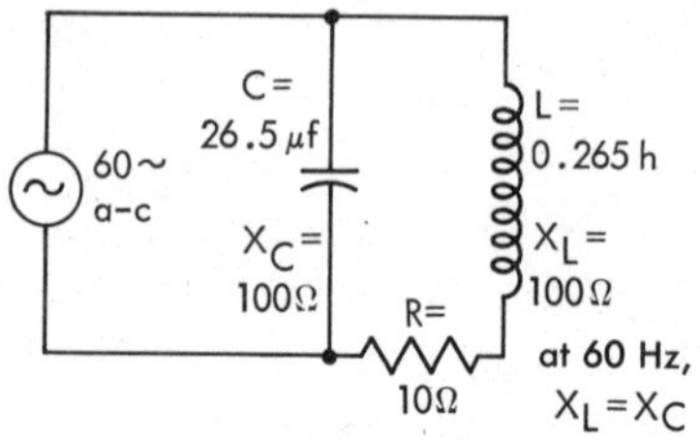

Fig. 21·134

21·135 (parallel) In this circuit, the reactance of the 26.5-μf capacitor at 60 Hz is shown to be 100 ohms. The reactance of the 0.265-henry coil at 60 Hz is shown to be _____ ohms.

21·136 (100) When the inductive and capacitive reactances are equal, the circuit exhibits definite resonant characteristics. Since $X_L = X_c$, the same equation for resonant frequency holds here as in the series case. This equation is resonant frequency = $f =$ _____ .

21·137 $[1/(2\pi\sqrt{LC})]$ Consider first a perfect coil (zero internal resistance) in parallel with a perfect capacitor as in Fig. 21·137. At any source frequency, the current in the capacitor must lead the voltage by _____°.

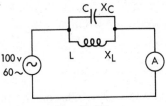

Fig. 21·137

21·138 (90) In Fig. 21·137, at any source frequency the current in the coil must lag behind the voltage by _____°.

21·139 (90) If the current in the capacitor leads the voltage by 90° and the current in the coil lags the voltage by 90°, then the two currents must be out of phase *with each other* by _____°.

21·140 (180) A phase difference of 180° between the current through the coil and the current through the capacitor means that these currents must be flowing in _____ directions.

21·141 (opposite) Since the same voltage is applied across both the capacitor and the coil, then when $X_L = X_c$ as it does at resonance, the intensity of the capacitor current must be _____ to the intensity of the coil current.

21·142 (equal) But if the two currents are *equal* and *opposite,* the net current flowing into the parallel resonant circuit and out at the other side must be _____.

21·143 (zero) Thus the ammeter A reads zero. If the current flowing in the external circuit is zero with an applied voltage of 100 volts, then the resonant circuit is behaving like an open circuit. Thus, the impedance of the resonant circuit appears to the external load to be _____ in size.

21·144 (infinite) The foregoing analysis applies to a *perfect* resonant circuit. In practice, the coil always has some resistance. In Fig. 21·144, this coil resistance has been symbolized by the letter _____.

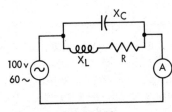

Fig. 21·144

21·145   (*R*) With X_L and R in series, the phase angle between current and voltage is more than $0°$ but definitely less than _____°.

21·146   (90) This means that the current in the capacitor and the current in the coil are not exactly $180°$ out of phase and, therefore, cannot be considered equal and _____.

21·147   (opposite) If the two currents are not exactly equal and opposite, there must be a net current flowing in the external load. If *R* is small and does not disturb the phase relationships severely, the net current will also be _____.

21·148   (small) This means that the impedance of the parallel resonant circuit, although not infinite as in the perfect case, is still very _____.

21·149   (large) Thus, in a practical parallel resonant system, the current flowing in the external circuit is quite _____, and the impedance of the parallel resonant circuit is quite _____.

21·150   (small, large) This is just the opposite of series resonance, since in series resonance the circuit current is usually quite _____ and the impedance is usually quite _____.

21·150   (large, small)

Off-resonance effects in parallel circuit operation

When any resonant circuit operates at the resonant frequency, the reactances may be considered to cancel. As we know, this occurs at one frequency and *one frequency only* for a given *LC* combination. A circuit in perfect resonance may, therefore, be said to be resistive.

At frequencies other than that of resonance the reactances do not cancel completely, leaving one or the other predominating. When the off-resonance operation is such that the coil predominates in its effect, the circuit is said to be inductive; when the capacitor predominates, the circuit is said to be capacitive.

21·151 Suppose we have the same circuit set up with a variable frequency generator as in Fig. 21·151. Assume that we have found the resonant frequency to be 60 Hz. If the source frequency is now dropped to 30 Hz, X_L will decrease (since $X_L = 2\pi fL$) and X_c will _____ .

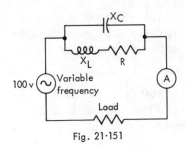

Fig. 21·151

21·152 (increase) At this new low frequency, therefore, the current through the coil will increase while the current through the capacitor will _____ .

21·153 (decrease) The current in the external load will now be due largely to the coil current. Hence, the *LC* circuit is now behaving in an *inductive* fashion; thus, the current in the load will _____ behind the applied voltage.

21·154 (lag) A general rule may now be stated: If the source frequency is _____ than that required for resonance in a given system, the *LC* circuit behaves *inductively*.

21·155 (lower) If the source frequency is higher than the resonant frequency, X_L will increase and X_c will _____ .

21·156 (decrease) At this new high frequency, therefore, the current through the coil will decrease, while the current through the capacitor will _____ .

21·157 (increase) The current in the external load will now be due largely to the capacitor current. Hence, the *LC* circuit is now behaving in a capacitive fashion; the current in the load will _____ the applied voltage.

21·158 (lead) A second general rule may now be stated: If the source frequency is _____ than that required for resonance, the *LC* circuit will behave *capacitively*.

21·158   (higher)

Summary of parallel resonance

With these short summary frames, we bring the program on basic a-c to its close. Those who have mastered d-c and a-c are now prepared for the introduction to the fascinating study of electronics.

21·159 Summarizing the characteristics of parallel resonant circuits, we can start by saying that, like series resonance, a condition of parallel resonance is obtained when $X_L =$ _____ .

21·160 (X_c) When $X_L = X_c$, the current in the capacitor is equal and opposite to the current in coil provided that the resistance of the coil is _____ .

21·161 (zero) Since no real coil can be built with zero resistance, the phase angle between coil current and capacitor current is not exactly _____ .

21·162 (180°) This results in a small external current showing that the impedance of the parallel resonant circuit is not infinite but is still very _____ .

21·163 (large) Since $X_L = X_c$ at resonance, the power factor is unity because the circuit acts as a pure _____ .

21·164 (resistance) When the frequency fed to a parallel LC circuit is below that of the resonant frequency, the circuit behaves _____ .

21·165 (inductively) When the frequency fed to a parallel LC circuit is above that of the resonant frequency, the circuit behaves _____ .

21·165 (capacitively)

MEASURABLE BEHAVIORAL OBJECTIVES

Upon completion of a section, you should be able to achieve the objectives listed for it. The frame or frames that cover the related subject matter are indicated immediately following each objective.

Introduction to resonance

Identify resonance in a series RCL circuit.   (21·1 to 21·12)
a   Recognize that $XL = X_c$ in resonance.   (21·1, 21·5, 21·10, 21·11)
b   State that $Z = R$ in resonance.   (21·2, 21·3, 21·5, 21·9)
c   Define Z as the phasor sum of R and $X = X_L - X_c$ in general. (21·6 to 21·8)
d   Realize that the impedance is minimum at resonance.   (21·11, 21·12)

The resonant frequency of an RCL circuit

1 Calculate the reactance of inductors and capacitors. $(21 \cdot 13$ to $21 \cdot 16)$
  a State the equation for X_L. $(21 \cdot 13, 21 \cdot 14)$
  b State the equation for X_c. $(21 \cdot 15, 21 \cdot 16)$
2 Derive the equation for the resonant frequency. $(21 \cdot 14, 21 \cdot 16$ to $21 \cdot 27)$
  a Realize that X_L increases as f increases. $(21 \cdot 14, 21 \cdot 18)$
  b Realize that X_c decreases as f increases. $(21 \cdot 16, 21 \cdot 18)$
  c Recognize that $X_L = X_c$ at some frequency which is by definition the resonant frequency. $(21 \cdot 19$ to $21 \cdot 22)$
  d State the formula for the resonant frequency. $(21 \cdot 23$ to $21 \cdot 27)$
3 Calculate the resonant frequency for a series RCL circuit. $(21 \cdot 28$ to $21 \cdot 34)$
4 List the characteristics of a resonant circuit. $(21 \cdot 39$ to $21 \cdot 42)$
  a Recognize that the current is maximum for the given voltage. $(21 \cdot 39)$
  b Realize that the current and voltage are in phase. $(21 \cdot 40)$
  c Realize that the power factor is unity. $(21 \cdot 41)$

Calculation of a series resonant circuit

1 Define voltage gain as the ratio of inductive voltage drop to applied voltage. $(21 \cdot 43$ to $21 \cdot 56, 21 \cdot 63)$
  a Recognize that the inductive and capacitive voltage drops are equal in magnitude but $180°$ out of phase at resonance. $(21 \cdot 52)$
  b Recognize that the resistive voltage drop equals the applied voltage at resonance. $(21 \cdot 54)$
  c Realize that the voltage gain $= X_L/R$ since the current throughout the circuit is the same. $(21 \cdot 46, 21 \cdot 49, 21 \cdot 55, 21 \cdot 56)$
2 Define the Q of a series circuit as X_L/R. $(21 \cdot 56$ to $21 \cdot 58, 21 \cdot 64)$
  a Realize that the Q is equal to the voltage gain. $(21 \cdot 56, 21 \cdot 57)$
  b Recognize that Q decreases as R increases. $(21 \cdot 58)$

The resonance curve

1 Describe the resonance curve of a series RCL circuit. $(21 \cdot 65$ to $21 \cdot 72)$
  a Define the resonance curve as a plot of current magnitude versus frequency. $(21 \cdot 65)$
  b Recognize that the curve is maximum at the resonant frequency and decreases for lower and higher frequencies. $(21 \cdot 66)$
2 Define the half-power points. $(21 \cdot 69, 21 \cdot 73$ to $21 \cdot 81)$
  a Recognize that the maximum power occurs at resonance and is equal to $P = I^2R$ where I is the resonant current. $(21 \cdot 69, 21 \cdot 75)$
  b Realize that $P1 = I1^2R = P/2$ occurs at two points, one on each side of the resonant frequency. $(21 \cdot 73, 21 \cdot 74)$
  c Derive $I1 = 0.707I$ is the half-power current. $(21 \cdot 74$ to $21 \cdot 80)$
3 Define the bandwidth as the frequency range between the half-power points. $(21 \cdot 82$ to $21 \cdot 86)$
  a Realize that the frequencies within the bandwidth are "useful" frequencies in that they provide an amount of power which is not substantially less than the maximum power. $(21 \cdot 83$ to $21 \cdot 86)$
  b Define the two half-power frequencies. $(21 \cdot 82, 21 \cdot 83, 21 \cdot 86)$

The meaning of selectivity

1 Define the passband of a resonant circuit. (21·87 to 21·97)

2 Describe the use of a resonant circuit as a frequency selective circuit. (21·98 to 21·100)

3 Differentiate between a circuit with broad selectivity and good selectivity in terms of passband and bandwidth. (21·98 to 21·100)

The effect of circuit Q on selectivity

1 Relate the resistance in a series RCL circuit to the bandwidth or passband. (21·101 to 21·118)

2 Realize that the higher the Q the better the selectivity. (21·119 to 21·124)

3 Recognize that the Q of the series RCL circuit is essentially that of the coil. (21·119)

A summary of series resonance

Summarize the characteristics of a resonant series RCL network. (21·125 to 21·133)

a Realize that $X_L = X_c$. (21·125)

b State the formula used for computing the resonant frequency. (21·126)

c Recognize that the current is maximum. (21·128)

d Realize that the impedance is minimum and equal to the resistance. (21·127)

e Identify the power factor value as unity. (21·129)

f Define the half-power frequencies, bandwidth, and passband. (21·130 to 21·132)

g Relate selectivity and Q. (21·133)

Parallel resonance

1 Describe a parallel resonant circuit and its characteristics. (21·134 to 21·150)

a The circuit is a series RL circuit in parallel with a capacitor. (21·134)

b The resonant frequency is identical with that of a series RCL circuit. (21·135, 21·136)

c The impedance of the circuit is very large at resonance. (21·143, 21·148, 21·149)

d The current is very small at resonance. (21·142, 21·147)

e The behavior of a parallel resonant circuit is opposite that of a series resonant circuit. (21·150)

2 Analyze the behavior of a parallel resonant circuit. (21·138 to 21·147)

Off-resonance effects in parallel circuit operation

Describe the characteristic of operation of a parallel circuit above and below resonance. (21·151 to 21·158)

a Indicate that at frequencies below resonance, the circuit behaves inductively with the current lagging the voltage. (21·151 to 21·154)

294

b Recognize that above resonance the circuit behaves capacitively with the current leading the voltage. (21·155 to 21·158)

Summary of parallel resonance

Summarize the characteristics of a parallel resonant circuit. (21·159 to 21·165)

a Recognize that $X_L = X_c$ at resonance. (21·159)
b Realize that with zero coil resistance the current would be zero but in practice the resistance is not zero and the current is small but not zero. (21·160 to 21·162)
c The impedance of a parallel resonant circuit is very large. (21·162)
d The power factor of a parallel resonant network is unity. (21·163)
e Identify the inductive and capacitive nature of the parallel resonant circuit below and above resonance. (21·164, 21·165)

resistor color code

In the manufacture of resistors, especially those of very small size, it is far easier to dab their bodies with spots or rings of color than it is to mark numbers on them. Each color is assigned a number. Color-code charts are available in many publications for ready reference; yet you can expedite your work to a considerable extent by memorizing the number assigned to each color.

Memorization is often facilitated by the use of mnemonic devices which establish an association between a number or word and some other easily remembered concept. In Table A · 1 below, these associations are clearly defined.

TABLE A · 1   USE OF MNEMONIC DEVICES

Color	Number	Mnemonic device
Black	0	**Black** midnight is the **zero** hour
Brown	1	**One brown** penny, lost among many
Red	2	A **red** devil has **two** horns
Orange	3	**Oranges** grow on **trees** (three)
Yellow	4	**Yellow** is **for** (four) cowards
Green	5	A **green** thumb is one of **five** fingers
Blue	6	Oceans **blue** have **six** letters, too
Purple	7	Deep **purple** twilight—**7th** heaven at 7
Gray	8	The **grey**hounds **ate** at 8
White	9	The **White** Sox have **nine** players

Study the associations carefully, then cover up the numbers associated with the colors and try to recall the numbers from the mnemonic sentences. Repeat this until you can do it unhesitatingly. Then cover the colors and try to elicit the numbers, using the mnemonic sentences. When you feel that you have mastered this group, go on to the program below without referring to the table at all.

A·1   The color *blue* should make you think of large bodies of water. Counting the letters in the name of such large bodies of water will tell you that blue should be associated with the number _____ .

A·2   (6) The color gray should make you think of a dog. Dogs like to eat. In the past tense, the word "eat" should recall the number _____ .

A·3   (8) Black means dark, and dark should recall midnight. Midnight is called the _____ hour, giving you the association needed to recall that black stands for the number _____ .

A·4   (zero, 0) The sky at the horizon after the sun has set turns to deep purple. During most of the year, twilight can be thought of as taking place around _____ P.M., which should remind you that purple ought to be associated with the number _____ .

A·5   (7, 7) An orange grows on a _____ . The number association is quite clear here because _____ sounds so much like three.

A·6   (tree, tree) A little verse like "One brown _____ , lost among many" is easy to remember and will always enable you to associate the number *one* with the color *brown*.

A·7   (penny) Visualize the horns on the head of a red devil. The number of horns is the number you need to associate with the color red. The number is _____ .

A·8   (2) Associate the color *green* with the word *thumb*. Immediately, the number that must come to mind is _____ , since this is the number of fingers on the hand that has the green thumb.

A·9   (5) Everyone knows that a baseball team has nine players on the field. The team you should associate with the number nine is the _____ Sox.

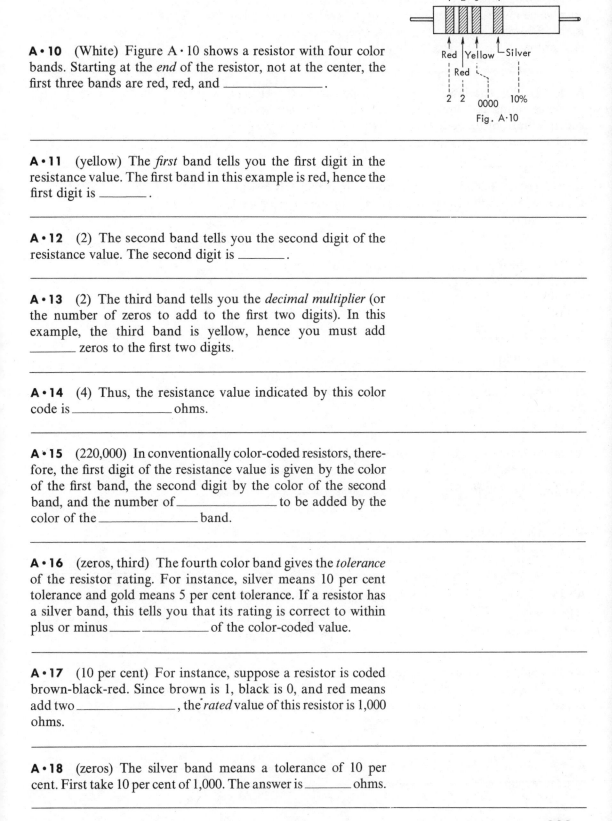

Fig. A·10

A·10 (White) Figure A·10 shows a resistor with four color bands. Starting at the *end* of the resistor, not at the center, the first three bands are red, red, and _____ .

A·11 (yellow) The *first* band tells you the first digit in the resistance value. The first band in this example is red, hence the first digit is _____ .

A·12 (2) The second band tells you the second digit of the resistance value. The second digit is _____ .

A·13 (2) The third band tells you the *decimal multiplier* (or the number of zeros to add to the first two digits). In this example, the third band is yellow, hence you must add _____ zeros to the first two digits.

A·14 (4) Thus, the resistance value indicated by this color code is _____ ohms.

A·15 (220,000) In conventionally color-coded resistors, therefore, the first digit of the resistance value is given by the color of the first band, the second digit by the color of the second band, and the number of _____ to be added by the color of the _____ band.

A·16 (zeros, third) The fourth color band gives the *tolerance* of the resistor rating. For instance, silver means 10 per cent tolerance and gold means 5 per cent tolerance. If a resistor has a silver band, this tells you that its rating is correct to within plus or minus _____ of the color-coded value.

A·17 (10 per cent) For instance, suppose a resistor is coded brown-black-red. Since brown is 1, black is 0, and red means add two _____ , the *rated* value of this resistor is 1,000 ohms.

A·18 (zeros) The silver band means a tolerance of 10 per cent. First take 10 per cent of 1,000. The answer is _____ ohms.

A·19 (100) Now if you add 100 to 1,000 this gives the *maximum* value the resistor can have for 10 per cent tolerance. That is, a 1,000-ohm 10 per cent resistor cannot have a value greater than _____ ohms.

A·20 (1,100) The lower limit established by a 10 per cent tolerance rating is found by subtracting 10 per cent of the coded value from the coded value. Thus, subtracting 10 per cent of 1,000 from 1,000 gives us _____ ohms.

A·21 (900) Therefore, the lowermost limit that this resistor is allowed to reach in manufacture without being rejected is _____ ohms.

A·22 (900) When you buy a 1,000-ohm 10 per cent resistor, it is therefore necessary to remember that its resistance may actually be as low as 900 ohms or as high as _____ ohms.

A·23 (1,100) Let us take another example. A resistor is coded yellow-purple-orange-gold. Since yellow is 4, purple is 7, and orange means add 3 zeros, the nominal value of this resistor is _____ ohms.

A·24 (47,000) The gold band means that the actual value of this resistor may be _____ per cent above or _____ per cent below its nominal value.

A·25 (5, 5) Taking 5 per cent of 47,000 gives a tolerance of plus or minus _____ ohms.

A·26 (2,350) Thus, at the most, this resistor may have an actual value of 49,350 ohms. At the least, its value will be _____ ohms.

A·27 (44,650) Let us try some very high values to practice the color code. The resistance of a resistor coded blue-black-blue is _____ megohms. (Remember 1 megohm = 1,000,000 ohms.)

A·28 (60) A resistor is coded white-green-green. Its nominal resistance value is _____ megohms.

A·29 (9.5) A 100-megohm resistor would be coded _____-

_____-_____ .

___

A·30 (brown-black-purple) A 3.3-megohm resistor with a 10
per cent tolerance would be coded _____-_____-

_____-_____ .

___

A·31 (orange-orange-green-silver) Let us try some low values.
The nominal resistance of a resistor coded brown-black-black
is 10 ohms. The third band (black) shows that we are to add
no _____ .

___

A·32 (zeros) Thus, the nominal resistance of a resistor green-
red-black is _____ ohms.

___

A·33 (52) And the nominal resistance of a resistor coded
brown-brown-brown is _____ ohms.

___

A·34 (110) To indicate resistances of less than 10 ohms, we
make the first and third bands black. Thus, black-red-black is
020 or 2 ohms; similarly black-green-black is _____ ohms.

___

A·35 (5) The color code of a 9-ohm resistor is, therefore,

_____-_____-_____ .

___

A·35 (black-white-black)

___

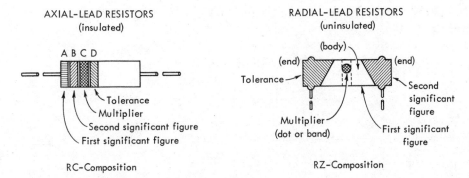

RESISTOR COLOR CODE MARKING
(mil–std resistors)

AXIAL–LEAD RESISTORS
(insulated)

A B C D

Tolerance
Multiplier
Second significant figure
First significant figure

RC–Composition

RADIAL–LEAD RESISTORS
(uninsulated)

(body)
(end)   (end)
Tolerance
Second
significant
figure
Multiplier
(dot or band)
First significant
figure

RZ–Composition

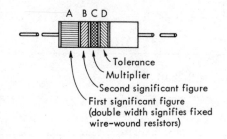

RU–Wire–Wound

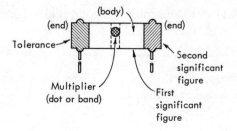

RZ–Composition

TABLE A·2   RESISTOR COLOR CODE

Band A or body*		Band B or end*		Band C or dot or band*		Band D or end*	
Color	First significant figure	Color	Second significant figure	Color	Multiplier	Color	Resistance tolerance, %
Black	0	Black	0	Black	1	Body	±20
Brown	1	Brown	1	Brown	10	Silver	±10
Red	2	Red	2	Red	100	Gold	±5
Orange	3	Orange	3	Orange	1,000		
Yellow	4	Yellow	4	Yellow	10,000		
Green	5	Green	5	Green	100,000		
Blue	6	Blue	6	Blue	1,000,000		
Purple (Violet)	7	Purple (Violet)	7				
Gray	8	Gray	8	Gold	0.1		
White	9	White	9	Silver	0.01		

* For wire-wound-type resistors, band A shall be double-width.
When body color is the same as the dot (or band) or end color, the colors are differentiated by shade, gloss, or other means.

Examples (band marking):
10 ohms ±20 per cent: brown band A; black band B; black band C; no band D. 4.7 ohms ±5 per cent: yellow band A; purple band B; gold band C; gold band D.

Examples (body marking):
10 ohms ±20 per cent: brown body; black end; black dot or band; body color on tolerance end.
3,000 ohms ±10 per cent: orange body; black end; red dot or band; silver end.

appendix B
capacitor color codes

Capacitor manufacturing methods and techniques have undergone many changes through the years. One of the unfortunate results of this has been the accompanying changes in color-coding systems. It is often difficult to determine which of the various obsolete systems applies to a given capacitor, particularly if its history is not known.

In these frames we shall be concerned only with current systems as applied to *ceramic, mica,* and *molded paper* capacitors. For the most part, the colors used in the resistor color code remain unchanged in significance; here and there, in the ratings of temperature coefficients and tolerances, we encounter a variation in the significance of a color. These must be carefully noted to avoid confusion.

Most capacitors are now coded in terms of the standards of the Electronic Industries Association (EIA). The only exception covered in these frames is the color code for mica capacitors which is given for both EIA and Joint Army-Navy (JAN) standards.

TABLE B·1 CAPACITOR COLOR CODES

Color	First significant figure	Multiplier	High C tolerance, %*	Low C tolerance, pf †	Temperature coefficient, ppm/°C
Black	0	1	20	2.0	−0
Brown	1	10	1		−30
Red	2	100	2		−80
Orange	3	1,000			−150
Yellow	4	10,000			−220
Green	5		5	0.5	−330
Blue	6				−470
Violet	7				−750
Gray	8	0.01		0.25	+30
White	9	0.1	10	1.0	+120 to −750

*For nominal capacitances greater than 10 pf.

†For nominal capacitances of 10 pf or smaller.

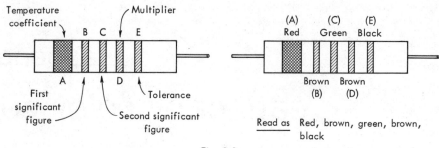

Fig. B·1

B·1   Refer to Fig. B·1. This figure deals with the color code for _____-type capacitors.

B·2   (ceramic) The coding system on ceramic capacitors is based upon the use of five bands of color. There is one wide band, and there are _____ narrow bands.

B·3   (four) The wide band is at the left side of the capacitor and is identified by the letter _____ .

B·4   (A) The four narrow bands are labeled from left to right with the letters B, _____, _____, _____ .

B·5   (C, D, E) Band A will be ignored temporarily. Band B, however, has exactly the same significance as it does in the resistor color code. It gives the first _____ figure of the *capacitance* value in this case, as opposed to the resistor code which gives the first _____ figure of the resistance.

B·6   (significant, significant) For example, a capacitor of 5 pf would have a green band B; a capacitor of 50 pf would have a green band B; and a capacitor of 500 pf would have a _____ band B.

B·7   (green) Or a 30-pf capacitor would have an orange band B; a 3,000-pf capacitor would have an _____ band B.

B·8   (orange) A 250-pf capacitor would have a _____ band B.

B·9   (red) The second narrow band, band C, gives the _____ significant figure in the capacitance value.

B·10 (second) For example, when band C is yellow, the second significant figure in the capacitance value is 4. When band C is white, the second significant figure is 9. When band C is violet, the second significant figure is _____ .

B·11 (7) When band C is green, the second significant figure of the capacitance value is _____ .

B·12 (5) When band C is black, the second significant figure of the capacitance value is _____ .

B·13 (0) If band B on a ceramic capacitor is brown and band C is blue, the first two significant figures in the capacitance value are _____ and _____ .

B·14 (1, 6) A capacitor of 26 pf would have a red-blue sequence for bands B and C. A capacitor of 260 pf would have a red-blue sequence for bands B and C. A capacitor of 2,600 pf would have a _____-_____ sequence for bands B and C.

B·15 (red-blue) A capacitor of 46 pf would have a yellow-blue sequence for bands B and C. A capacitor of 4,600 pf would have a _____-_____ sequence for bands B and C.

B·16 (yellow-blue) A 68-pf capacitor would have a _____-_____ sequence for bands B and C.

B·17 (blue-gray) A 100-pf capacitor would have a _____-_____ sequence for bands B and C.

B·18 (brown-black) A 92-pf capacitor woud have a _____-_____ sequence for bands B and C.

B·19 (white-red) Band D gives the _____ which must be applied to the values given by bands B and C.

B·20 (multiplier) For example, if band D is red, this tells you that you are to multiply the figures given by bands B and C by _____ .

B・21 (100) Or if band D is gray, you are to use a multiplier having the value _____ .

B・22 (0.01) Or if band D is orange, the figure given by bands B and C is to be multiplied by _____ .

B・23 (1,000) Suppose the capacitor BCD sequence is brown-black-brown. The brown-black tells you that the first two significant figures are _____ and _____ , respectively.

B・24 (1, 0) The band D brown tells you that the multiplier is _____ .

B・25 (10) Thus, we have 10 multiplied by 10 to give us a capacitance value of _____ pf.

B・26 (100) The BCD sequence on a ceramic capacitor is yellow-violet-red. The first two significant figures are _____ and _____ , respectively.

B・27 (4, 7) The multiplier for this sequence is _____ .

B・28 (100) The capacitor has a capacitance of 47×100 or _____ pf.

B・29 (4,700) The BCD sequence on a ceramic capacitor is orange-orange-black. The first two significant figures are _____ .

B・30 (33) The multiplier is _____ .

B・31 (1) Thus, the capacitor has a capacitance of _____ pf.

B・32 (33) The capacitance of a ceramic capacitor having a BCD sequence of gray-blue-red is _____ pf.

B・33 (8,600) A ceramic capacitor having a BCD sequence of blue-gray-white has a capacitance of 68×0.1 pf. This is, therefore, a capacitance of _____ pf.

B·34 (6.8) A capacitor with a BCD sequence of red-green-gray has a capacitance of 25×0.01 pf. Its capacitance is _____ pf.

B·35 (0.25) The BCD sequence on a capacitor is green-black-white. Its capacitance is _____ pf.

B·36 (5.0) The BCD sequence on a capacitor is red-violet-black. Its capacitance is _____ pf.

B·37 (27) The BCD sequence on a capacitor is violet-green-brown. Its capacitance is _____ pf.

B·38 (750) The BCD sequence on a 130-pf capacitor is _____-_____-_____ .

B·39 (brown-orange-brown) The BCD sequence on a 4.7-pf capacitor is _____-_____-_____ .

B·40 (yellow-violet-white) The BCD sequence on a 43-pf capacitor is _____-_____-_____ .

B·41 (yellow-orange-black) The BCD sequence on a 9,100-pf capacitor is _____-_____-_____ .

B·42 (white-brown-red) Band E of the ceramic color code states the _____ of the rating.

B·43 (tolerance) See Table B·1. The "High C tolerance" column gives the tolerance in per cent for capacitors greater than _____ pf.

B·44 (10) The "Low C tolerance" column gives the tolerance in _____ for capacitors of 10 pf or smaller.

B·45 (pf) A 180-pf capacitor with a band E of black would have a tolerance of 20 per cent, because this capacitor falls in the group of capacitance higher than _____ pf.

B·46 (10) A 3.3-pf capacitor with a band E of black would have a tolerance of _____ pf, because this capacitor has a value of less than 10 pf.

B·47 (2) If band E on a 270-pf capacitor is green, its tolerance is 5 per cent. If band E on a 6.8-pf capacitor is green, its tolerance is _____ pf.

B·48 (0.5) A capacitor has a BCDE sequence of orange-blue-brown-white. Its capacitance and tolerance are _____ and _____.

B·49 (360 pf, 10 per cent) A capacitor has a BCDE sequence of gray-black-white-white. Its capacitance and tolerance are _____ and _____.

B·50 (8 pf, 1 pf) A capacitor has a BCDE sequence of violet-green-red-green. Its capacitance and tolerance are _____ and _____.

B·51 (7,500 pf, 5 per cent) A capacitor has a BCDE sequence of green-black-gray-gray. Its capacitance and tolerance are _____ and _____.

B·52 (0.5 pf, 0.25 pf) A capacitor has a BCDE sequence of orange-orange-brown-red. Its capacitance and tolerance are _____ and _____.

B·53 (330 pf, 2 per cent) The *temperature coefficient* of a capacitor is given in parts per million/centigrade degree. In the last column of Table B·1, the abbreviation shown for this rating is _____.

B·53 (ppm/°C)

Information Panel

It is assumed that this rating is familiar to students who have studied electronic technology. For those who do not need a review, Frames B·54 to B·71 may be omitted.

In review, consider the variation in capacitance that would take place in a 750-pf capacitor whose temperature coefficient is +120 ppm/°C when the temperature changes from 20 to 100°C.

The first step consists in placing a decimal point after the last digit in 750, thus 750. Next, zeros are added until the total number of digits is six, making the millions place. Thus, 750.000. Third, the temperature coefficient (120) is multiplied by the change of temperature (100 − 20°C = 80°C). The product in this case is 120 × 80 = 9,600 ppm. Fourth, the sign of the coefficient is noted. If it is positive, then the capacitance *rises* with *increasing* temperature; if it is negative, then the capacitance *falls* with increasing temperature. In our example, the coefficient is +120 ppm/°C, hence we must add the total change of capacitance (9,600 ppm) as follows:

$$
\begin{array}{r}
750.000 \\
+9.600 \\
\hline
759.600
\end{array}
$$

Since capacitances are given to two significant figures, this final result should be rounded back to two significant figures. Thus, in our example, the new capacitance would be taken as 760 pf.

B·54   A capacitor has a nominal rating of 47 pf. Its band E color is yellow. Its temperature coefficient is _____ ppm/°C.

B·55   (−220) Suppose the capacitor is subjected to a temperature change of +50°C. The total change of capacitance will then be the product of the coefficient and Δt, or 220 × 50 = _____ ppm.

B·56   (11,000) The temperature coefficient is *negative*, hence the nominal capacitance will be _____ by 11,000 ppm.

B·57   (decreased, lowered, etc.) Writing 47 pf to the millions place, we have _____ .

B·58   (47.0000) Then *subtracting* the capacitance change of 11,000 ppm we have _____ pf.

B·59   (45.9) And rounding back to two significant figures, we can express the final value of capacitance as _____ pf.

B·60　(46)　Take another example: A capacitor has an ABCDE band sequence of violet-white-brown-black-green. Since its nominal capacitance is given by the BCD sequence, this capacitor has a nominal value of _____ pf.

B·61　(91)　Its tolerance rating is _____ per cent.

B·62　(5)　Its temperature coefficient is _____ ppm/°C.

B·63　(−750)　Suppose it is measured and found to have an actual capacitance of 92 pf at 25°C. This is well within its tolerance rating. Now suppose that the temperature rises to 150°C. The change of temperature is _____°C.

B·64　(+125)　The change of capacitance in parts per million is 750 × 125 = _____ ppm.

B·65　(93,750)　Writing 92 pf to the millions place we have

_____ .

B·66　(92.0000)　Subtracting the change of capacitance from the nominal capacitance to the millions place, we can write

$$\begin{array}{r} 92.0000 \\ -\ 9.3750 \\ \hline \end{array}$$

which gives an answer of _____ .

B·67　(82.6250 pf)　Rounding back to two significant figures, the final value of capacitance thus obtained is _____ .

B·68　(83 pf)　Try another example: A capacitor has a band sequence of red-orange-white-red-red. Its temperature coefficient is _____ (give units).

B·69　(−80 ppm/°C)　Its nominal capacitance is _____ pf.

B·70　(3,900)　Its tolerance is _____ per cent.

B·71 (2) Assuming its actual value at 20° is 3,900 pf, its capacitance at 180° will be _____ _____ (to 2 significant figures).

B·71 (3,800 pf)

Information Panel

Two color-code systems are in current use for *mica* capacitors. One of these is the EIA code, and the other is the JAN code. These codes are essentially identical, except in one respect. For the EIA code, the A dot color (see Fig. B·72) is *white*, while for the JAN system, the A dot color is *black*. In short, the A dot informs the user whether he is dealing with a capacitor having standard EIA specifications or with one that meets the generally more rigorous JAN specifications. All capacitors, regardless of the color-code system used, are read in exactly the same way; the A dot merely informs the user of the specifications to which the capacitor has been built.

Note: Molded *paper* capacitors sometimes resemble mica types; to distinguish these, the JAN code uses a *silver* A dot, but the remainder of the code is unchanged.

B·72 Refer to Fig. B·72. The top row of dots starting with either *black* or _____ is read from left to right; the lower row is read from right to left as the order of the letters indicates.

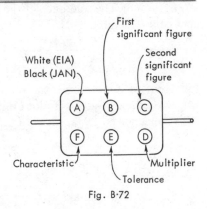

Fig. B·72

B·73 (white) Note that the B dot and C dot taken together give the first and second _____ figures of the capacitance.

B·74 (significant) The multiplier is given by the _____ dot, and the tolerance is given by the _____ dot.

B·75 (D, E) Suppose a mica capacitor has an ABCDE sequence like this: black-red-violet-red-green. From the A dot, we know that this capacitor will meet _____ specifications.

B·76 (JAN) The B dot and C dot tell us that the first two significant figures are _____ .

B·77 (27) The multiplier is _____ .

B·78 (100) The nominal capacitance value is, therefore, _____ pf.

B·79 (2,700) The tolerance is read off in terms of the color (E dot) with a per cent sign added. Since the E dot is green, and green means 5, then the tolerance on the capacitance rating is _____ (see Table B·1).

B·80 (5 per cent) Thus, the complete rating is JAN 2,700 $\pm$ 5 per cent pf. (Note that we have omitted the F dot for the moment.) Try this one: The sequence is white-green-blue-brown-black (F dot omitted). This is an EIA capacitor having a nominal capacitance value of _____ pf.

B·81 (560) The tolerance of the capacitance value is _____ per cent (see Table B·1).

B·82 (20) The complete rating is, therefore, EIA 560 $\pm$ 20 per cent pf. One more example: The dot sequence is white-brown-red-black-green (F dot omitted). The complete rating of this capacitor is _____ .

B·82 (EIA 12 $\pm$ 5 per cent pf)

Information Panel

The *characteristic* of mica capacitors is related to the temperature coefficient, method of testing, working voltages, etc. Except in rare cases, the uses to which mica capacitors are put do not require knowledge of the exact characteristic, hence we shall omit further reference to it. Mica capacitors may be taken to be rated at 500 working volts, unless the manufacturer states otherwise. For temperature compensation, ceramic capacitors are normally used; it was for this reason that we went into considerable detail with respect to temperature coefficients when we discussed this type of capacitor.

B·83 Tubular molded paper-dielectric capacitors are often color-coded, although many have stamped values. Refer to Fig. B·83. Bands A, B, C, and D have the same significance as for ceramic capacitors. However, bands E and F provide information relative to the _____ _____ of the capacitor.

Fig. B·83

B·84 (working voltage) Most voltage ratings are obtained by multiplying the normal color significance by 100. Thus, if band E is green, the WV = 5 × 100 = 500 volts. If band E is orange, the WV is _____ volts (ignore band F for a moment).

B·85 (300) A capacitor with a band E color of *blue* has a working voltage rating of _____ volts (ignore band F).

B·86 (600) A paper capacitor with a red E band has a working voltage rating of _____ volts (ignore band F).

B·87 (200) Band F gives the second significant figure of the voltage rating. For example, if band E is green and band F is black, then the rating is 5.0 × 100 or _____ working volts.

B·88 (500) But if band E is red and band F is green, the working voltage of the capacitor is 2.5 × 100 = _____ volts.

B·89 (250) Similarly, if the voltage color sequence is blue-green then the working voltage of the capacitor is _____ WV.

B·90 (650) Also, a *gold* band E represents a first significant group of 10. Thus, a gold-black sequence means a working voltage of 10.0 × 100 = _____ volts.

B·91 (1,000) And a gold-green sequence means _____ WV.

313

B·92 (1,500) If the color of band E is *silver,* then the first significant group is 20. Thus silver-black means 20×100 or _____ WV.

B·93 (2,000) And silver-green means _____ WV.

B·94 (2,500) Let us try a few complete examples for tubular molded paper capacitors. A capacitor has an A, B, C, D, E, F sequence of brown-black-orange-black-yellow-black. The brown A dot signifies a first significant figure of _____ .

B·95 (1) The black B dot signifies a second significant figure of _____ .

B·96 (0) The orange C dot signifies a multiplier of _____ .

B·97 (1,000) Thus the nominal capacitance is _____ pf.

B·98 (10,000) This is better expressed as _____ μf.

B·99 (0.01) The black D dot indicates that the tolerance is _____ .

B·100 (20 per cent) The yellow dot gives us the first significant figure of the working voltage rating. This is _____ .

B·101 (4) The black F dot shows that the second significant figure of the voltage rating is zero. Thus, the working voltage is $4.0 \times 100 =$ _____ volts.

B·102 (400) The complete rating is 0.01 μf $\pm$ 20 per cent at 400 volts. Try this example: The sequence is blue-red-red-white-gold-red. The nominal capacitance is _____ pf.

B·103 (6,200) Expressed in microfarads, the nominal rating is _____ .

B·104 (0.0062 μf) The tolerance is shown by the white D band (see Table B·1). This is _____ per cent.

B • 105 (10) The first significant group in the voltage rating is 10. The second significant figure is 2. Thus, put together, the voltage rating is $12 \times 100 =$ _____ volts.

B • 106 (1,200) Hence, the complete rating of this capacitor is $0.0062 \ \mu f \pm 10$ per cent, 1,200 WV. As a final example try this: The sequence is red-red-orange-black-gold-blue. The complete rating of this capacitor is _____ .

B • 106   (0.022 $\mu f \pm 20$ per cent, 1,600 WV.)

---

appendix C
criterion check tests

CHAPTER 1

1 Matter can be found in three states, one of which is
  a atom   *b* gas
  c crystal   *d* water

2 If a substance has a given shape and volume it is called a(n)
  a compound   *b* electron
  c solid   *d* oxygen

3 The three states of iron are
  a gas, solid, and liquid
  b hematite, steel, and chrome
  c electrons, atoms, and molecules
  d elements, compounds, and mixtures

4 A substance that cannot be broken down into simpler substances is called a(n)
  a oxide   *b* solid
  c compound   *d* element

5 Table salt dissolved in water is an example of a
  a mixture   *b* solid
  c distillation   *d* compound

6 The building blocks of an element are
  a atoms   *b* molecules
  c electrons   *d* liquids

7 The building blocks of a compound are
  a atoms   *b* molecules
  c electrons   *d* liquids

8 If the electrons are removed from an atom, the part that remains is called the
  a molecule   *b* gas
  c nucleus   *d* neutrons

9 If two glass rods are rubbed with silk, the two rods will
  a break   *b* attract each other
  c move   *d* repel each other

10 If rod *A* and rod *B* attract each other, then
  a Rods *A* and *B* are rubber.
  b Rod *A* is rubber and rod *B* is glass.
  c Rods *A* and *B* are glass.
  d None of the above is correct.

11 A rubber rod stroked with fur is charged
  a negatively   *b* positively
  c positively or negatively   *d* neutrally

12 A positively charged rubber rod and a positively charged glass rod will
  a attract each other
  b repel each other
  c have no effect on each other
  d none of the above

13 The fundamental positive charge is a(n)
  a electron   *b* ion
  c proton   *d* atom

14 If a substance is stroked, it loses two electrons per atom. The net atomic charge for the stroked substance is
  a -2 *b* $+2$
  c 0 *d* 2×2

15 Neutral atoms must have the same number of
  a neutrons and protons
  b protons and electrons
  c electrons and neutrons
  d compounds and mixtures

16 Ions are formed by losing or gaining
  a electrons   *b* atoms
  c neutrons   *d* gas

17 The correct form of Coulomb's law is

  a $F = \dfrac{d_1 \times d_2}{q^2}$ *b* $F = \dfrac{d_1 \times q_2}{d_1{}^2}$

  c $F = ma$ *d* $F = \dfrac{q_1 \times q_2}{d^2}$

18 The force between charged bodies is inversely proportional to
  a the charges   *b* the distance
  c the distance squared   *d* electrons

19 The force between two charged bodies will double if we
  a double both charges
  b double one of the charges
  c double the distance between charges
  d halve both charges

20 The ability of charged bodies to exert a force on one another is attributed to the existence of

    a compounds   *b* electric fields

    c neutrons   *d* electrons

21 The convention for assigning direction to an electric field due to a negative charge is in a direction

    a away from the charge   *b* toward the charge

    c up   *d* down

22 The direction of lines of force due to charged particles is

    a always straight   *b* always up

    c sometimes curved   *d* none of the above

23 An electroscope can be used to detect

    a compounds   *b* atoms

    c electrons   *d* neutrons

24 For an electroscope to operate, it

    a first must be charged

    b does not have to be charged

    c must have a switch installed on it

    d none of the above

25 The charge distribution on an egg-shaped solid metal is

    a uniform   *b* nonuniform

    c never negative   *d* never positive

CHAPTER 2

1 Electric current consists of a flow of

    a elements   *b* neutrons

    c atoms   *d* electrons

2 The direction of the current flow in a conductor is

    a from a positively charged body to a negatively charged body

    b from a negatively charged body to a positively charged body

    c from left to right

    d from top to bottom

3 One coulomb contains

    a one electron   *b* 6.3×10^{18} atoms

    c 6.3×10^{18} electrons   *d* one ampere

4 A wire carries a current of one ampere if

    a One coulomb flows through it each minute.

    b One coulomb flows through it each second.

    c Ten coulombs flow through it each second.

    d One hundred coulombs flow through it each second.

5 The resistance of a wire depends on its
  a color
  b number of neutrons
  c temperature
  d humidity

6 A material is called an insulator if it has
  a many free neutrons
  b many free electrons
  c few free electrons
  d few free neutrons

7 An example of a good electrical conductor is
  a silver
  b glass
  c water
  d electrons

8 The correct equation for resistance is

  a $R = \dfrac{I}{V}$

  b $R = \rho \dfrac{L}{A}$

  c $R = \dfrac{P^2}{I}$

  d $R = \dfrac{A}{L}$

9 Resistance is expressed in units of
  a volts
  b amperes
  c ohms
  d watts

10 The resistance of a wire will double if we double its
  a area
  b temperature
  c length
  d weight

11 A potential difference exists between two bodies if
  a They are charged equally.
  b They are both charged negatively and equally.
  c They are both charged positively and equally.
  d Only one of them is charged.

12 If a body having 120 free electrons is connected to another body with 60 electrons, there will be a shift of
  a 30 electrons
  b 60 electrons
  c 90 electrons
  d 120 electrons

13 A circuit is called complete if
  a A voltage difference exists.
  b A battery is present.
  c Electrons are present.
  d Electrons can flow.

14 The current in a circuit will flow
  a from − to + plates of the battery
  b from + to − plates of the battery
  c from left to right
  d from right to left

15 In an incomplete circuit, the current
  a is high
  b cannot flow
  c can flow from + to −
  d can flow from − to +

16 A generator of electricity produces a current that increases to a maximum and falls to zero periodically. The current is called
   a   alternating current
   b   direct current
   c   pulsating direct current
   d   pulsating alternating current

17 The schematic diagram representation of a ground is

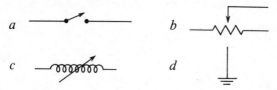

CHAPTER 3

1 A common reference point in a circuit
   a   is always the most negative point
   b   is always the most positive point
   c   is always the battery terminal
   d   may be at any potential

2 The unit for resistance can be expressed as
   a   volts   *b*   amp
   c   volts/amp   *d*   amp/volt

3 When the applied potential across a 15-ohm resistor is 60 volts, the current is
   a   125 amp   *b*   2 amp
   c   4 amp   *d*   15 amp

4 A circuit consists of a 20-volt battery and a resistor. If the current in the circuit is 4 amp, the resistor is
   a   4 ohms   *b*   5 ohms
   c   6 ohms   *d*   20 ohms

5 When the current in a 1-kilohm resistor is 2 milliamp, the potential across the resistor is
   a   1 volt   *b*   2 volts
   c   20 volts   *d*   200 volts

6 One nanosecond is equivalent to
   a 10^{-9} second   *b* 10^{-12} second
   c 10^{-3} second   *d* 10^3 second

7 If the current in a circuit doubles when the resistance remains the same, then the voltage must
   a   reduce to half   *b*   reduce four times
   c   increase four times   *d*   increase two times

8 The current in a circuit is 2 amp when the resistance is 10 ohms. If we double the value of the resistance, the new current will be

a 4 amp   *b* 2 amp
c 1 amp   *d* 0.5 amp

9 To measure current in a circuit, we must connect the ammeter in

a series with the resistor
b parallel with the resistor
c close to the battery
d any fashion, so long as the terminals fit

10 The direction of current flow in a circuit will be determined by

a the number of resistors
b the position of the ammeter
c the value of the resistor
d the polarity of the battery

11 The voltage across a 4.5-volt and a 1.5-volt battery connected in series is

a 1.5 volts   *b* 2.0 volts
c 4.5 volts   *d* 6.0 volts

12 The voltage across four parallel 1.5-volt batteries is

a 1.5 volts   *b* 6.0 volts
c 4.0 volts   *d* 6.5 volts

13 Fifteen Edison cells in series have a total output voltage of

a 18 volts   *b* 3.0 volts
c 5.0 volts   *d* 9.0 volts

14 The total current drawn from two 3.0-volt batteries in series is 1 amp. Each battery supplies

a 1 amp   *b* 0.5 amp
c 2 amp   *d* 3 amp

15 The total current drawn from two 3.0-volt batteries in parallel is 1 amp. Each battery supplies

a 1 amp   *b* 0.5 amp
c 2 amp   *d* 3 amp

16 The primary function of a switch is to

a prevent excessive current
b protect the battery
c open a circuit at the will of the operator
d it has no function

17 The primary function of a fuse is to

a prevent excessive current
b protect the battery
c open a circuit
d close a circuit

CHAPTER 4

1 The joule is a unit of
   a charge   b power
   c energy   d current

2 Joules/second is equivalent to
   a watts   b coulombs
   c energy   d work

3 Power is measured in units of
   a charge   b watts
   c work   d volts

4 The equation that does not equal the power dissipated in a
   resistor is

   a $P = I^2R$ b $P = \dfrac{V^2}{R}$

   c $P = VI$ d $P = \dfrac{R}{V^2}$

5 A 120-volt source connected across a resistor produces a
   2-amp current. The power dissipated by the resistor is
   a 240 watts   b 120 watts
   c 60 watts   d 30 watts

6 The current through a 100-watt lamp is 0.5 amp. The
   voltage across the lamp is
   a 200 volts   b 120 volts
   c 50 volts   d 100 volts

7 A 50-ohm resistor dissipates 2 watts of power. The voltage
   across the resistor is
   a 100 volts   b 10 volts
   c 25 volts   d 12.5 volts

8 A 50-watt light bulb burns an average of 10 hr a day for
   one week. The total kilowatthour consumption is
   a 3.5   b 35
   c 0.35   d 0.035

9 If a series circuit consists of three resistors and a battery,
   the following statement is always true
   a The voltage drop across each resistor is the same.
   b The current through each resistor is the same.
   c The power dissipated in each resistor is the same.
   d The energy consumption in each resistor is the same.

10 A circuit consists of two resistors, one 10 ohms and the
   other 40 ohms, in series with a 200-volt battery. The current in the circuit is
   a 5 amp   b 8 amp
   c 4 amp   d 10 amp

11 To find the net resistance in a series circuit, we must

   a Add the resistors and then divide by two.

   b Add the resistors and then divide by zero.

   c Add the resistors and then divide by one.

   d Add the resistors and then divide by ten.

12 A series circuit consisting of a 1-ohm, a 2-ohm, and a 3-ohm resistor will develop a voltage drop of 4 volts across the 2-ohm resistor. The voltage across the 1-ohm resistor is

   a 2 volts   *b* 1 volt

   c 6 volts   *d* 3 volts

13 A circuit consists of several resistors in series with a battery. The voltage drop across the resistors is equal to

   a the voltage drop across two resistors

   b the voltage drop across four resistors

   c the current divided by the net resistor

   d the emf of the battery

14 In the circuit of Fig. C 4·14 the voltage drop across the 5-ohm resistor is 20 volts. The battery emf is

   a 105 volts   *b* 140 volts

   c 175 volts   *d* 200 volts

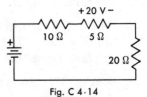

Fig. C 4·14

15 The current in the circuit of Fig. C 4·14 is

   a 3 amp   *b* 5 amp

   c 6 amp   *d* 4 amp

16 The voltage drop across the 10-ohm resistor in the circuit of Fig. C 4·14 is

   a 20 volts   *b* 40 volts

   c 80 volts   *d* 100 volts

17 A series circuit consists of two resistors $R1$ and $R2$ in series with a voltage source E_t.
The voltage $E1$ across $R1$ can be found by

   a $E1 = \dfrac{R1 + R2}{R1} E_t$ *b* $E1 = \dfrac{I1}{R1}$

   c $E1 = \dfrac{R1}{R1 + R2} E_t$ *d* $\dfrac{R1}{E1} = \dfrac{R2}{E_t}$

18 To determine the voltage polarity across a resistor, we have to know

   a the value of the resistor

   b the battery voltage

   c the temperature of the resistor

   d the direction of current

19 Current flows into terminal A and departs at terminal B for a resistor; therefore, terminal A is

   a negative with respect to terminal B

   b positive with respect to terminal B

   c at zero potential with respect to terminal B

   d at ground potential

20 In the circuit of Fig. C 4·20, the voltage drop from *B* to *C* is

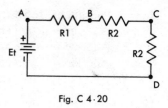

Fig. C 4·20

 a negative
 b more positive than that from *A* to *D*
 c positive
 d cannot be determined from this diagram

21 To indicate the polarity of the voltage drop from *D* to *C* in Fig. C 4·20, we can put a "+" sign at
 a D   *b* C
 c B   *d* A

22 Kirchhoff's voltage law states
 a The voltage drop across a resistor is equal to the current mutiplied by the resistance.
 b The sum of emfs and voltage drop in a series circuit must be equal to zero.
 c The total voltage drop in a series circuit cannot be zero.
 d None of the above.

23 In Fig. C 4·23 Kirchhoff's voltage law is

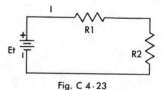

Fig. C 4·23

 a $E_t + IR1 + IR2 = 0$ *b* $E_t = -1(R1 + R2)$
 c $E_t - IR2 - IR1 = 0$ *d* $E_t - IR2 + IR1 = 0$

24 Kirchhoff's voltage law cannot be used
 a with parallel circuit
 b to find current in a circuit
 c to find voltage across a resistor in a series circuit
 d none of the above

25 The circuit in Fig. C 4·23 has
 a three junctions   *b* a large current
 c one ground point   *d* a high voltage

26 Kirchhoff's current law states
 a The sum of the currents entering a junction is zero.
 b The sum of the currents in a series circuit is zero.
 c The sum of the currents in a parallel circuit is zero.
 d None of the above.

CHAPTER 5

1 In a parallel circuit with resistors *R*1, *R*2, and *R*3 shunted across a battery
 a The current is the same in each resistor.
 b The voltage is the same across each resistor.
 c The voltage is proportional to the net resistance.
 d The voltage across each resistance is dependent on the value of the resistors.

2 To determine the value of the net resistance for three parallel resistors $R1$, $R2$, and $R3$, we can use the following equation:

a $\quad R_t = R1 + R2 + R3$

b $\quad R_t = \dfrac{1}{R1} + \dfrac{1}{R2} + \dfrac{1}{R3}$

c $\quad \dfrac{1}{R_t} = \dfrac{1}{R1} + \dfrac{1}{R2} + \dfrac{1}{R3}$

d $\quad \dfrac{1}{R_t} = R1 + R2 + R3$

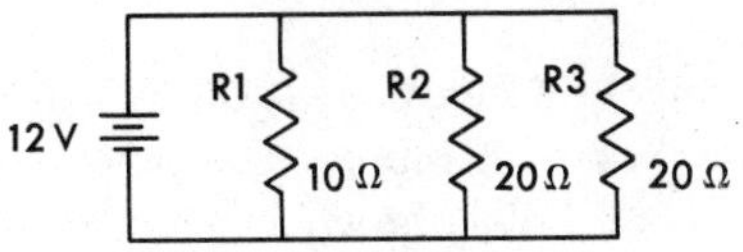

3 The value of the voltage across $R3$ in Fig. C 5·3 is

a 12/20 volt   b 20/12 volts

c 20 × 12 volts   d 12 volts

Fig. C 5·3

4 The net resistance across the battery is

a 5 ohms   b 15 ohms

c 10 ohms   d 20 ohms

5 With two resistors in parallel one of which is a 100-ohm resistor and the other one is not known, the only likely value for the net resistance is

a 101 ohms   b 1,000 ohms

c 90 ohms   d 110 ohms

6 The current in resistor $R1$ in Fig. C 5·3 is

a 2.4 amp   b 1.2 amp

c 0.6 amp   d 1.8 amp

7 The power dissipated in resistor $R1$ in Fig. C 5·3 is

a 14.4 joules   b 144 watts

c 14.4 watts   d 28.8 watts

8 An 18-ohm and a 9-ohm resistor are in parallel with each other. The effective resistance is

a 6 ohms   b 5 ohms

c 8 ohms   d 10 ohms

9 A 30-volt battery is applied to the parallel combination of the 18-ohm and the 9-ohm resistor. The battery current will be

a 5 amp   b 6 amp

c ³⁰⁄₈ amp   d 3 amp

10 For a parallel circuit the battery current

a goes through each resistor

b goes through some of the resistors

c equals the sum of the branch currents

d cannot be found

CHAPTER 6

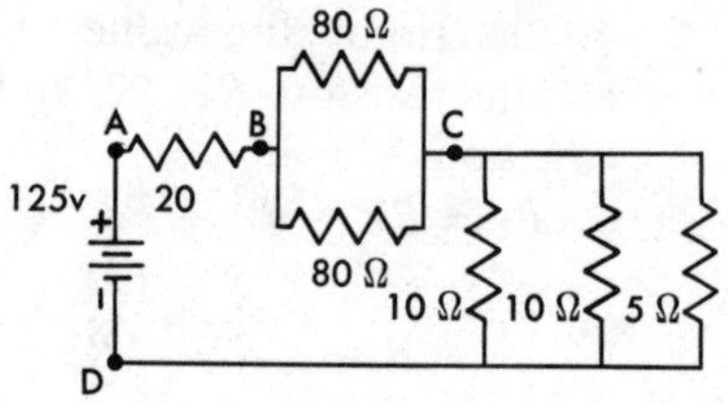

1 For Fig. C 6·1, the resistance between points *A* and *B* is
   a 40 ohms   *b* 20 ohms
   c 62.5 ohms   *d* 2.5 ohms

2 For Fig. C 6·1, the resistance between points *B* and *C* is
   a 40 ohms   *b* 80 ohms
   c 160 ohms   *d* 25 ohms

3 For Fig. C 6·1, the resistance between points *C* and *D* is
   a 25 ohms   *b* 15 ohms
   c 2.5 ohms   *d* 20 ohms

4 For Fig. C 6·1, the resistance between points *A* and *D* is
   a 205 ohms   *b* 120 ohms
   c 105 ohms   *d* 62.5 ohms

5 For Fig. C 6·1, the current through the 20-ohm resistor is
   a 2 amp   *b* 1 amp
   c 0.5 amp   *d* 2.5 amp

6 For Fig. C 6·1, the current through one of the 80-ohm resistors is
   a 2 amp   *b* 1 amp
   c 0.5 amp   *d* 2.5 amp

7 For Fig. C 6·1, the current through the 5-ohm resistor is
   a 2 amp   *b* 1 amp
   c 0.5 amp   *d* 2.5 amp

8 For Fig. C 6·1, the voltage drop from *A* to *B* is
   a 125 volts   *b* 40 volts
   c 80 volts   *d* 5 volts

9 For Fig. C 6·1, the voltage drop from *B* to *C* is
   a 125 volts   *b* 40 volts
   c 80 volts   *d* 5 volts

10 For Fig. C 6·1, the voltage drop across the 5-ohm resistor is
   a 10 volts   *b* 5 volts
   c 2.5 volts   *d* 40 volts

Fig. C 6·1

CHAPTER 7

1 Voltage-divider circuits use
   a parallel circuits   *b* series-parallel circuits
   c only series circuits   *d* none of the above

2 The values of the resistors used for voltage division are determined by the
   a battery voltage   *b* bleeder current
   c load resistor   *d* power dissipation

3 The current in Fig. C 7·3 with *S*1 open is
  a 5 amp   *b* 2 amp
  c 1 amp   *d* 0.1 amp

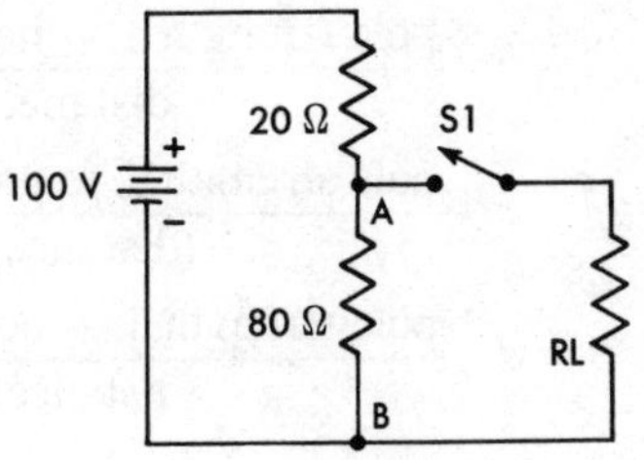

4 The voltage drop from *A* to *B* in Fig. C 7·3 is
  a 100 volts   *b* 80 volts
  c 60 volts   *d* 20 volts

5 The current in Fig. C 7·3 with *S*1 closed and $R_L = 48$ is
  a 5 amp   *b* 2 amp
  c 1 amp   *d* 0.1 amp

6 The voltage drop from *A* to *B* in Fig. C 7·3 with *S*1 closed and $R_L = 48$ ohms is
  a 100 volts   *b* 80 volts
  c 60 volts   *d* 20 volts

7 The current in Fig. C 7·3 with *S*1 closed and $R_L = 1$ kilohm is about
  a 5 amp   *b* 2 amp
  c 1 amp   *d* 0.1 amp

8 The voltage drop from *A* to *B* in Fig. C 7·3 with *S*1 closed and $R_L = 1$ kilohm is about
  a 100 volts   *b* 80 volts
  c 60 volts   *d* 20 volts

9 The current in the 80-ohm resistor in Fig. C 7·3 is called the
  a load current   *b* voltage-divider current
  c battery current   *d* bleeder current

10 The main disadvantage of using resistors as voltage dividers is the
  a large power dissipation
  b complicated calculations
  c small current in the load
  d high voltage of the battery

Fig. C 7·3

CHAPTER 8

1 A magnet would not attract
  a iron   *b* nickel
  c cobalt   *d* copper

2 Magnets made of low retentivity iron are
  a temporary magnets   *b* permanent magnets
  c magnets with one pole only *d* weak magnets

3 The force of magnetic attraction or repulsion between magnetic poles is determined by the formula
  a $\dfrac{\text{pole strength 1} \times \text{pole strength 2}}{\text{distance}}$

$$b \quad \frac{\text{pole strength } 1 + \text{pole strength } 2}{\text{distance}}$$

$$c \quad \frac{\text{pole strength } 1 \times \text{pole strength } 2}{(\text{distance})^2}$$

$$d \quad \frac{\text{pole strength } 1 + \text{pole strength } 2}{(\text{distance})^2}$$

4 The terminology which is incorrect is
  a electric charge   b magnetic charge
  c magnetic pole   d none of the above

5 If the strength of each pole is increased by a factor of 3, the magnetic force will increase by
  a 9   b 6
  c 3   d 2

6 The direction of the magnetic lines of force is
  a from + to − charges
  b from south to north pole
  c from one end of the magnet to the other
  d from north to south pole

7 A permeable substance is one which
  a is a strong magnet
  b is a permanent magnet
  c magnetic lines of force readily travel through
  d conducts electricity

8 Materials slightly repelled by a strong magnetic field are called
  a paramagnetic   b diamagnetic
  c temporary magnets   d permanent magnets

9 The permeability of a ferromagnetic substance would be
  a less than one   b one
  c slightly more than one   d about 7,000

10 A magnetic field can be found around
  a stationary charges   b moving charges
  c iron   d steel

11 The left-hand rule for single conductors carrying current states:
  a The fingers of the left hand will encircle the conductor in the direction of the lines of force if the thumb points toward the positive end of the battery.
  b The fingers of the left hand will encircle the conductor in the direction of the lines of force if the thumb points toward the negative end of the battery.
  c If the fingers of the left hand encircle the conductor, the thumb will point in the direction of the north pole.
  d None of the above.

12 If a wire loop cuts magnetic lines of force
  a a current is induced

  b nothing will happen
  c charges will be formed
  d the wire will become magnetic

13 For the solenoid of Fig. C 8 · 13, the following statement is true:
  a Pole *A* is a south pole.
  b Pole *B* is a north pole.
  c Pole *A* is a north pole.
  d Not enough information is given.

Fig. C 8·13

14 The magnitude of the induced emf in a conductor moving through a magnetic field is not determined by
  a the strength of field
  b the diameter of the wire
  c the number of conductors
  d the relative speed between the conductor and the field

CHAPTER 9

1 Voltage can be induced in a wire coil by
  a a steady magnetic field
  b positive charges
  c positive and negative charges
  d a changing magnetic field

2 With two coils near each other, but not touching, and with one connected to an a-c generator and the other to a load, the following statement is correct:
  a The coil connected to the generator is called the secondary.
  b The coil connected to the load is called the secondary.
  c The coil connected to the load is called the primary.
  d Either one is called the primary.

3 A coil has an inductance of 1 henry if a current changing at the rate of 1 amp/sec
  a induces 1 volt in another coil
  b causes a back emf of 1 volt
  c causes an aiding emf of 1 volt
  d causes transformer action

4 A coil of 6 henrys develops a counter emf of 12 volts. The rate of change of current flow must be
  a 1 amp/sec *b* 6 amp/sec
  c 2 amp/sec *d* 12 amp/sec

5 A collapsing field around a coil
  a helps the decay of coil current
  b tends to aid current flow reversal
  c tends to oppose the decay of coil current
  d does not affect coil current flow

6 Maximum current is induced in a conductor if the conductor cuts a magnetic field at

    a   0°   *b*   45°

    c   180°   *d*   90°

7 Which way must the conductor be moving in Fig. C 9·7 for the current flow to be as shown?

    a   up   *b*   down

    c   left   *d*   right

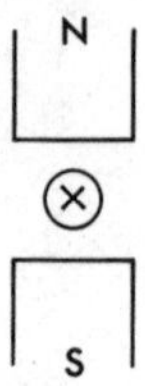

8 The effect of an inductance is such that current flowing through it

    a   cannot change instantaneously

    b   can change instantaneously

    c   cannot change

    d   is opposed by the inductance

9 Mutual inductance is measured in units of

    a   ohms   *b*   henrys

    c   volts   *d*   farads

10 Generator action can be explained by

    a   Ohm's law   *b*   Kirchhoff's law

    c   Lenz's law   *d*   Newton's law

Fig. C 9·7

CHAPTER 10

1 A component that is not part of a generator is

    a   field magnet   *b*   slip ring

    c   resistor   *d*   brushes

2 Which statement is correct for an a-c generator?

    a   The induced emf under the north pole has a polarity opposite that under the south pole.

    b   Maximum emf is induced in a conductor in the interpolar space.

    c   Each brush always has the same polarity output voltage.

    d   The output voltage of the generator is independent of its speed.

3 The rotating portion of the generator is known as the

    a   poles   *b*   armature

    c   stator   *d*   slip rings

4 The voltage output of a generator is 100 volts when the armature is at 45°. The maximum output voltage from the generator will be

    a   70.7 volts   *b*   100 volts

    c   142 volts   *d*   200 volts

5 For an a-c generator with two poles, two complete rotations of the armature will produce

    a   one complete sinusoidal voltage cycle

b two complete sinusoidal voltage cycles
c three complete sinusoidal voltage cycles
d zero complete sinusoidal voltage cycles

6 To convert an a-c generator to a d-c generator, we must replace the

a commutator	*b* split ring
c armature	*d* slip rings

7 A rectifier can be used to

a convert d-c to a-c	*b* increase voltage
c decrease the ripple	*d* convert a-c to d-c

8 The output voltage of an eight-coil d-c generator is a

a steady d-c voltage	*b* steady a-c voltage
c pulsating d-c voltage	*d* pulsating a-c voltage

9 A d-c generator with six coils rotating at 100 Hz will deliver an ouput voltage that has a

a 1,200-Hz ripple	*b* 600-Hz ripple
c 300-Hz ripple	*d* 150-Hz ripple

CHAPTER 11

1 A component that is not part of a d'Arsonval meter movement is

a spring	*b* coil
c magnet	*d* gears

2 Deflection of the d'Arsonval meter movement is caused by
a the spring and the magnet
b the magnetic field only
c the pivots and springs
d the current in the coil and the magnet

3 If a d'Arsonval meter movement is rated at 50 μa, and only 10 μa is passing through its coil, the deflection will be
a 10 per cent of full scale
b 20 per cent of full scale
c 50 per cent of full scale
d 100 per cent of full scale

4 The sensitivity of a meter movement is given as 50 mv, 0–20 μa. The d-c resistance of the coil is

a 2,500 ohms	*b* 2,000 ohms
c 25 ohms	*d* 200 ohms

5 If the coil resistance of a 1-ma meter is 200 ohms, the sensitivity would be given as

a 1 ma, 200 ohms	*b* 1 ma, 200 mv
c 1 ma, 2,000 ohms	*d* 1 ma, 2,000 mv

6 The function of a shunt in an ammeter is to
  a bypass the current
  b increase current in the coil
  c decrease the voltage drop
  d increase the meter's resistance

7 We are to use a d'Arsonval meter with a 100-ohm coil and 0–1 ma sensitivity to yield an ammeter with a full-scale reading of 10 amp. The shunt resistance should be
  a 100 ohms   *b* 10 ohms
  c 0.001 ohm   *d* 0.01 ohm

8 Using the same meter as in question 7, we are to design an ammeter for 10 ma full-scale reading. The shunt resistance should be
  a 111 ohms   *b* 11.1 ohms
  c 1.11 ohms   *d* 1.11×10^{-2} ohm

9 The sensitivity in ohms/volt of a voltmeter using a 0–5 ma meter movement is
  a 50 ohms/volt   *b* 100 ohms/volt
  c 200 ohms/volt   *d* 500 ohms/volt

10 We are to use a d'Arsonval meter with a 100-ohm coil and 0–1 ma sensitivity to design a voltmeter with a full-scale reading of 10 volts. The value of the multiplier should be
  a 1 kilohm   *b* 10 kilohms
  c 9,900 ohms   *d* 900 ohms

11 The multiplier and the meter movement in a voltmeter are always in
  a parallel   *b* series
  c series-parallel   *d* parallel-series

12 The function of the "safety" resistor in an ohmmeter is to
  a protect the battery
  b increase the current in the coil
  c increase the voltage drop across the coil
  d limit the current in the coil

13 An ohmmeter uses a 0–100 μa, 50-ohm meter movement. The value of the safety resistor with a 1.2-volt battery should be
  a 11,950 ohms   *b* 119.50 ohms
  c 7,850 ohms   *d* 650 ohms

14 For the meter in question 13, a half-scale reading will be produced by
  a 50 ohms   *b* 12 kilohms
  c 1.3 kilohms   *d* 100 ohms

15 When we measure a-c voltages with a d'Arsonval meter movement the meter will respond to
  a an a-c signal   *b* a d-c signal
  c a pulsating d-c signal   *d* a rectified d-c signal

16 To reduce the effect of a voltmeter upon the circuit being measured we should

   a decrease the multiplier resistance

   b get a more sensitive movement

   c use a parallel resistor

   d use an a-c meter with a rectifier

CHAPTER 12

1 The direction of current in an a-c circuit

   a cannot be determined

   b is always in one direction

   c can be found instantaneously

   d is from north to south

2 A frequency of 900 Hz is called

   a audio frequency   *b* radio frequency

   c high frequency   *d* ultrahigh frequency

3 A frequency of 455,000 Hz is the same as

   a 45.5 kHz   *b* 0.455 mHz

   c 45.5 mHz   *d* 455 ma

4 The period of a periodic curve is

   a the same as frequency

   b expressed in volts

   c measured in wavelengths

   d the time required to complete 1 cycle

5 The period for a sine wave is ⅟₁₀₀ sec. The frequency of the wave is

   a 100 Hz   *b* 1,000 Hz

   c ⅟₁₀₀ Hz   *d* 10 Hz

6 The velocity of radio waves is

   a 186,000 m/sec   *b* 3×10^6 m/sec

   c 3×10^8 m/sec   *d* 3×10^{10} m/sec

7 A radio wave having a frequency of 30 mh has a wavelength of

   a 1 m   *b* 10 miles

   c 10 cm   *d* 10 m

8 A wave in the ocean travels at 0.005 mile/sec and has a frequency of 0.1 Hz. The distance between wave crests is

   a 0.005 mile   *b* 0.05 mile

   c 0.5 mile   *d* 0.2 mile

9 Two waves of the same frequency are 180° out of phase; then

   a The maxima will occur at the same instant.

   b The minima will occur at the same instant.

c The maximum of one will occur at the same instant as the minimum of the other.

d The two waves are unrelated.

10 The peak value of a sine wave is 20 volts. The average value for a single alternation is

   a 12.72 volts   *b* 6.36 volts

   c 636 volts   *d* 0.1272 volt

11 The effective value of a sinusoidal voltage is 14.14 volts, and so its peak value is

   a 10 volts   *b* 20 volts

   c 30 volts   *d* 7.07 volts

12 If the average value of a wave is 6 volts, its effective value is

   a 3.53 volts   *b* 3.18 volts

   c 66.6 volts   *d* 6.66 volts

CHAPTER 13

1 The property of a coil carrying a changing current to induce a counter emf is called

   a mutual inductance

   b series aiding inductance

   c series opposing inductance

   d self-inductance

2 The formula for determining the inductance of two coils connected in series aiding is

   a $LT = L1 + L2 + M$ *b* $LT = L1 - L2 + 2M$

   c $LT = L1 + L2 + 2M$ *d* $LT = L1 + L2 - 2M$

3 When two coils, one 5 henrys and the other 3 henrys, are connected in series and are so far apart that they cannot influence each other, the total inductance will be

   a 2 henrys   *b* 8 henrys

   c $1\frac{5}{8}$ henrys   *d* $\frac{8}{15}$ henry

4 Two 3-henry coils are connected in series aiding so that the mutual inductance between them is 1.5 henrys. The total inductance is

   a 6 henrys   *b* 4.5 henrys

   c 9 henrys   *d* 0 henrys

5 Two 3-henry coils are connected in series opposing so that the mutual inductance between them is 1.5 henrys. The total inductance is

   a 6 henrys   *b* 4.5 henrys

   c 9 henrys   *d* 3 henrys

6 In a pure inductor, the current-voltage relationship is

   a current lags voltage by 90°

   b voltage lags current by 90°

c   current leads voltage by 90°
d   current and voltage are in phase

7 The opposition of an inductor to current flow
a   depends on the magnitude of the applied voltage
b   varies directly with frequency
c   varies inversely with frequency
d   depends only on the resistance of the coil

8 The reactance of a 4-henry coil at 100 Hz is
a   400 ohms   b   628 ohms
c   2,512 ohms   d   5,024 ohms

9 The reactance of a 4-henry coil at 200 Hz is
a   400 ohms   b   628 ohms
c   2,512 ohms   d   5,024 ohms

10 The total inductive reactance of two 3-henry coils connected in series aiding with a mutual inductance of 0.5 henry at 1 kHz is
a   43,960 ohms   b   31,400 ohms
c   6,280 ohms   d   55,760 ohms

CHAPTER 14

1 Dielectric material is a(n)
a   good conductor   b   insulator
c   resistor   d   capacitor

2 The function of a capacitor is to
a   stop current flow   b   help current flow
c   store energy   d   store heat

3 An electric circuit consists of a 5-volt battery and a 1-farad capacitor across it. The current in the circuit after a long time period will be
a   5 amp   b   0.2 amp
c   2 amp   d   0 amp

4 The capacitance of a capacitor is not influenced by the
a   thickness of the conducting plates
b   area of the conducting plates
c   distance separating the plates
d   nature of the insulator

5 The units of capacitance are
a   ohms   b   henrys
c   coulombs   d   coulombs/volt

6 A capacitor that stores 1.2 coulombs at 2 volts has a capacitance of
a   0.6 farad   b   1.2 farads
c   1.8 farads   d   2.4 farads

7 0.01 farad is the same as
  a 10 μf   *b* 100 μf
  c 10,000 μf   *d* 1 μf

8 A two-plate air capacitor has an area of 3 sq in., and the separation between plates is 0.1 in. Its capacitance is
  a 6.75 farads   *b* 6.75 μf
  c 6.75 pf   *d* 30 pf

9 For a pure capacitor, the voltage-current relationship is
  a voltage lags current by 90°
  b voltage leads current by 90°
  c current lags voltage by 90°
  d current leads voltage by 180°

10 The capacitive reactance of a 0.01-farad capacitor at 159 Hz is
  a 0.1 farad   *b* 0.1 ohm
  c 0.01 ohm   *d* 159 ohms

11 If a 120-volt 159-Hz source is connected across a 10-μf capacitor, the current in the circuit is
  a 9 ma   *b* 12 ma
  c 10 μa   *d* 1.2 amp

12 If four 80-μf capacitors are connected in parallel, the net capacitance is
  a 20 μf   *b* 40 μf
  c 160 μf   *d* 320 μf

13 If four 80-μf capacitors are connected in series, the net capacitance is
  a 20 μf   *b* 40 μf
  c 160 μf   *d* 320 μf

14 The dielectric-absorption loss in a capacitor is due to
  a leakage current
  b molecular distortion
  c insufficient dielectric constant
  d charging of dielectric

15 Capacitors lose energy due to dielectric distortion. This type of loss is called
  a dielectric-hysteresis loss
  b dielectric-absorption loss
  c dielectric-distortion loss
  d leakage loss

16 A capacitor used on a 240-volt a-c line should have a peak voltage rating of
  a 240 volts   *b* 340 volts
  c 120 volts   *d* 720 volts

17 A capacitor used on a 240-volt d-c line should have a working voltage rating of
  a 240 volts   *b* 340 volts
  c 120 volts   *d* 720 volts

CHAPTER 15

1 The mutual inductance of a transformer with perfect coupling and a primary inductance of 100 henrys and secondary inductance of 2.25 henrys is
   - a 102.25 henrys
   - b 97.75 henrys
   - c 15 henrys
   - d 225 henrys

2 For a 100 per cent efficient transformer the primary has 1,000 turns and the secondary has 100 turns. If the power input to the above transformer is 1,000 watts, the power output is
   - a 1,000 watts
   - b 100 watts
   - c 10 watts
   - d 10 kw

3 A transformer has 1,000 primary turns and 500 secondary turns. If the secondary voltage is 120, the primary voltage is
   - a 120 volts
   - b 240 volts
   - c 60 volts
   - d 1,000 volts

4 A 3:1 step-down transformer is 95 per cent efficient. The power input is 300 watts; the power output is
   - a 100 watts
   - b 900 watts
   - c 300 watts
   - d 285 watts

5 If a 1:4 step-up ideal transformer has a primary voltage of 100 volts, the secondary voltage is
   - a 25 volts
   - b 400 volts
   - c 60 volts
   - d 141 volts

6 If a 1:4 step-up ideal transformer has a primary current of 16 ma, the secondary current is
   - a 4 ma
   - b 16 ma
   - c 32 ma
   - d 64 ma

7 A transformer used on the 120-volt line has a primary of 60 turns and 720 volts output. The secondary winding should have
   - a 240 turns
   - b 10 turns
   - c 360 turns
   - d 720 turns

8 An autotransformer having 200 turns is connected to a 120-volt line to get 72 volts output; the transformer should be tapped at turns number
   - a 36
   - b 120
   - c 140
   - d 72

9 A 90 per cent efficient autotransformer has a power output of 30 watts; the input power is
   - a 27 watts
   - b 30 watts
   - c 270 watts
   - d 33 watts

CHAPTER 16

1 A series circuit consists of a 500-ohm resistor and an a-c source of an effective value of 100 volts. The power dissipated in the resistor is
a 20 watts   *b* 5,000 watts
c 200 watts   *d* 25,000 watts

2 The effective voltage across a resistor is 12 volts, and the current through it is 0.5 amp. The power dissipated in the resistor is
a 6 watts   *b* 24 watts
c 288 watts   *d* 12 watts

3 A 4-ohm resistor dissipates 64 watts. The effective current in the resistor is
a 16 amp   *b* 256 amp
c 18 amp   *d* 4 amp

4 A 120-ohm resistor is connected across an a-c line having a peak voltage of 171 volts. The effective value of the current in the resistor is
a 0.7 amp   *b* 1 amp
c 1.4 amp   *d* 2 amp

5 A pure capacitor of 1,000 ohms reactance is connected across a 100-volt (eff) a-c line. The current in the capacitor is
a 10 amp   *b* 0.1 amp
c 0.07 amp   *d* 1.41 amp

6 The current through a pure inductor of 700-ohm reactance is 10 ma. The power dissipated by the inductor is
a 0.07 watt   *b* 70,000 watts
c 7 watts   *d* 0 watts

7 The peak current through a 700-ohm resistor is 10 ma. The power dissipated by the resistor is
a 0.07 watt   *b* 35 mw
c 7 watts   *d* 700 watts

8 For a practical capacitor
a There is no power loss.
b We cannot find its reactance.
c There will be some power dissipation.
d None of the above is true.

CHAPTER 17

1 In an a-c resistive circuit, the current _____ the voltage by _____°.
a lags, 90   *b* leads, 90
c lags, 0   *d* lags, 30

2 For the circuit of Fig. C 17·2 $E = 100$ volts is the effective value of the voltage. The effective value of the current is _____ amp.

    a 20   *b* 2,000
    c 5   *d* 52

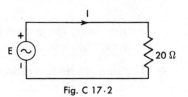

Fig. C 17·2

3 If *E* in Fig. C 17·2 is represented by phasor *E* in Fig. C 17·3, then *I* is represented by phasor _____ .

    a *A*   *b* *B*
    c *C*   *d* *D*

4 In Fig. C 17·3 phasor *B* has a phase angle of _____°.

    a 0   *b* +90
    c −90   *d* 180

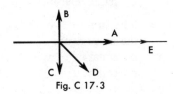

Fig. C 17·3

5 In Fig. C 17·3, phasor *D* _____ phasor *A* by about _____°.

    a lags, 25   *b* lags, 65
    c leads, 25   *d* leads, 65

6 In Fig. C 17·6, phasor _____ has the greatest magnitude.

    a *A*   *b* *B*
    c *C*   *d* *D*

7 In Fig. C 17·6, which quadrant contains no phasors?

    a I   *b* II
    c III   *d* IV

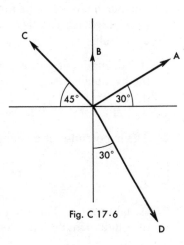

Fig. C 17·6

8 In Fig. C 17·6, phasor *C* _____ phasor *A* by _____°.

    a lags, 45   *b* lags, 30
    c leads, 105   *d* leads, 75

9 In Fig. C 17·6 the phasor having the smallest magnitude _____ the phasor having the largest magnitude by _____°.

    a lags, 30   *b* lags, 45
    c leads, 60   *d* leads, 150

10 The 0° axis lies between quadrants _____ and _____.

    a I, II   *b* II, III
    c III. IV   *d* IV, I

CHAPTER 18

1 The voltage across a resistor _____ the current through it by _____°.

    a lags, 90   *b* lags, 45
    c leads, 90   *d* leads, 0

2 The voltage across an inductor _____ the current through it by _____°.

    a lags, 90   *b* lags, 45
    c leads, 90   *d* leads, 0

3 Two phasors can _____ be added algebraically.

    a always
    b never

   c when they are in phase
   d when they are perpendicular

4 The sum of any two phasors can be found geometrically as the diagonal of a _____ .
   a square   *b* rectangle
   c parallelogram   *d* quadrilateral

5 The sum of two phasors is found using a rectangle when the phasors are _____ .
   a equal   *b* perpendicular
   c collinear   *d* skew

6 If the two legs of a right triangle are given, the length of the hypotenuse may be found using _____ .
   a the Pythagorean theorem   *b* addition
   c calculus   *d* multiplication

7 If the lengths of two legs are 4 and 6 units, the length of the hypotenuse is _____ units.
   a 10   *b* 24
   c $\sqrt{10}$ *d* $2\sqrt{13}$

8 The hypotenuse of a triangle whose legs are 3 and 4 in. is _____ in.
   a 5   *b* 6
   c 7   *d* $\sqrt{7}$

9 A right triangle has a hypotenuse 13 units long and a leg of 5 units length. The other leg has a length of _____ units.
   a 8   *b* $\sqrt{8}$
   c $\sqrt{15}$ *d* 12

10 In a series *RL* circuit the inductor voltage _____ the resistor voltage by _____°.
   a lags, 0   *b* lags, 90
   c leads, 45   *d* leads, 90

11 The total voltage applied to a series *RL* circuit is found from the resistor and inductor voltages using a _____ .
   a square   *b* right triangle
   c skew parallelogram   *d* quadrilateral

12 A phasor diagram for a series *RL* circuit is shown in Fig. C 18·12. The resistor voltage is shown as E_R. *A* represents the _____ and *B* represents the _____ .
   a resistor current, inductor
   b resistance, reactance
   c inductor voltage, current
   d inductor voltage, total voltage

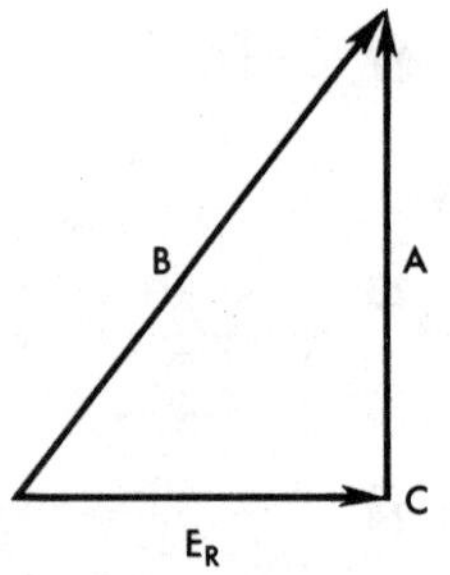

Fig. C 18·12

13 Impedance represents a force _____ the flow of current and is analogous to _____ in a d-c circuit.
   a opposing, resistance   *b* opposing, conductance
   c aiding, resistance   *d* aiding, conductance

14 Ohm's law for a-c circuits is the same as Ohm's law for d-c circuits except that _____ is replaced by _____ .
a voltage, current
b resistance, impedance
c amperes, volts
d average value, effective value

15 The symbol for impedance is _____ .
a R
b G
c Z
d Y

16 The inductive reactance is symbolized by _____ and is defined by the ratio _____ .
a $R_L, E_L/I_L$
b $R_L, I_L/E_L$
c $X_L, E_L/I_L$
d $X_L, I_L/E_L$

17 The total impedance of an RL circuit is found as the _____ of the sum of the _____ of the resistance and inductive reactance.
a square, square roots
b square root, squares
c rms value, averages
d none of these

18 The side opposite angle ϕ in a right triangle has length p, the adjacent side has length a, and the hypotenuse has length h. The sin ϕ, cos ϕ, and tan ϕ are defined by _____ , _____ , and _____ respectively.
a $a/p, p/h, h/a$
b $p/h, h/a, a/p$
c $a/p, h/a, p/a$
d $p/h, a/h, p/a$

19 The sides of a 30-60-90 triangle are in the ratio _____ .
a 1 to $\sqrt{3}$ to 2
b 1 to 2 to 3
c 1 to 1 to 2
d 1 to $\sqrt{2}$ to 2

20 The sides of a 45-45-90 triangle are in the ratio _____ .
a 1 to 1 to 2
b 1 to $\sqrt{2}$ to $\sqrt{2}$
c 1 to 1 to $\sqrt{2}$
d $\sqrt{2}$ to $\sqrt{2}$ to $\sqrt{3}$

21 sin 0° = _____ and sin 90° = _____ .
a $0, \infty$
b $0, 1$
c $1, 0$
d $1, \infty$

22 cos 0° = _____ and tan 90° = _____ .
a $0, \infty$
b $0, 1$
c $1, 0$
d $1, \infty$

23 cos 90° = _____ and tan 0° = _____ .
a $0, 0$
b $0, 1$
c $1, 0$
d $1, \infty$

24 Trigonometric functions of arbitrary angles are defined in terms of a set of coordinates. The angle corresponding to a given point is measured as the _____ rotation between the positive _____ axis and a line connecting the point and the origin.
a clockwise, vertical
b clockwise, horizontal

    c counterclockwise, vertical
    d counterclockwise, horizontal

25 The line from the point to the origin is called the hypotenuse. The vertical coordinate of the point is the _____ and the horizontal coordinate is the _____ .
    a abscissa, ordinate   *b* ordinate, abscissa
    c cosine, sine   *d* sine, cosine

26 The _____ is always positive while the _____ or _____ may be negative.
    a abscissa, hypotenuse, ordinate
    b ordinate, hypotenuse, abscissa
    c hypotenuse, ordinate, abscissa
    d abscissa, ordinate, hypotenuse

27 The sine of an angle is defined as _____/_____ .
    a abscissa, ordinate   *b* abscissa, hypotenuse
    c ordinate, abscissa   *d* ordinate, hypotenuse

28 The cosine of an angle is defined as _____/_____ .
    a abscissa, ordinate   *b* abscissa, hypotenuse
    c ordinate, abscissa   *d* ordinate, hypotenuse

29 The tangent of an angle is defined as _____/_____ .
    a abscissa, ordinate   *b* abscissa, hypotenuse
    c ordinate, abscissa   *d* ordinate, hypotenuse

30 In the first quadrant, the sin, cos, and tan are _____, _____, and _____ respectively.
    a +, +, +   *b* +, −, +
    c −, −, +   *d* −, −, −

31 In the second quadrant, the sin, cos, and tan are _____, _____, and _____ respectively.
    a +, +, +   *b* +, −, +
    c −, −, +   *d* +, −, −

32 In the third quadrant the sin, cos, and tan are _____, _____, and _____ respectively.
    a +, +, +   *b* −, +, −
    c +, −, −   *d* −, −, +

33 In the fourth quadrant, the sin, cos, and tan are _____, _____, and _____ respectively.
    a +, +, +   *b* −, +, −
    c +, −, −   *d* −, −, +

34 In a series *RL* circuit the resistor voltage _____ the current by _____°.
    a lags, 0   *b* lags, 90
    c leads, 45   *d* leads, 90

35 In a series *RL* circuit, the inductor voltage _____ the current by _____°.
    a lags, 0   *b* lags, 90
    c leads, 45   *d* leads, 90

36 The total voltage in a series RL circuit is equal to the
_____ .
a resistor voltage
b inductor voltage
c algebraic sum of the resistor and inductor voltages
d phasor sum of the resistor and inductor voltages

37 The total voltage in a series RL circuit _____ the current
by an angle _____ .
a lags, of 90°
b lags, between 0 and 90°
c leads, between 0 and 90°
d leads, between 90 and 180°

38 In a series RL circuit, the inductor current _____ the
resistor current.
a leads   b lags
c is equal to   d is the negative of

39 The impedance triangle is similar to the _____ triangle
with the resistance phasor in place of the _____ .
a current, resistor current   b current, resistor voltage
c voltage, impedance   d voltage, resistor voltage

40 In the impedance triangle the inductive reactance and impedance phasors are analogous to the _____ and _____
phasors respectively in the voltage triangle.
a inductive voltage, total voltage
b inductive current, total current
c inductive voltage, resistive voltage
d inductive current, resistive current

41 In a series RL circuit phasor diagram, the _____ phasor
and the _____ voltage phasor are in phase.
a current, resistor   b total voltage, resistor
c current, inductor   d total voltage, inductor

42 In a series RL circuit phasor diagram, the total voltage
may be represented by the _____ phasor and the resistor
voltage may be represented by the _____ phasor.
a current, voltage
b impedance, resistance
c current, resistance current
d impedance, inductance

43 The phase angle of a series RL circuit is the angle between
the _____ phasor and the _____ phasor.
a resistance, inductive reactance
b resistance, impedance
c inductive reactance, impedance
d none of these

44 The phase angle of a series RL circuit may be computed as
_____ or _____ or _____ .
a $\cos^{-1}R/X_L$, $\sin^{-1}X_L/R$, $\tan^{-1}R/Z$

b $\cos^{-1}R/Z$, $\sin^{-1}X_L/R$, $\tan^{-1}R/X_L$
c $\cos^{-1}Z/X_L$, $\sin^{-1}R/Z$, $\tan^{-1}X_L/Z$
d $\cos^{-1}R/Z$, $\sin^{-1}X_L/Z$, $\tan^{-1}X_L/R$

45 The phase angle of an *RL* series circuit is defined as the angle between the _____ phasor and the _____ phasor.
  a resistance, reactance
  b current, total voltage
  c reactance, impedance
  d resistance voltage, reactance voltage

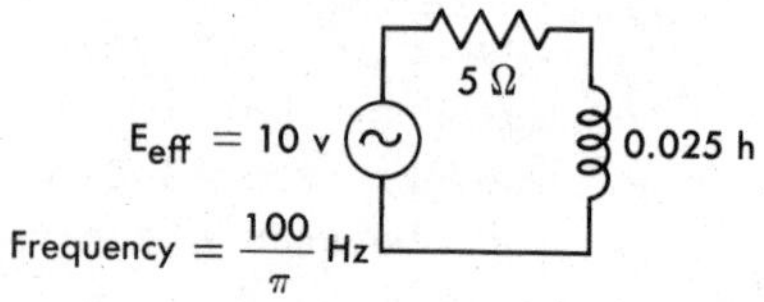

46 For the circuit of Fig. C 18·46 the inductive reactance is _____ ohms.
  a 2.5 b 5
  c 25 d 2.5/π

$E_{eff} = 10$ v,   5 Ω,   0.025 h

Frequency $= \dfrac{100}{\pi}$ Hz

Fig. C 18·46

47 The impedance of the circuit of Fig. C 18·46 is _____ ohms.
  a 7.5 b 10
  c $\sqrt{31.25}$ d $5\sqrt{2}$

48 The current in the circuit of Fig. C 18·46 has an effective value of _____ amp.
  a 2 b 1
  c $\sqrt{2}$ d $1/\sqrt{2}$

49 In the circuit of Fig. C 18·46, the effective value of the resistor voltage is _____ volts.
  a $5\sqrt{2}$ b 5
  c $5/\sqrt{2}$ d 10

50 In the circuit of Fig. C 18·46, the effective value of inductor voltage is _____ volts.
  a 5 b 0.025
  c $0.125\sqrt{2}$ d $5\sqrt{2}$

51 The phase angle for the circuit of Fig. C 18·46 is _____°.
  a 0 b 30
  c 45 d 60

52 A(n) _____ stores and returns energy to a circuit while a(n) _____ dissipates energy.
  a resistor, impedance b resistor, inductor
  c inductor, resistor d inductor, reactance

53 The apparent power is _____ .
  a the power dissipated b I^2R
  c I^2Z d I^2X_L

54 The true power is _____ .
  a I^2R b I^2Z
  c I^2X_L d the power stored

55 The power factor is defined as the ratio _____/_____ .
  a true power, apparent power
  b apparent power, true power

c stored power, apparent power

d true power, stored power

56 The power factor for a purely resistive circuit has a value of _____ while a purely inductive circuit results in a value of _____ .

a 0, 1   *b* 1, 0

c 0, −1   *d* −1, 0

57 For an *RL* circuit, the power factor cannot be less than _____ or greater than _____ .

a 0, 1   *b* −1, 0

c 1, 1   *d* −∞, +∞

58 The power factor for a series *RL* circuit is equal to _____ / _____ .

a R/X_L *b* X_L/R

c R/Z *d* X_L/Z

CHAPTER 19

1 Charge is transported from one plate of a capacitor to the other through the external circuit. This process gives the appearance of a current flowing through the _____ although there is no such _____ .

a battery, current   *b* dielectric, current

c dielectric, voltage   *d* battery, voltage

2 The voltage across a capacitor _____ the current through it by _____ °.

a lags, 45   *b* lags, 90

c leads, 0   *d* leads, 90

3 If the resistance in a series *RC* circuit is increased the magnitude of the phase angle _____ .

a increases

b remains the same

c decreases

d changes in an indeterminate manner

4 In a series *RC* circuit, the current _____ the total voltage by an angle _____ .

a lags, of 45°   *b* lags, of 0°

c leads, between 0 and 90°   *d* leads, of 90°

5 The resistance phasor for a series *RC* circuit points to the right. The capacitive reactance phasor points _____ while the diagonal of the rectangle having these two phasors as sides represents the _____ .

a up, impedance   *b* down, impedance

c left, current   *d* up, total voltage

6 The impedance for a series *RC* circuit is computed as $Z = \sqrt{\underline{\quad}^2 + \underline{\quad}^2}$.

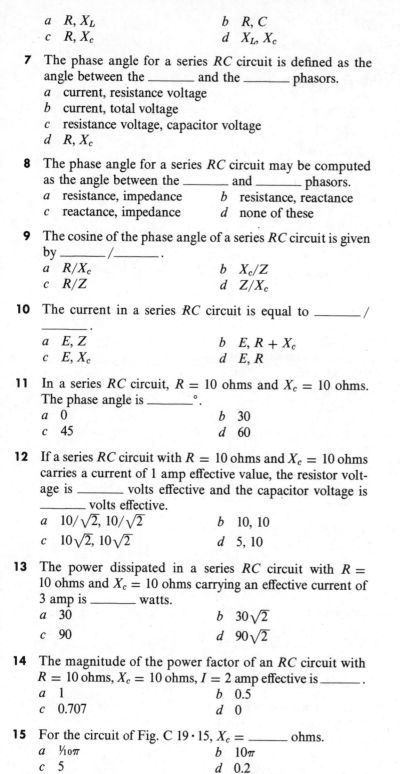

a R, X_L b R, C
c R, X_c d X_L, X_c

7   The phase angle for a series RC circuit is defined as the angle between the _____ and the _____ phasors.
   a   current, resistance voltage
   b   current, total voltage
   c   resistance voltage, capacitor voltage
   d R, X_c

8   The phase angle for a series RC circuit may be computed as the angle between the _____ and _____ phasors.
   a   resistance, impedance   b   resistance, reactance
   c   reactance, impedance   d   none of these

9   The cosine of the phase angle of a series RC circuit is given by _____ / _____ .
   a R/X_c b X_c/Z
   c R/Z d Z/X_c

10   The current in a series RC circuit is equal to _____ / _____ .
   a E, Z b $E, R + X_c$
   c E, X_c d E, R

11   In a series RC circuit, $R = 10$ ohms and $X_c = 10$ ohms. The phase angle is _____ °.
   a   0   b   30
   c   45   d   60

12   If a series RC circuit with $R = 10$ ohms and $X_c = 10$ ohms carries a current of 1 amp effective value, the resistor voltage is _____ volts effective and the capacitor voltage is _____ volts effective.
   a $10/\sqrt{2}, 10/\sqrt{2}$ b   10, 10
   c $10\sqrt{2}, 10\sqrt{2}$ d   5, 10

13   The power dissipated in a series RC circuit with $R = 10$ ohms and $X_c = 10$ ohms carrying an effective current of 3 amp is _____ watts.
   a   30   b $30\sqrt{2}$
   c   90   d $90\sqrt{2}$

14   The magnitude of the power factor of an RC circuit with $R = 10$ ohms, $X_c = 10$ ohms, $I = 2$ amp effective is _____ .
   a   1   b   0.5
   c   0.707   d   0

15   For the circuit of Fig. C 19·15, $X_c =$ _____ ohms.
   a $\frac{1}{10}\pi$ b 10π
   c   5   d   0.2

16   For the circuit of Fig. C 19·15, $Z =$ _____ ohms.
   a   50.2   b   55
   c $5\sqrt{101}$ d $\sqrt{55}$

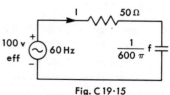

Fig. C 19·15

17 For the circuit of Fig. C 19 · 17, I_{eff} = _____ amp.
    a 1.43   *b* 2
    c $\sqrt{2}$ *d* 1

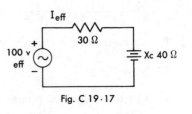

Fig. C 19·17

18 For the circuit of Fig. C 19 · 17, the phase angle magnitude
is _____ .
    a 0.75   *b* 1.33
    c $\cos^{-1}0.75$ *d* $\cos^{-1}0.60$

19 The power dissipated in the circuit of Fig. C 19 · 17 is
_____ watts.
    a 60   *b* 80
    c 100   *d* 120

20 The power factor for the circuit of Fig. C 19 · 17 has a
magnitude of _____ .
    a 0.30   *b* 0.40
    c 0.50   *d* 0.60

CHAPTER 20

1 In a series *RCL* circuit the _____ voltage is in phase with
the current.
    a resistor   *b* inductor
    c capacitor   *d* total

2 In a series *RCL* circuit the inductor voltage _____ the
current by _____° while the capacitor voltage _____
the current by the same angle.
    a leads, 90, lags   *b* lags, 90, leads
    c leads, 45, lags   *d* lags, 45, leads

3 If the inductor voltage phasor points up, the _____ phasor
points to the right and the capacitor voltage phasor points

_____ .
    a total voltage, down   *b* current, down
    c resistor voltage, left   *d* resistor voltage, up

4 The impedance diagram is similar to the _____ diagram
with the resistor voltage replaced by the _____ .
    a voltage, current   *b* current, impedance
    c voltage, resistance   *d* current, reactance

5 The phase angle between the inductive and capacitive reactance phasors is _____° .
    a 0   *b* 45
    c 90   *d* 180

6 The net reactance in an *RCL* circuit is
    a X_L *b* X_c
    c $X_C - X_L$ *d* $X_L - X_c$

7 The impedance of a series *RCL* circuit is _____ .
    a $\sqrt{R^2 + X_L{}^2 + X_c{}^2}$ *b* $\sqrt{R^2 + X_L{}^2 - X_c{}^2}$

$$c \quad \sqrt{R^2 + (X_L + X_c)^2} \qquad d \quad \sqrt{R^2 + (X_L - X_c)^2}$$

8 An impedance is capacitive if _____ .
   a $R = 0$ *b* $X_L > X_c$
   c $X_L < X_c$ *d* only if $X_L = 0$

9 The net reactance phasor of a series *RCL* circuit can be found _____ .
   a only by vectorial addition
   b by algebraic addition
   c using calculus
   d only by using trigonometry

10 The reactance and resistance are added _____ to find the impedance.
   a algebraically   *b* using calculus
   c by phasors   *d* arithmetically

CHAPTER 21

1 In a series *RCL* circuit Z is the phasor sum of _____ and _____ .
   a R, X_L *b* $R, X_L - X_c$
   c X_L, X_c *d* X, V

2 At resonance in a series *RCL* circuit _____ and Z has its _____ value equal to _____ .
   a $X_L = 0$, minimum, $R + X_c$
   b $R = 0$, maximum, $X_L - X_c$
   c $X_L = X_c$, minimum, R
   d $X = 0$, minimum, R^2

3 Inductive reactance is computed as _____ .
   a fL *b* $R + fL$
   c $2\pi fL$ *d* $1/(2\pi fL)$

4 Capacitive reactance is given by _____ .
   a $R + 2\pi fC$ *b* fC
   c $2\pi fC$ *d* $1/(2\pi fC)$

5 As frequency increases inductive reactance _____ and capacitive reactance _____ .
   a increases, increases   *b* increases, decreases
   c decreases, increases   *d* decreases, decreases

6 There will _____ be a frequency, called the _____ frequency, at which _____ .
   a sometimes, natural, $X_L = X_c$
   b always, natural, $R = 0$
   c always, resonant, $X_L = X_c$
   d sometimes, resonant, $X = 0$

7 The formula for the resonant frequency is $f =$ _____ .

$$a \quad \sqrt{LC} \qquad\qquad b \quad 1/\sqrt{LC}$$
$$c \quad 2\pi\sqrt{LC} \qquad\quad d \quad 1/2\pi\sqrt{LC}$$

8 In a series RCL circuit $R = \pi$ ohms, $L = 1/\pi$ henry, $C = 2/\pi$ farad, and the applied voltage has an effective value of 10 volts. The resonant frequency is _____ Hz.
$$a \quad \sqrt{2}/4 \qquad\qquad b \quad 10$$
$$c \quad 5 \qquad\qquad\quad d \quad \sqrt{\pi}$$

9 For a series RCL circuit at resonance the current amplitude is _____ for a fixed voltage amplitude and the power factor is _____ .
a minimum, zero   b minimum, unity
c maximum, zero   d maximum, unity

10 The phase angle between current and total voltage for a series RCL circuit at resonance is _____°.
a 0   b between 0 and 90
c 90   d 180

11 The voltage gain of a series RCL circuit may be defined as the ratio of _____ to _____ .
a applied voltage, resistive voltage drop
b applied voltage, inductive voltage drop
c inductive voltage drop, capacitive voltage drop
d inductive voltage drop, applied voltage

12 At resonance in a series RCL circuit the applied voltage equals the _____ voltage drop.
a resistive   b inductive
c capacitive   d reactive

13 The voltage gain is equal to _____ .
$$a \quad R/Z \qquad\qquad b \quad X_L/R$$
$$c \quad Z/R \qquad\qquad d \quad X_L/X_c$$

14 The voltages across the _____ and _____ in a resonant series RCL circuit are equal in magnitude but _____° out of phase.
a resistor, inductor, 90
b inductor, capacitor, 180
c resistor, capacitor, 180
d resistor, impedance, 45

15 The Q of a series RCL circuit is equal to the _____ .
a bandwidth   b voltage gain
c impedance   d resonant frequency

16 As _____ increases, the Q _____ .
a R, increases   b R, decreases
c z, decreases   d E, increases

17 The Q of a series RCL circuit can generally be computed as _____ .
$$a \quad Z/R \qquad\qquad b \quad R/X_c$$
$$c \quad X_L/R \qquad\qquad d \quad P/E$$

18 A resonance curve for a series *RCL* circuit is a plot of _____ magnitude versus _____ .
  a   current, voltage   *b*   current, frequency
  c   voltage, frequency   *d*   impedance, frequency

19 The curve is _____ at the _____ frequency and decreases on both sides.
  a   minimum, resonant   *b*   minimum, half-power
  c   maximum, resonant   *d*   maximum, half-power

20 The power dissipated by a series *RCL* circuit is _____ at the resonant frequency and is equal to _____ .
  a   minimum, I^2R *b*   minimum, $I^2R/2$
  c   maximum, I^2R *d*   maximum, $I^2R/2$

21 There is (are) _____ frequency(ies) called the half-power point(s) at which $P = \frac{1}{2}P_{max}$.
  a   0   *b*   1
  c   2   *d*   3 or more

22 There is a half-power point on _____ .
  a   the lower side of resonance
  b   the upper side of resonance
  c   both sides of resonance
  d   either side of resonance, but not both sides

23 At a half-power point the current is _____ times the maximum current.
  a   2   *b* $\sqrt{2}$
  c $\frac{1}{2}$ *d* $1/\sqrt{2}$

24 The bandwidth of a series *RCL* circuit is the _____ of the upper half-power point _____ the _____ of the lower half-power point.
  a   current, minus, current
  b   current, plus, current
  c   frequency, minus, frequency
  d   frequency, plus, frequency

25 The "useful" frequencies are the _____ .
  a   half-power frequencies
  b   frequencies between the half-power points
  c   frequencies outside the region between the half-power points
  d   frequencies above resonance

26 The half-power frequencies of a series *RCL* circuit are those frequencies at which the current is _____ times the maximum current.
  a   2   *b*   1.414
  c   0.15   *d*   0.707

27 The _____ of a resonant curve is the set of frequencies between the _____ frequencies.
  a   resonant frequency, half-power

b   passband, maximum and minimum
c   selectivity, maximum and minimum
d   passband, half-power

28   A circuit that can pass one frequency and _____ neighboring frequencies has _____ selectivity.
   a   reject, poor   *b*   reject, good
   c   pass, good   *d*   pass, narrow

29   The _____ the passband, the broader the selectivity, and the _____ the bandwidth.
   a   narrower, larger   *b*   narrower, smaller
   c   wider, larger   *d*   wider, smaller

30   A circuit with good selectivity has a _____ passband and a _____ bandwidth.
   a   broad, large   *b*   broad, small
   c   narrow, large   *d*   narrow, small

31   The higher the resistance in a series *RCL* circuit, the _____ the passband and the _____ the bandwidth.
   a   broader, smaller   *b*   broader, larger
   c   narrower, smaller   *d*   narrower, larger

32   As the *Q* of a circuit _____ the _____ gets better.
   a   decreases, selectivity   *b*   decreases, bandwidth
   c   increases, bandwidth   *d*   increases, selectivity

33   In general, the *Q* of a series *RCL* circuit is essentially that of the _____ .
   a   source   *b*   resistance
   c   coil   *d*   condensor

34   In a resonant series *RCL* circuit _____ , resulting in a resonant frequency of _____ .
   a $R = 0$, $\sqrt{LC}$ *b* $X_L = X_c$, $1/\sqrt{LC}$
   c $X_L = 0$, 0 *d* $X_L = X_c$, $1/2\pi\sqrt{LC}$

35   In a resonant series *RCL* circuit the impedance is _____ and is equal to _____ , resulting in a _____ current amplitude.
   a   minimum, *R*, minimum
   b   minimum, *R*, maximum
   c   maximum, *X*, maximum
   d   maximum, *X*, minimum

36   The power factor for a resonant series *RCL* circuit is equal to _____ .
   a   0   *b*   +0.5
   c   −0.5   *d*   1

37   At the half-power frequencies the current is $I_{max}/$_____ .
   a   1   *b*   2
   c $\sqrt{2}$ *d*   0.707

38 The bandwidth is the _____ of the half-power frequencies while the set of frequencies between the half-power frequencies is called the _____ .

    a   sum, bandwidth   *b*   sum, passband
    c   difference, bandwidth   *d*   difference, passband

39 As the Q of a circuit _____ the selectivity gets _____ .

    a   increases, better   *b*   increases, worse
    c   decreases, better   *d*   increases, broader

40 A parallel resonant circuit consists of a _____ circuit in parallel with a _____ .

    a   parallel RC, coil   *b*   parallel RL, capacitor
    c   series RC, coil   *d*   series RL, capacitor

41 The resonant frequency of a parallel RCL circuit is given by $f =$ _____ .

    a RC *b* $1/\sqrt{LC}$
    c $\sqrt{LC}/2\pi$ *d* $\tfrac{1}{2}\pi\sqrt{LC}$

42 At resonance the impedance is very _____ and the current is very _____ in a parallel RCL circuit.

    a   large, large   *b*   large, small
    c   small, large   *d*   small, small

43 The behavior of a parallel resonant RCL circuit is essentially _____ to that of a series resonant RCL circuit.

    a   similar   *b*   opposite
    c   unrelated   *d*   identical

44 In an ideal parallel resonant circuit $R =$ _____ and the resonant current is _____ whereas in a practical circuit the current is _____ but not _____ .

    a   0, 0, small, 0   *b*   0, ∞, large, ∞
    c   ∞, 0, small, 0   *d*   ∞, ∞, large, ∞

45 A parallel RCL circuit below resonance behaves _____ with the current _____ the voltage.

    a   inductively, lagging   *b*   inductively, leading
    c   capacitively, lagging   *d*   capacitively, leading

46 A parallel RCL circuit above resonance behaves _____ with the current _____ the voltage.

    a   inductively, lagging   *b*   inductively, leading
    c   capacitively, lagging   *d*   capacitively, leading

47 In a practical parallel RCL resonant circuit _____ , the current is _____ , and the impedance is _____ .

    a $R = 0$, large, small   *b* $R = 0$, large, large
    c $X_L = X_c$, large, small   *d* $X_L = X_c$, small, large

48 The power factor for a resonant parallel RCL circuit is _____ .

    a   0   *b*   ½
    c $1/\sqrt{2}$ *d*   1

49 A parallel *RCL* circuit behaves inductively _____ and capacitively _____ .
  a at d-c, at resonance
  b at resonance, at d-c
  c above resonance, below resonance
  d below resonance, above resonance

ANSWERS FOR CRITERION CHECK TESTS

CHAPTER 1
1.	*b*	8.	*c*	14.	*b*	20.	*b*
2.	*c*	9.	*d*	15.	*b*	21.	*b*
3.	*a*	10.	*d*	16.	*a*	22.	*c*
4.	*d*	11.	*a*	17.	*d*	23.	*c*
5.	*a*	12.	*b*	18.	*c*	24.	*b*
6.	*a*	13.	*c*	19.	*b*	25.	*b*
7.	*b*						

CHAPTER 2
1.	*d*	6.	*c*	10.	*c*	14.	*a*
2.	*b*	7.	*a*	11.	*d*	15.	*b*
3.	*c*	8.	*b*	12.	*a*	16.	*c*
4.	*b*	9.	*c*	13.	*d*	17.	*d*
5.	*c*						

CHAPTER 3
1.	*d*	6.	*a*	10.	*d*	14.	*a*
2.	*c*	7.	*d*	11.	*d*	15.	*b*
3.	*c*	8.	*c*	12.	*a*	16.	*c*
4.	*b*	9.	*a*	13.	*a*	17.	*a*
5.	*b*						

CHAPTER 4
1.	*c*	8.	*a*	15.	*d*	21.	*b*
2.	*a*	9.	*b*	16.	*b*	22.	*b*
3.	*b*	10.	*c*	17.	*c*	23.	*c*
4.	*d*	11.	*c*	18.	*d*	24.	*d*
5.	*a*	12.	*a*	19.	*a*	25.	*a*
6.	*a*	13.	*d*	20.	*c*	26.	*a*
7.	*b*	14.	*b*				

CHAPTER 5
1.	*b*	4.	*a*	7.	*c*	9.	*a*
2.	*c*	5.	*c*	8.	*a*	10.	*c*
3.	*d*	6.	*b*				

CHAPTER 6
1.	*b*	4.	*d*	7.	*b*	9.	*c*
2.	*a*	5.	*a*	8.	*b*	10.	*b*
3.	*c*	6.	*b*				

CHAPTER 7
1.	*b*	4.	*b*	7.	*c*	9.	*d*
2.	*c*	5.	*b*	8.	*b*	10.	*a*
3.	*c*	6.	*c*				

CHAPTER 8	1. *d*	5. *a*	9. *d*	12. *a*
	2. *a*	6. *d*	10. *b*	13. *c*
	3. *c*	7. *c*	11. *a*	14. *b*
	4. *b*	8. *b*		

CHAPTER 9	1. *d*	4. *c*	7. *c*	9. *b*
	2. *b*	5. *c*	8. *a*	10. *c*
	3. *b*	6. *d*		

CHAPTER 10	1. *c*	4. *c*	6. *d*	8. *c*
	2. *a*	5. *b*	7. *d*	9. *b*
	3. *b*			

CHAPTER 11	1. *d*	5. *b*	9. *c*	13. *a*
	2. *d*	6. *a*	10. *c*	14. *b*
	3. *b*	7. *d*	11. *b*	15. *c*
	4. *a*	8. *b*	12. *d*	16. *b*

CHAPTER 12	1. *c*	4. *d*	7. *d*	10. *a*
	2. *b*	5. *a*	8. *b*	11. *b*
	3. *b*	6. *c*	9. *c*	12. *d*

CHAPTER 13	1. *d*	4. *c*	7. *b*	9. *d*
	2. *c*	5. *d*	8. *c*	10. *a*
	3. *b*	6. *a*		

CHAPTER 14	1. *b*	6. *a*	10. *b*	14. *d*
	2. *c*	7. *c*	11. *d*	15. *a*
	3. *d*	8. *c*	12. *d*	16. *b*
	4. *a*	9. *a*	13. *a*	17. *a*
	5. *d*			

CHAPTER 15	1. *c*	4. *d*	6. *a*	8. *b*
	2. *a*	5. *b*	7. *c*	9. *d*
	3. *b*			

| CHAPTER 16 | 1. *c* | 3. *d* | 5. *b* | 7. *b* |
| | 2. *a* | 4. *b* | 6. *d* | 8. *c* |

CHAPTER 17	1. *c*	4. *b*	7. *c*	9. *d*
	2. *c*	5. *a*	8. *c*	10. *d*
	3. *a*	6. *d*		

CHAPTER 18

1. d	16. c	31. d	45. b
2. c	17. b	32. d	46. b
3. c	18. d	33. b	47. d
4. c	19. a	34. a	48. c
5. b	20. c	35. d	49. a
6. a	21. b	36. d	50. d
7. d	22. d	37. c	51. c
8. a	23. a	38. c	52. c
9. d	24. d	39. d	53. c
10. d	25. b	40. a	54. a
11. b	26. c	41. a	55. a
12. d	27. d	42. b	56. b
13. a	28. b	43. b	57. a
14. b	29. c	44. d	58. c
15. c	30. a		

CHAPTER 19

1. b	6. c	11. c	16. a
2. b	7. b	12. b	17. b
3. c	8. a	13. c	18. d
4. c	9. c	14. c	19. d
5. b	10. a	15. c	20. d

CHAPTER 20

1. a	4. c	7. d	9. b
2. a	5. d	8. c	10. c
3. b	6. d		

CHAPTER 21

1. b	14. b	26. d	38. d
2. c	15. b	27. d	39. a
3. c	16. b	28. b	40. d
4. d	17. c	29. c	41. d
5. b	18. b	30. d	42. b
6. c	19. c	31. b	43. b
7. d	20. c	32. d	44. c
8. a	21. c	33. c	45. a
9. d	22. c	34. d	46. d
10. a	23. d	35. b	47. d
11. d	24. c	36. d	48. d
12. a	25. b	37. c	49. d
13. b			

index